Agrarian Dreams

1. *Changing Fortunes: Biodiversity and Peasant Livelihood in the Peruvian Andes*, by Karl S. Zimmerer

2. *Making the Invisible Visible: A Multicultural Planning History*, edited by Leonie Sandercock

3. *Imperial San Francisco: Urban Power, Earthly Ruin*, by Gray Brechin

4. *Imposing Wilderness: Struggles over Livelihood and Nature Preservation in Africa*, by Roderick P. Neumann

5. *Shady Practices: Agroforestry and Gender Politics in The Gambia*, by Richard A. Schroeder

6. *On Holiday: A History of Vacationing*, by Orvar Löfgren

7. *Spaces of Hope*, by David Harvey

8. *Even in Sweden: Racisms, Racialized Spaces, and the Popular Geographical Imagination*, by Allan Pred

9. *American Empire: Roosevelt's Geographer and the Prelude to Globalization*, by Neil Smith

10. *Disabling Globalization: Places of Power in Post-Apartheid South Africa*, by Gillian Hart

11. *Agrarian Dreams: The Paradox of Organic Farming in California*, by Julie Guthman

Agrarian Dreams

The Paradox of Organic Farming in California

Julie Guthman

UNIVERSITY OF CALIFORNIA PRESS
Berkeley · Los Angeles · London

University of California Press
Berkeley and Los Angeles, California

University of California Press, Ltd.
London, England

© 2004 by the Regents of the University of California

Library of Congress Cataloging-in-Publication Data

Guthman, Julie.
    Agrarian dreams : the paradox of organic farming in
California / Julie Guthman.
        p.   cm.
Includes bibliographical references (p.   ) and index.
    ISBN 0-520-24094-4 (cloth : alk. paper) —
    ISBN 0-520-24095-2 (pbk. : alk. paper)
    1. Organic farming—California. I. Title.
S605.5 .G88   2004
631.5'84'09794—dc22   2003016040

Manufactured in the United States of America

13   12   11   10   09   08   07   06   05
10   9   8   7   6   5   4   3   2

To Mel
For Sierra

Contents

Tables

Abbreviations

BIFS	Biologically Integrated Farming Systems
BIOS	Biologically Integrated Orchard Systems
BSE	bovine spongiform encephalopathy
Bt	*Bacillus thuringiensis*
CAFF	Community Alliance with Family Farmers
CAN	California Action Network
CCOF	California Certified Organic Farmers
CDFA	California Department of Food and Agriculture
CIRS	California Institute of Rural Studies
COFA	California Organic Farmers Association
	California Organic Foods Act
CSA	community supported agriculture
EPA	Environmental Protection Agency
FAIR	Federal Agriculture Improvement and Reform Act
FDA	Food and Drug Administration
FIFRA	Federal Insecticide, Fungicide, and Rodenticide Act
FQPA	Food Quality Protection Act
FVO	Farm Verified Organic

GATT   General Agreement on Tariffs and Trade

GEO   genetically engineered organism

IFOAM   International Federation of Organic Agriculture Movements

IPM   integrated pest management

IRS   Internal Revenue Service

LISA   Low-Input Sustainable Agriculture program

NAFTA   North American Free Trade Agreement

NGO   nongovernment organization

NOP   National Organic Program

NOSB   National Organic Standards Board

OC   Organic Certifiers

OCC   Organic Certifiers Council

OCIA   Organic Crop Improvement Association

OFARM   Organic Farmers for Relationship Marketing

OFPA   Organic Food Production Act

OFPANA   Organic Foods Production Association of North America

OFRF   Organic Farming Research Foundation

OGBA   Organic Growers and Buyers Association

OMRI   Organic Materials Research Institute

OTA   Organic Trade Association

QAI   Quality Assurance International

SARE   Sustainable Agriculture Research and Education program

SCS   Scientific Certification Systems

UC-SAREP   University of California's Sustainable Agriculture Research and Education Program

UFW   United Farm Workers

USDA   United States Department of Agriculture

Acknowledgments

As with all work products, this book has resulted from the efforts, ideas, and personal support of many different people. Gaining access to usable data was probably the biggest challenge of this research project. I would like to thank Don Villarejo, Merissa Wright, and other folks at the California Institute for Rural Studies for access to and assistance with their all-important database of California growers. I am equally grateful to Ray Green, who heads the organic program at the California Department of Food and Agriculture (CDFA), for his help in obtaining what is allegedly public information of California organic growers and certifiers. Erica Walz at the Organic Farming Research Foundation (OFRF) graciously sent me database information, as Libby McCulley did at California Certified Organic Farmers (CCOF); Libby also gave me access to some of CCOF's archival materials. In general, I have appreciated CCOF's policy of organizational transparency, often lacking among other organic certification agencies.

I am deeply grateful to the many growers who let me into their trucks, fields, offices, and homes, where almost all of my interviews occurred. Most of them were eager to have someone come look at and talk about their operations, and I found them to be both forthcoming and generous in our discussions. On several occasions I returned from interview trips with bags full of avocados, apples, garlic, melons, dates, raisins, almonds, and so forth, a nice side benefit of such research. I also appreciate the honesty and willingness of others with whom I spoke at length:

representatives from all the certifiers with significant operations in California (except for the always elusive Quality Assurance International) and various industry advocates. Bob Scowcroft (of OFRF), especially, continues to be a vocal and generous contributor to the growing body of oral history regarding the organic movement.

I am indebted to several people at the University of California at Santa Cruz whose work parallels my own. Sean Swezey, at the Center for Agroecology and Sustainable Food Systems (who has since become the director of the Sustainable Agriculture Research and Education Program at Davis), gave me invaluable technical advice in devising a system by which to evaluate growers' agroecological practices. I have also benefited from the ongoing discussions, formal and otherwise, with others in the "agro-foodie" group, including Patricia Allen, Melanie DuPuis, Margaret FitzSimmons, Bill Friedland, David Goodman, Mike Goodman, and Tim Vos, among others.

I am profoundly thankful to members of my dissertation committee, who helped shape my thinking and guided the process. Michael Watts, my chair, provided both sage advice and uncanny perceptiveness; his unspoken standards of academic excellence pushed me to go further and deeper than I might have otherwise thought possible. Dick Walker has been both a friend and an invaluable mentor, particularly in the postdoctoral phases of preparing this piece; thanks to DW, I now see through a new lens the California landscapes I know so well from past work and play. Rachel Schurman introduced me to what turned out to be a critical body of theory for the book. Miriam Wells's research on strawberry production along California's central coast turned out to be an exemplar of the type of commodity study I wanted to do, both in its depth of method (which I could not hope to replicate) and its analytical coherence. I am also thankful to others whose course work was particularly influential in my academic training: Laura Enriquez, Louise Fortmann, Paul Groth, Gillian Hart, Nancy Peluso, and Allen Pred.

In the course of graduate training and preparing this book, I also benefited from the intellectual and personal support of Aaron Bobrow-Strain, William Boyd, Sharad Chari, Jill Esbenshade, Susanne Freidberg, Christy Getz, Denny Kelso, Jake Kosek, Kathy McAfee, Liz Oglesby, Scott Prudham, and Victoria Randlett, among others. I want to acknowledge especially James McCarthy, who, without any formal incentive, was a dependable mentor through every important milestone of graduate school, as well as an enthusiast of the well-timed snide remark. Likewise, I credit Amy Ross, who, without failure, sometimes aggravatingly so, made me think about everything in entirely new and different ways. Wendy Wolford remains an exemplar of unbridled enthusiasm and tenacity and a loyal friend.

Chris Benner, Jill Esbenshade, Jonathan London, Liz Oglesby, Wendy Wolford, and Steve Wolf gave both substantive feedback and editorial attention to earlier drafts. Much appreciation is extended to Jerry Kohn, lifelong friend and intellectual fellow traveler, for a thorough read of an earlier version of the manuscript. I am grateful for the intellectually generous comments of Sally Fairfax, Melanie DuPuis, and one anonymous reviewer, as well as ongoing advice and assistance from Monica McCormick at the University of California Press. Many thanks to Jacqueline Volin for ushering the production process along and Robin Whitaker for careful copyediting.

This research was financially supported by grants from the National Science Foundation (SBR-9711262), UC Sustainable Agriculture Research and Education Program, the Association of American Geographers, and the Geography Department at UC Berkeley. Nat Vonnegut of the Geography Department displayed supreme competence in dealing with administrative matters related to my dissertation.

Finally, when we think of a dissertation and book as a collective work enterprise of the academy, we often forget to acknowledge the labor of those who make it possible to devote such efforts to reading, thinking, researching, and writing. For this, I express deep gratitude to the teachers at UC Child Care and Emerson Elementary, who competently and lovingly helped raise my child for several years in the course of my graduate training and postdoctoral work. I also want to acknowledge the producers at the Berkeley farmers' market (especially Full Belly, Blue Heron, Riverdog, Kashiwase, and Woodleaf, whose principals have been intellectually generous as well in terms of this study, but also Swanton Berry Farms, the only strawberry or organic grower with a United Farm Workers contract), and the many workers they employ, for providing the gorgeous, fresh, seasonal, tasty, nutritious, and, yes, mainly organic foods that my family and I have come to make the cornerstone of our daily food intake. Of course, my deepest gratitude extends to my partner, Michael McCormick, for all that he does, and to Sierra, my beautiful daughter, for continuing to flourish with a mom pulled in many directions.

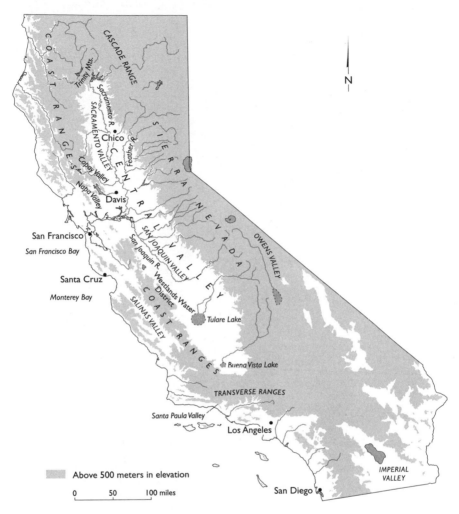

N

COAST RANGES

CASCADE RANGE

Trinity Mts.

Sacramento R.

SACRAMENTO VALLEY

SIERRA

CENTRAL

Chico

Feather R.

Capay Valley

Napa Valley

Davis

San Francisco

San Francisco Bay

SAN JOAQUIN VALLEY

San Joaquin R.

Westlands Water District

NEVADA

OWENS VALLEY

Santa Cruz

Monterey Bay

COAST RANGES

SALINAS VALLEY

VALLEY

Tulare Lake

Buena Vista Lake

TRANSVERSE RANGES

Santa Paula Valley

Los Angeles

IMPERIAL VALLEY

San Diego

Above 500 meters in elevation

0   50   100 miles

Map 1. California

Far North

Trinity

Humboldt

Cascade-
Sierra

North
Valley

Butte

Mendocino

North
Coast

Yolo

Sonoma   Napa

Solano

Marin

Solano-
Yolo

Santa Cruz

Merced

East
Valley

Cascade-
Sierra

San
Benito

Fresno

Central
Coast

Monterey

Kings

Tulare

San Luis
Obispo

Kern

West
Valley

San Bernardino

South
Coast

Santa
Barbara

Ventura

Southwest

Desert
Valleys

Riverside

Southwest

Imperial

San Diego

N

0   50   100 miles

Map 2. Study regions

CHAPTER I

Agrarian Dreams

Care about social justice issues? Labor and employment practices by agribusiness, health problems related to pesticides [ap-
plied] by farm labor, and the security of the small family
farmer are related issues. If corporate farms continue their
takeover of our food supply, then these businesses and their
giant trading corporate partners can set the price of basic food
commodities, dictate the wages and working conditions of
farmworkers, and put family farms out of business through
the consolidation of landholdings and economies of scale. Pol-
luting farming practices and poor labor conditions are cheaper
and are more likely to occur if corporations are allowed to
continue taking over our food production. Preserving the family and small-scale farm that can employ alternative methods
and that can produce food for local consumption ensures food
safety and is more environmentally sound than industrialized
farming methods, and the organic industry is made up of primarily small-sized producers. We have not fully addressed the
issues of sustainability within the growing organic industry,
but that question may become moot if these laws [the first set
of organic rules proposed by the USDA in 1997] are passed.
Lower standards will allow for a greater takeover of organic
farming by agribusiness and put the small producer out of
work and off the land.

> Claire Cummings, commentator on food
> and farming on KPFA radio

I feel that the motivation of the people growing this way coin-
cides with my concerns about the health of the planet. . . .
[Organic farmers] are motivated by belief, not profit margin.

> Patricia Unterman, food writer,
> *San Francisco Examiner,* 1998

The turn-of-the-millennium years have been nothing less than extraordinary in exposing the public health, environmental, and moral risks of industrialized agriculture. Each new round of news stories, whether about genetically engineered foods, mad cow disease, hoof-and-mouth disease, *E. coli* contamination, or pesticide poisoning, reinforces the idea that our system for growing and processing food has run amok. The surprising popularity of books such as Eric Schlosser's *Fast Food Nation,* Michael Pollan's *Botany of Desire,* and Marion Nestle's *Food Politics,* in addition to a wealth of titles focused on individual food commodities, speaks to heightened public interest in the production and consumption of food. It is becoming increasingly difficult not to think about what goes into our mouths.

In this era of escalating food politics, Claire Cummings has voiced what many believe: organic farming is the agrarian answer. Not only does it counter all of the objectionable by-products of industrial agriculture; it is also the clear antidote to corporate food provision, enabling the resuscitation of the small family farm. Echoing her sentiments, many writers such as Pollan, Schlosser, and others have concluded their books with accolades for organic farming, emphasizing its difference from industrial agriculture. Pollan suggests that organic farming "can't be reconciled to the logic of a corporate food chain" (2001a, 224); Schlosser waxes rhapsodic about an organic-cattle rancher who claims "nature is smart as hell" (2001a, 255). Meanwhile, many practitioners and loyal consumers link organic farming to a new agrarianism that will save the family farm. Some even talk about a "rural renaissance" in reference to the current vigor of direct marketing that supports farms of relatively small size.[1]

This book casts doubt on the current wisdom about organic food and agriculture, at least as it has evolved in California. In an empirical sense, it refutes these popular portrayals. Many people presume that institutions within the organic sector operate according to a different logic than that of the agribusiness firms that drive the industrialization and globalization of food provision. This book shows that the organic sector itself is "industrializing" and "globalizing" at a rapid pace. It tells how organic farming rarely meets the ideal of "farming in nature's image" (Soule and Piper 1992). And it argues that the organic movement has fallen woefully short of addressing the social justice issues that are often assumed to be part and parcel of organic farming. However, it is not good enough—indeed it could be construed as highly irresponsible—simply to recount the ways in which organic farming does not live up to the discourses that support it. The main purpose of this book is to explain *how* organic farming has replicated what it set out to oppose. First, however, it is important to take stock of what organic agriculture was intended to be.

THE ORGANIC CRITIQUE

Unfortunately, the only serious critics of industrial
farming per se [are] those who comprise what can be
loosely called "the organic-farming movement."

Colin Duncan, *The Centrality of Agriculture*

At first glance, organic farming seems to represent a clear opposition to industrial agriculture, defined for the moment as that which is made more factorylike in order to be more productive and profitable.[2] Organic farming ostensibly incorporates and builds upon complicated natural systems, in sharp contrast to the simplification and standardization that often characterize industrial agriculture (Ikerd 2001). Organic producers putatively embrace farm self-sufficiency and whole foods to the certain detriment of agribusiness, which commodifies inputs and processes that were once produced or carried out on the farm or in household kitchens (Goodman, Sorj, and Wilkinson 1987). The organic movement supposedly puts rural livelihoods first, suggesting an attention to the social justice issues that have been shunted to the side in the interest of farm productivity and "feeding the world."

In truth, it is impossible to divine a singular argument and meaning for organic agriculture. The unification of themes into an organic movement has not been without contradictions and exclusions, and many contemporary understandings of organic agriculture are not even complementary.[3] Moreover, there has always been a tension between those who see organic agriculture as simply a more ecologically benign approach to farming and those who seek a radical alternative to a hegemonic food system. These unresolved tensions continue to surface in ongoing battles over the regulation of "organically grown food," and as this book will show, even the idea of regulation is contested. But even though the organic movement has never agreed on the extent to which its alternatives should be embedded in noncapitalist forms of production, it has gained coherence and momentum through the shared awareness that the undesirable aspects of mass food production are at least in part the result of profit-driven agricultural industrialization.

Most observers of the organic farming movement would also agree that its ideological compass derives from four broadly defined social movements: the various campaigns centered on alternative production technologies, the health and pure food crusades, the 1960s counterculture, and modern environmentalism.[4] Also present in each of these movements—although not without controversy—were elements of a more radical interpretation of the industrialization critique. What follows is a brief sketch of how each of these movements has contributed to the industrialization critique.[5]

Clearly the most influential critique, as far as organic *farming* goes, turns on the consequences of intensive agricultural production.[6] Although interest in the relationship between agricultural practices and soil fertility goes at least as far back as the sixteenth century (Thirsk 1997), strong concern about the effects of modern agricultural practices materialized in the late nineteenth century, when "mining the soil" was associated with a worldwide glut in wheat production. An Englishman, Sir Albert Howard, considered by many to be the father of organic agriculture, was one of the first to articulate an alternative to agriculture as usual, on the basis of his work in India in the early part of the twentieth century. Over the course of his lifetime, he published several books describing composting techniques, touting the importance of humus and the reuse of agricultural wastes on the farm, and urging the elimination of chemical inputs because of their effects on soil fertility (see, e.g., Howard 1940). It was this work that inspired Lady Eve Balfour to found, in 1946, the Soil Association, the United Kingdom's first organic farming organization (Mergentime 1994). In some of Howard's writings he also made an explicit connection between the quest for profit and the degenerative aspects of modern agriculture (Peters 1979).

In the United States, a critique of productivity-focused agriculture emerged in the 1930s, a confluence of depressed agricultural prices and the ecological disaster of the dust bowl (Worster 1979). A "permanent agriculture" movement arose, calling for soil conservation measures such as terracing and cover cropping. Occasionally those in the permanent agriculture movement made the claim that the problem with conventional agricultural was its dependence on technology and science, which stressed the domination of nature for production and profit (Beeman 1995). In 1940, J. I. Rodale purchased an experimental organic farm in Emmaus, Pennsylvania, to test Howard's theories, as well as his own ideas about health and nutrition.[7] Although Rodale steered clear of left-wing critiques of agriculture, the raison d'être for his farm was to ex-

periment with techniques that were clearly being shunned by the agricultural research establishment (Peters 1979).

Earlier food movements made a second major contribution to the industrialization critique. The original movement for the U.S. Pure Food
Act began in the late nineteenth century to address both intentional and
unintentional contamination of food. Its initial concern was food adul-
teration, a widespread phenomenon when processed food was first marketed in impersonal, extraregional markets and bulk-producing additives
were introduced as a cost-reduction measure. The Pure Food Act established a system of regulation, although that system primarily benefited
the major food manufacturers, who could most easily comply with the
new bureaucratic standards (Levenstein 1988). It also unleashed a still-
to-be-quieted concern that food safety could easily be compromised in
the pursuit of profit and productivity.[8] Moreover, the journalistic muck-
raking (such as Upton Sinclair's *The Jungle*) that produced the necessary
political momentum for the Pure Food Act suggested an important connection between poor working conditions and compromised food. Recent exposés, such as Nicols Fox's *Spoiled* (1997), Schlosser's *Fast Food
Nation* (2001), and Pollan's article "Power Steer" in the *New York
Times Magazine* (2002), continue in that vein, driving home the point
that intensified methods of livestock production and handling are largely
to blame for recent problems with bacterial contamination in food.

The connections between the organic farming movement and the
health food movement are even more explicit, as both Belasco (1989)
and Peters (1979) show. The most direct connection was first made by
Rodale Press, publisher of both *Prevention,* a popular health-focused
magazine, and the magazine *Organic Gardening.* Each promoted the
messages of the other. But there was an important idiomatic association,
as well, for *organic* connoted both "natural" and "whole," the two
words most often used to suggest foods that have been minimally transformed by human manipulation. Starting in the 1830s with the whole
wheat crusade, led by Sylvester Graham of graham cracker fame, health
food advocates saw a unique value in whole, or less-processed, foods,
suspecting that they offer important synergies, undiscovered life-
enhancing properties (e.g., antioxidants), and protection from dangerous
additives. Adelle Davis, a popular health food writer of the 1960s, lam-
basted the food processing industry for promoting foods that were nu-
tritionally debilitated, the sort of critique that was furthered in the 1970s
by groups such as the Center for Science in the Public Interest, Ralph
Nader's "Raiders," and a rash of book publications that denounced the

food system (Levenstein 1993). Since food processing is such an important source of profit in the American economy, this critique, too, had radical implications.

Utopian experiments and back-to-the-land movements provided a third major influence on the organic farming movement. As early as the 1930s, at least two rural experiments that combined nonchemical agriculture with communal living had emerged. One was associated with Ralph Borsodi; the other with Scott Nearing. Borsodi was avowedly antagonistic to capitalism and favored decentralized subsistence agriculture, not a reinvigoration of the one- or two-crop capitalist family farm (Beeman 1995). Nearing was a disaffected radical academic who through fifty years of "homesteading" with his partner, Helen, became an icon of the counterculture (Jacob 1997). Both served as models for a new back-to-the-land movement that started in the late 1960s.

By 1965, the so-called New Left—differentiated from the Old Left by interest in decentralized, utopian, and non-class-based forms of political action—was looking at alternative institutions as a way of modeling social change (Gottleib 1993). Between 1965 and 1970, disaffected urban radicals formed thirty-five hundred communes in the U.S. countryside, where small groups of individuals and families pooled their resources to create subsistence-style farms (Belasco 1989). Most of these communes practiced what were later codified as organic techniques, not necessarily by intention, but because self-sufficiency was a cornerstone of their ideology. Though their success was marginal at best—many of the failures were attributed to shortages of food—what was radical was the link between an alternative farming system and a collective form of ownership. Following the Nearings' path, there was also a significant migration to rural areas of individual families who sought a more private existence, mostly on privately owned land (Jacob 1997).

The urban component of food politics was equally critical, not only modeling alternative food-delivery institutions, but also forging direct links with the countryside. Food cooperatives, which involved direct employee ownership and management of retail stores or food businesses (many of which were bakeries), and so-called food conspiracies, in which members pooled money and bought weekly from nearby suppliers, became commonplace in many cities and college towns. Between 1969 and 1979, five thousand to ten thousand such institutions were established, grossing more than $500 million a year (Belasco 1989). Many linked up with nearby organic farms as sources of supply. In addition, many paid at least vague attention to issues of hunger and poverty, offering discount prices to low-income consumers, food-for-work programs, or even free handouts.

During this period, *organic* most clearly became understood as a critique. According to Belasco, *organic* and *natural* were used more or less interchangeably, although *organic* had "wider implications," since it addressed not only what happens during factory processing but also what occurs at the farm. Organic agriculture was envisioned as a system of small-scale local suppliers whose direct marketing, minimal processing, and alternative forms of ownership explicitly challenged the established food system. Thus, the "organic paradigm" straddled three countercurrents: "therapeutic self-enhancement, consumerist self-protection, and alternative production. . . . Organically raised food required a completely new system of food production and distribution, and with that, major social decentralization" (1989, 69). So, while the "counter-cuisine" incorporated several different themes—including survivalist (i.e., getting along on little), antimodernist (i.e., valorizing craft production), "health foodist," or explicit criticism of the food industry—*organic* agriculture was considered oppositional indeed.

The fourth movement to contribute substantially to the ideology of the organic farming movement is environmentalism, although not as directly as one might imagine. Rachel Carson's publication of *Silent Spring* in 1962 is considered by many to be the birth of the modern U.S. environmental movement, but it did not immediately awaken significant interest in organic agriculture. Carson put considerable distance between herself and the organic movement. For its part, the U.S. environmental movement was focused on the conservation of pristine nature at the expense of other environmental considerations and did not take seriously Carson's pronouncements of the dangers of pesticide use (Gottleib 1993).

By 1970, the year of the first Earth Day, the environmental movement had broadened its issue base. A groundswell of apocalyptic thinking, sparked by stories of famine in South Asia and Africa, pronouncements of uncontrollable population growth, and the experience of the worldwide oil crisis of 1973, reignited concerns about energy use and the finiteness of resources in general. These typically neo-Malthusian concerns, along with on-the-ground failures of the green revolution, gave birth to "sustainable development," the idea that economic development had to proceed with attention to the resource needs of future generations. In some circles, notions of sustainability also incorporated social justice concerns, particularly to the extent that existing poverty was linked with environmental degradation.[9] A key treatise of this era was Francis Moore

Lappé's *Diet for a Small Planet* (1971), an argument for vegetarianism that based its claim on the resource intensiveness of the feed grain–livestock complex and its implications for world hunger. This justification for vegetarianism was particularly powerful in moving the emphasis out of the realm of individual ethics to the international political economy of agriculture. The implicit link between vegetarianism and organic agriculture arguably imbued the latter with similar justification.

Another way in which the idea of sustainable development has influenced organic farming is through the "appropriate technology" movement, emboldened by Barry Commoner's slogan "small is beautiful" (Buttel 1994). The gist of the appropriate technology critique is the notion that technology and science have been captured by large state and agribusiness interests. Were the institutions that produce and disseminate technology more decentralized and popularly controlled, they would better serve those excluded from or hurt by so-called big science. The failure of earlier utopian experiments in actually producing food reinforced the idea that more attention had to be paid to the science of agriculture (Levenstein 1993). New Alchemy Institute, a Massachusetts-based ecological think tank formed in the early 1970s, was one such institution established to meet that goal; its purpose was to make small-scale farming and other smallholding ventures viable (Belasco 1989; Peters 1979).

In addition, the organic farming movement has drawn from the more recently articulated environmentalist notion of bioregionalism (Sale 1985; Kloppenberg, Henrickson, and Stevenson 1996). The appropriation of the idea of "foodsheds"—a term that plays on John Wesley Powell's exhortations regarding the importance of watershed-based regions (see Stegner 1953)—is to draw attention to seasonality and other agronomic constraints, which, if followed, presumably would put less pressure on land and other elements of nature. Locally scaled distribution networks might also substantially reduce the number of "food miles" necessary for trading food, leading to a dramatic savings of fossil fuel energy. Insofar as the globalization of food distribution has turned on overcoming obstacles of distance and durability (Friedmann 1994), bioregionalist notions also intersect with a critique of globalization.[10]

The "scientization" of the environmental movement—as scientific legitimacy has routinely been attached to claims of environmental degradation—has also given organic farming heretofore missing legitimacy (Buttel 1992). The energy crisis of the early 1970s opened up scientific discussion of the relationship between energy and agriculture. Subsequently, the National Science Foundation, with a good deal of outside encouragement, commissioned a study that compared organic and conventional farming systems. Its chief investigator, William Lockeretz, had strong credentials in mainstream science (Peters 1979). The study, published in 1975, demonstrated that organic systems use less energy derived from fossil fuels. Then a USDA report in 1980 gave "grudging respect" to organic agriculture by dismissing previous misconceptions and noting the scientific methods being employed in organic farms (Beeman 1995). Separately, the scientific linkage of pesticides with cancer, ozone depletion, and other such horrors, though ceaselessly contested, continued to generate careful scrutiny of agricultural chemicals, even though regulation of these chemicals remained woefully inadequate.

This link to science potentially has undermined the radical critique of industrial agriculture that all four formative movements have in some sense shared. The increased support of science has reinforced a technical approach to environmental problem solving, relegating social issues to the status quo (Buttel 1994).[11] But what of the agrarianist vision for organic agriculture? How does it stand in relation to these formative movements?

THE AGRARIANIST VISION

A mind overloaded with work, which in agriculture
means too much acreage, covers the place like a
stretched membrane—too short in some places, broken
by strain in others, too thin everywhere. The overloaded mind tries to solve its problems by oversimplify-
ing itself and its place—that is, by industrialization. It
ceases to work at the necessary likeness between the
processes of farming and the processes of nature and
beings to order the farm on the assumption that it
should and can be like a factory. It gives up diversity
for monoculture. It gives up the complex strategies of
independence (the use of manure, of crop rotations, of
solar and animal power, etc.) for a simple dependence
on industrial suppliers (and on credit).

> Wendell Berry, "Whose Head Is the Farmer Using?
> Whose Head Is Using the Farmer?"

We must see again, as I think the founders of our government saw, that the most appropriate governmental
powers are negative—those, that is, that protect the

small and weak from the great and powerful. .... the
governmental power that can be used most effectively
to assure the equitable distribution of property, which
alone can give some measure of strength and independence to ordinary citizens, is that of taxation. As our
present economy clearly shows, the small can survive
only if the great are restrained.

Wendell Berry, *The Unsettling of America*

Cutting across all four of the movements mentioned, contemporary agrarian populism shares many of the same elements of this broadly construed
"industrialization" critique, in, for example, its concern with corporate
power, the role of big science in agro-industrialization, and the implicit
links between the social organization of farming and ecological outcomes.
A key difference, though, is that agrarian populism specifically locates
these problems with the growth and consolidation of the corporate input
and food processing sectors *at the expense of the family farm*. As such, the
new agarianism sees the family-owned and -operated, small-scale farm as
the locus of, indeed the key to, social justice and ecological sustainability.[12] Moreover, and in contrast to the counterculture critique, it places
tremendous value on farmer independence rather than collective action.

The agrarian vision is, of course, deeply rooted in U.S. political and
cultural history and has emerged repeatedly as a trope of anticorporate
sentiment. It originated with Thomas Jefferson, who opposed the cen-
tralized power sought by the Federalists. He preferred a weak federal
government and argued that only agriculture and landownership could
ensure independence and virtue, thereby providing the basis for a re-
publican democracy (White 1991, 63). The vision of a nation of small,
like-sized, and, ultimately, white farmers undergirded the clearance of
Indians, as well as the major land giveaways of the nineteenth century,
including the Homestead Act of 1862. After the so-called closing of the
frontier, agrarianism was revitalized during the populist moment of the
1890s, when western farmers fought the monopoly power of the rail-
roads and middlemen. Agrarianism saw another resurgence after the
dust bowl tragedy of the 1930s, when the dust storms were attributed to
agricultural consolidation and mechanization, which had pushed poor
tenant farmers west to become "sodbusters" (Worster 1979). The link
between ecology and farm structure first articulated by the permanent
agriculture movement evolved into a call for reinvigoration of the family unit of production.

This battle cry was taken up by Wendell Berry, who became a key spokesperson for the agrarianist vision in the latter part of the twentieth century. He explained the problem of soil degradation specifically in terms of an ecological breakdown of the grain-based family farming unit, which had been compelled to overproduce to make up for falling prices, exhausting its presumably freehold land. Wes Jackson, currently affiliated with the Land Institute in Kansas, became another carrier of these arguments, also emphasizing notions of cultural renewal and ethical revival (Beeman 1995). Jackson and Berry continue to be influential. The coupling of sustainable agriculture with the salvation of the family farm is explicitly spelled out in Marty Strange's 1988 book, *Family Farming: A New Economic Vision.*

Because the agrarianist vision has become so potent within organic agriculture, it is worth elaborating the assumptions underlying the descriptors of "the family-owned and -operated, small-scale farm." First, freehold ownership is the desired form of land tenure, as it putatively provides the basis of economic security and, hence, farmer independence. Drawing from Locke's political philosophy positing that he who mixes his labor with land to put it to productive use is the rightful owner, the specific norm here is a yeoman farmer, one who works his own land and nothing more. In newer iterations of agrarianism, notions of individual ownership are also tightly coupled with notions of stewardship; only owners, it is presumed, have interest in the long-term viability of the land.[13] As Strange puts it, the family-owned farm "encourages (imperfectly) the responsible use of resources" (1984, 19). Then, in return for valuing the long-term fertility of the farm and practicing ecological farming methods, the farmer-owner will generate greater returns in the market and stave off the demise of this family-owned farm.

The agrarian ideal is also an owner-*operated* farm, self-sufficient to the extent that family members provide all the necessary labor, and farm income is sufficient to pay all farm and family needs. In the more explicitly Christian vision of Berry, the household is the last bastion against cultural estrangement (Berry 1986).[14] In the more secularized version, "farms are family centered because the family is the logical unit of production within which to transfer skills and to provide inter-generational continuity in the farm's management" (Strange 1984, 118). Either way, hiring outside labor is considered a sort of moral failing. The ecological link is that a diversified cropping system ostensibly smoothes labor demands, mitigates market risks, and reduces the need for inputs, thereby

improving the possibilities of meeting the condition of family operator-
ship (Strange 1988).

The small scale of such farms is equally critical to this vision. Not
only is smallness considered a social good in its own right; this norm
also assumes a symbiosis between the scale of a unit of production and
its ecological ramifications. "A healthy farm not only will have the right
proportion of plants and animals; it will have the right proportion of
people. There will not be so many as to impoverish themselves and the
farm, but there will be enough to care for it fully and properly without
overwork" (Berry 1986, 182). A farm with too many acres will also
give way to simplification, the progenitor of ecological destruction.
Jackson sees the problem as one of information management. As he
puts it, the inevitable loss of biological diversity in a managed farm
means that "the price for sustainability must be paid from elsewhere.
[One must] substitute cultural information for biological information"
(1984, 226). The necessity of a low "eyes-to-crop ratio" is one of the
reasons that the family farm is seen as the ideal organizational form.
This assumes, of course, that only family members are seen as adequately enfranchised to monitor and act on what happens in the field.[15]

Finally, the new agrarianism, like all agrarian populism, is deeply sus-
picious of state intervention, does not question the individuation of markets, and, most fundamentally, remains a defense of private property
(Brass 1997). So, deeply suspect of scientific and bureaucratic rational-
ity precisely for its effect on the social aspects of farming, the agrarianist social vision could be construed as deeply conservative. Yet, these last
qualities are exactly what has made it so attractive to the organic farming movement. The organic movement has always been distrustful of
government intervention, given the ways that federal farm programs and
the USDA have encouraged and even subsidized the worst sort of farming practices. Many back-to-the-landers, moreover, value their independence and have become property owners themselves.

In short, many in the organic movement have come to embrace these
elements of the new agrarianism, equating both social justice and ecological sustainability with small-scale family farming. Because of this
conceptualization, the movement has come to focus largely on *form*, in
particular the proportionality of big farms versus small farms. Instead,
as this book will show, the movement would do better to pay attention
to the *processes* of social and ecological exploitation that gave rise to the
organic critique in the first place.

THE PLACE OF CALIFORNIA

I'm a small family farmer in the Central Valley. . . .
Organic farming is a way of gaining independence from
the corporate structures that undermine the agrarian
tradition.

> Ted Willey, T & D Willey Farms, California Studies
> Conference, San Francisco State University,
> February 1997

California never had much of an agrarian smallholder tradition. Land was never farmed in a mode resembling premodern peasant societies. Most California native groups were not agriculturists, and the relics of mission agriculture were mostly eradicated shortly after statehood in 1848. Nor was California settled by a large class of landowning farmers who had holdings of similar size and nature, where family members performed the necessary labor. Large landholdings became the basis of farming from shortly after the gold rush, when an elite few brought much of its hinterland under monopolistic control (McWilliams [1935] 1971; Liebman 1997). When these landholdings were finally split up in the late part of the nineteenth century, they were made viable by intensive and specialized fruit production, which fundamentally depended on hired labor, racialized and marginalized to ensure the cheapness and flexibility to meet intermittent labor requirements (Almaguer 1994; Daniel 1981; Leibman 1983; among others). In other words, California agriculture was industrial from the get-go, characterized by what Carey McWilliams termed "factories in the field," an observation echoed by the likes of Walter Goldschmidt and John Steinbeck, two other published critics of California's industrial agriculture.

Today, California ranks sixth among nations in its agricultural economy and has been the number-one agricultural state in the United States for more than fifty years. Its 1997 output was $26.8 billion, approximately 10 percent of total U.S. production, with Texas a distant second at $15.9 billion. This rank is largely due to California's preeminence in high-value specialty-crop production; that same year it accounted for more than half of all U.S. production in fruit, nut, and vegetable crops and exported 20 percent of what it grew (California Department of Food and Agriculture 2000). Furthermore, all this production took place on only 3 percent of the state's acreage, suggesting an extraordinary degree of intensification (U.S. Bureau of the Census 1999). California has led the way in technologies that both reduce the risks of nature and speed up crop turnover, from cooperative fruit marketing, plant breeding, bi-

ological control, in-field transplant and harvest mechanization, to the
generous use of petroleum-based fertilizers. California has the highest
rate of pesticide application in the country (Liebman 1997).

As for the agricultural landscape, it is marked by

> fields and orchards [that] were designed to produce great quantities of
> cheap food. And to accomplish that . . . there must be high-input industrial
> efficiency. Fields are laser-leveled as flat as tabletops. Rows are precision-
> spaced with food crops bred to accommodate machinery and to last on
> store shelves. First the earth is drilled with synthetic fertilizers developed
> from the same research that perfected explosives and poison gas in World
> War II and then it's pumped with fumigants and doused with herbicides to
> inhibit soil-borne disease and retard the growth of weeds. Crops are
> sprayed and dusted with broad-spectrum insecticides that kill harmful in-
> sects, along with most others, in order to maintain high yields and guaran-
> tee consistency of appearance. (Ableman 1993, 74)

> You assume these are farms, but this is not what you see when you close your
> eyes and think "farms." Farms are in the country and this is definitely not the
> country. . . . Only the cars and trucks that occasionally speed by along the
> two-lane roads that frame these anonymous fields suggest human life. (68)

Finally, virtually all farms are organized as capitalist enterprises, relying
heavily on the employment of wage labor.[16] But this sort of observation has
never stopped agriculturists from evoking agrarian dreams; to be sure, the
rhetoric of the family farm remains pervasive. Victor Davis Hanson, a fruit
grower (i.e., de facto employer) and classics scholar, in *Field without
Dreams* (1996), laments, "The American yeoman is doomed; his end is part
of an evolution of long duration; and so for historical purposes his last generation provides a unique view of the world—a superior view I will argue—
that is to be no more" (xi). Later, "the most perilous family farms seem to
be those in our own size range, between 80 and 200 acres" (266).

Organic California

Just as California agriculture has been characterized as "the great exception" (McWilliams 1949), so can the same be said for organic agriculture within California. For alongside this industrial rurality arose one
of the most countercultural branches of the organic farming movement.
Predominantly urban in origin, many of California's first organic farmers were first-generation growers who saw organic farming as an explicit
antidote to the excesses of industrial agriculture. In the interests of creating a different kind of agrarian dream, these growers carved their
farms from the leftover spaces—the hillsides, pastures, abandoned or-

chards, urban sand lots, and tiny river valleys—making "farms" of one, two, or perhaps ten arable acres. Farming to them was not a business but a lifestyle. Having such small farms, some households were able to do all the work themselves; others relied on the occasional support of neighbors, visiting friends, and interested college students. They grew basic fruits and vegetables such as apples, oranges, peaches, lettuce, carrots, and tomatoes. They made their own compost from kitchen scraps, cow or horse manure, and the inedible portions of the crops they grew. They rarely worried about bugs or fungi, content to grow fruit with a few worms and blemishes and vegetables with holey leaves. Most of the produce was sold to local health food stores and food cooperatives, where customers did not expect their purchases to be cosmetically perfect. Indeed, perfection would be cause to doubt that they were grown organically.

These farms did not just spring up out of the blue. California had long hosted the sort of experimentation that gave rise to the organic farming movement. Southern California, for example, was a formative center of the health food movement. As early as the 1870s, people suffering from tuberculosis and other such infirmities began migrating to southern California for the sunny climate and restful nights; sanatoriums and health resorts were built all over the region. Many "health seekers" went into small-scale beekeeping and citrus farming, then seen as the perfect profession for the elderly and infirm (Baur 1959). Well before the 1960s revolution, southern California was sprinkled with health food stores.

The San Francisco Bay Area, meanwhile, was a key node for what Belasco called the "counter-cuisine." The San Francisco–based Diggers gave out free food to urban dwellers in city parks, procuring their produce from Morning Star Ranch, a nearby organic farm. Far-Fetched Foods, a health food store in San Francisco's Haight Ashbury district, sought organic truck gardeners as sources of supply. Hundreds of other food cooperatives, collectively run bakeries, and alternative restaurants thrived there as well.

Most famously, in 1971 Alice Waters opened a small café in Berkeley, California, named it Chez Panisse, and began to serve simple meals to her friends. Feeling that the best food was made from fresh, local, and seasonal ingredients, Waters bought most of her produce from local farms and was the first to put "organic" on the menu in what later came to be a world-renowned culinary institution. There is little question that Alice Waters pioneered a revolution in food tastes, not only inventing "California cuisine," but also, through her penchant, bringing local, organically produced food into the mix. Waters inspired a rash of imitation—many Bay Area chefs trained with Waters and went on to open their own restaurants and become celebrity chefs in their own right—and quite instrumentally contributed to the diffusion of organic consumption.[17]

The alternative production movement also had its adherents in California. In 1967, Alan Chadwick, a British-born Shakespearean actor, began a garden club at the University of California at Santa Cruz based on the premise that gardening is best done without chemical pesticides and fertilizers (Gaura 1997). Eventually the garden expanded to a twenty-five-acre farm and became the only university-run research and extension service devoted solely to organics. The program was decidedly countercultural; prevailing leftish political sentiments and a cultural milieu of what Belasco (1989) called "communal bare bones living, vegetarianism, and sexual and pharmaceutical libertarianism" created an image for organic farming that lasted long after the 1960s had passed. Nevertheless, the program played an important role in diffusing organic farming. Not only were many organic technologies tried, tested, and extended through the now-named Center for Agroecology and Sustainable Food Systems, but also its apprenticeship program spawned many private farms as well as public service gardening and farming programs.

As a result, Santa Cruz, in particular, was to become a center for the California organic farming movement as it began to take more institutional forms. The first certification agency, California Certified Organic Farmers (CCOF), began there in 1973 as a grassroots organization of small organic farmers. In 1990, Bob Scowcroft and Mark Lipson, formerly of CCOF, started the Organic Farming Research Foundation with the purpose of fostering the improvement and widespread adoption of organic farming practices (OFRF 1999).

Somewhat later, a second node of the California organic farming movement materialized in Yolo County, in proximity to the University of California at Davis (in spite of its teaching and research emphasis on industrialized farming).[18] In the late 1970s, graduates of UC Davis started the California Action Project—later to become the California Action Network (CAN)—to promote organic and sustainable agriculture. So that CAN could focus on advocacy and legislative work, a second organization was created to be the research arm: the California Institute of Rural Studies (CIRS), under the leadership of Don Villarejo. With the aid of California Rural Legal Assistance, these two organizations brought a lawsuit against the University of California for failing to fulfill its land grant mission by solely promoting large-scale chemical-intensive agriculture. Although the plaintiffs lost in appeal, as a result of this suit, the university created the Small Farm Center at UC Davis and funded the agroecology program at UC Santa Cruz.

Later, CAN was to change its name to CAFF (Community Alliance with Family Farmers) and take on a more explicitly agrarian agenda, emphasizing "family farms as the cornerstone of healthy communities." CAFF was also active in getting the federal Sustainable Agriculture Research and Education bill passed. When it received its first congressional appropriations in 1988, CAFF helped start the Sustainable Agriculture Research and Education Program at UC Davis (UC-SAREP), an organization dedicated to expanding and disseminating technical knowledge on ecological methods, as well as promoting socially responsible practices and policies. Following a divergent course, CIRS bolstered its focus on farmworker justice, although all of these Yolo County–based organizations continued to collaborate, especially in the area of ecological farming and pesticide reduction.

Meanwhile, Paul Muller and Dru Rivers, the latter of whom had helped found the organic student farm at UC Davis, met at the 1982 annual ecological farming conference, held at the Asilomar conference center. They began Full Belly Farms, choosing the Capay Valley, on the west side of Yolo County, for its beauty, pockets of rich soil, and relatively clean water from Cache Creek. The modal size of Capay Valley farms also suggested the possibility for a community of like-minded farmers (Kraus 1991). In 1989, Muller and Rivers took on as partners Judith Redmond, former executive director of CAFF, and Raoul Adamchak, who also had worked in organic farming organizations. Together, they pioneered the subscription farm, a version of community supported agriculture (CSA), which was to become the California model for directly linking farms with consumers.[19]

In short, California played a formative role in the development of the organic farming movement, as the site of several key institutions that were critical in diffusing the techniques and meanings of organic farming, and as the place where regulations for organic production first evolved. And though agrarian populism tended to dominate the more broadly defined U.S. sustainable agriculture movement, the California organic movement was, at least initially, more countercultural, borrowing heavily from the New Left critique of the 1960s. This ideological sway was largely the result of the California organic movement's growth from urban sources, reflecting California's high degree of urbanization and the deep economic conservatism of much of the state's farming pop-

ulation. Arguably, it also resulted from California agriculture representing the very pinnacle of the sort of agricultural industrialization that the
organic movement sought to criticize.

Today, California holds far more organic farms than any other state
(extrapolated from Klonsky and Tourte 1998b), is second to Idaho in the
amount of certified organic cropland, and grows 47 percent of the certified organic vegetables in the country and 66 percent of the organic fruits
(Economic Research Service 2000b). It is safe to assume that California
is a world leader in the value of organic crops sold, given both the high
value of produce crops and the projection that the United States as a
whole was to have 40 percent of world sales in 2000 (El Feki 2000). California's organic agriculture, in this way, has come to parallel the economic success of the state's agriculture in general. The possibility that
California's organic agriculture is as exceptional as the state's style of industrial agriculture, which it seeks to counter, speaks to its importance
in setting wider trends for the rest of the world. For that reason alone, it
is important to examine the outcome of this experimental cross between
a putatively radical social movement and the most industrial agriculture
in the world.

THE STUDY

This book draws from the first extensive, in-depth social science study of
organic production in California. The project emerged from earlier, more
preliminary research on northern California's organic vegetable sector
that I conducted with two colleagues in the fall of 1995 (Buck, Getz, and
Guthman 1996, 1997). At the time, we found a significant disjuncture
between the discourses of organic farming and what was taking place in
the fields, warehouses, and markets that constitute the organic vegetable
commodity chain. Our impression was that the highest-value crops and
the most lucrative segments of such chains were being appropriated by
agribusiness firms, many of which were abandoning the putatively sustainable agronomic and marketing practices associated with organic
agriculture, such as composting and direct marketing.

The much larger study on which this book is based was designed to
examine that apparent anomaly in more depth: to understand how the
organic sector evolved in the way that it did, to see if obvious patterns
exist in the organization and practices of production, and, finally, to look
at how the regulatory mechanisms that define what it is to be organic in-

fluence the structure of the sector and the ways in which production is individually managed. My findings modify our original insight considerably. For one thing, traditional agribusiness entry has been fairly protracted and remains limited. However, the organic movement has sprouted its own industry, raising the question of how agribusiness came to be replicated in the organic sector. For another thing, and more important, the original study suggested that agribusiness producers are the only ones altering the practices of organic farming. This study shows that agribusiness's impacts are more far-reaching. One might ask how agribusiness involvement in organics affects even those who strive to do things differently.

In 1997, the baseline year for the statistical portion of this study, there were 1,533 organic growers registered with the state of California, 374 (32 percent) more than the first official count in 1992 (Klonsky et al. 2001; Klonsky and Tourte 1995). There were 67,826 acres in organic production, 22,333 (49 percent) more than in 1992, and reported gross sales of $158 million, $83 million (111 percent) more than in 1992.[20] Fruit, nut, and vegetable crops accounted for 92 percent of total organic sales and 74 percent of organic acreage (Klonsky et al. 2001). In certified acreage, grapes were the most prevalent crop, followed by rice, mixed vegetables, safflower, lettuce, tree nuts, citrus, and tomatoes (Economic Research Service 2000b).

The study involved compiling survey and archival data on all 1,533 growers. The qualitative portion was primarily based on interviews with 150 growers, attendance at industry conferences, and interviews with regulatory agents, technical experts, and industry advocates. Virtually all interviews took place in 1998 and 1999. It is important to note that the grower interviews were not taken from a random sample. Instead, the sample was purposefully stratified according to region, crop mix, scale of operation, and certification status, precisely to evaluate the ways in which these variables matter in terms of practice. Most significant, a large number of what I call mixed growers (i.e., growers with both conventional and organic acreage) were sampled to better understand the dynamics of conversion to organic production, as well as to assess this prior claim of agribusiness appropriation. Moreover, the sample of mixed growers serves as a proxy to compare conventional and organic growers. Readers should refer to the appendix for a further discussion of the research approach.

THE BOOK

The story of organic agriculture's origins presented so far was designed to account for the radical origins of organic farming. Yet, embedded in the movements I have just discussed were people and ideas that brought heretofore missing legitimacy to organic agriculture. Most significant among them was the growing acceptance of environmentalism. As suggested above, increased public concern with the environmental and health effects of industrial farming was already generating support for organic farming in the late 1970s and early 1980s. This concern was sharpened with two chemical-related food scares in the late 1980s, regarding the use of Aldicarb and Alar.[21]

In addition, the 1980s saw significant changes in diet and food taste, generated by a complicated interplay of the growth of a higher income-earning professional class, breakthroughs in nutritional science, heightened global travel and migration (leading to interest in exotic and ethnic foods), and enhanced concern with bodily health (Levenstein 1993). Organic food became more desirable for its association with health food, to be sure, but also for its association with gourmet food, thanks to chef-led advocacy of organics. In particular, the gentrification of organic food, spurred, in part, by the Alice Waters diaspora, gave organic food entirely new meanings, ultimately imbuing it with more market value as well (Guthman 2003). These changes, along with the hard work of organic advocates bent on institutional legitimacy, substantially modulated organic farming's contrarian bent. Effectively, the way was cleared for an entirely new set of actors to participate in organic production.

This, then, is where my analysis picks up again, to investigate the material forces that generated such unprecedented growth and, consequently, change in the organic sector. For, I argue, it is only because these ideational shifts articulated so strongly with changes in agrarian capitalism and its regulation that erstwhile conventional growers began to experiment with organic production beginning in the 1980s. Chapter 2 details the motivations for these conversions in the context of major restructuring and regulatory changes within the global agrofood economy. Chapter 3 looks at the structure and practices of the actual existing organic sector—outcomes of this recent growth—in regard to how organic agriculture is often imagined.

Still, the analysis previewed thus far addresses only the proximate causes of organic agriculture's transformation. One might be left wondering if organic agriculture would have strayed from its ideals without these grower conversions. The ensuing analysis seeks to answer this question. It delves into the respective logics of agrarian capitalism (as it evolved in California) and regulation (as it evolved within the organic sector) to illustrate how they directly shaped organic production, particularly when they intersected in unexpected ways.

Chapters 4 and 5, accordingly, focus on the development of agrarian capitalism in California and its legacies for organic farming. Chapter 4 recapitulates California's agrarian history through the lens of three processes that have characterized industrialization in California agriculture—what I will call intensification, appropriation, and valorization. Chapter 5 considers the uneven spatial development of California agriculture to illustrate how it has affected organic agriculture.

Chapters 6 and 7 turn to the effects of regulation. But, as opposed to consideration in chapter 2, which looks at how regulation external to the organic sector helped spur its growth, these chapters consider the effects of a regulatory framework that was largely of the organic sector's own choosing. Chapter 6 describes the origins and current character of organic regulation, in both its substance and its institutional support.[22] Chapter 7 analyzes the ramifications of these now-codified definitions of organic, in terms of both grower practices and industry structure.

As the organic sector has transformed to become what Michael Pollan dubbed "the organic-industrial complex" (2001b), two responses have emerged. Some, notably those who identify with an organic *industry,* counter that organic agriculture was never meant to engender a systemic reconstruction of the entire food system but instead had the more modest goal of a more ecologically benign and healthier food supply. The effort to promote a positive alternative is laudable, yet adherents of this perspective ignore the crucial question of how the existing structural conditions of agriculture potentially limit organic farming's success even in these more modest terms.

The other response comes from those who identify with the *movement.* Disappointed with the direction organic agriculture has taken, they offer a particularly *agrarian* answer, saying that the resuscitation of the small family farm will make for healthier food, better working conditions, and locally scaled distribution (e.g., Cummings 1998). This book challenges the agrarian vision as well. My contention is that the new agrarianism, while representing the most currently popular alternative vision of organic farming, is off the mark in its critique of agricultural industrialization, including that applied to organic agriculture. The conclusion of the book, chapter 8, is effectively a retort to both positions. In addition, I ask if there are other, more productive roads toward a more ecologically benign and socially just agriculture.

This occasionally harsh treatment of organic agriculture, and by implication many who advocate it, is likely to create a good deal of controversy, for there are people who would like to discredit organic agriculture permanently. I do not count myself among them, nor is that the purpose of this book. The fact is that I do buy and eat organic food— with a good deal of conviction, at that. Despite the inconsistencies in what are considered allowable inputs, there is no question in my mind that, as a rule, organic producers are exposing farmworkers, neighbors, and eaters to far less toxicity than their conventional counterparts are. The reader will discover that I am not convinced, however, that organic agriculture *as it is currently constructed* provides a trenchant alternative to the interwoven mechanisms that simultaneously bring hunger and surplus, waste and danger, and wealth and poverty in the ways food is grown, processed, and traded. This is the primary question I wish to explore in this book.

CHAPTER 2

Finding the Way

Roads to Organic Production

Variations in individual farmers' attitudes toward agriculture
are key to understanding what influences some farmers to
adopt alternative methods.

> Leslie Duram, *"A Pragmatic Study of Conventional
> and Alternative Farmers in Colorado"*

A generation of growers entered into organic production because of deeply
held political, environmental, philosophical, and/or spiritual values. Many
came out of the counterculture or were influenced by environmental ideas
in their college years and decided to try their luck at farming. Some followed the writings of the philosophical or practical giants in sustainable
agriculture (e.g., Wes Jackson and Robert Rodale, respectively) and deliberately made the effort to put these written ideas into practice. Others were
less circumspect and simply felt that organic agriculture was somehow
"the right thing to do." Whether they "always have been and always will
be" organic growers or whether they converted to organic farming out of
clear conviction, these early entrants set the tone for organic farming by
developing a set of idioms around organic food provision that were initially impenetrable by mainstream America, perhaps by design. These
growers are most accurately ascribed to the organic movement.[1] Before the
1980s, they were virtually the only growers to populate the organic sector.

The explosive rise in organic production came after 1980, however,
amid a major restructuring in the world's agrofood economy. Marsden
(1992) and others have referred to this new period of food regulation as
"post-productivist" in juxtaposition with a period when national food security was the basis of state intervention in agriculture (particularly in Europe) before the crises of overproduction—the so-called farm crisis—that
occurred in the 1980s. Though the distinctions are possibly overdrawn,

two key aspects of postproductivism bear on the growth of organic production.[2] First, changing national support for agriculture, including the
partial and uneven post-GATT withdrawals of commodity supports and
tariff barriers to trade, altered the supply conditions by which growers
make their planting decisions.[3] Second, the perception of (First World)
plenitude, increased environmental awareness, and changing tastes and
health concerns sharpened consumer awareness of how food is made.[4]
Occasionally consumers responded with demands for more state intervention (i.e., regulation); more often, they began to buy so-called high-
quality food as well as support alternative systems of provision.[5]

These two trends intersected to provide new opportunities for value
seeking, or what I will call valorization in chapter 4. So, for instance,
changes toward purportedly healthier diets gave renewed importance to
the international trade in so-called high-value foods, specifically those
that were once deemed precious (e.g., fruits and vegetables, poultry,
dairy products, and shellfish) (Goodman and Watts 1997; Jaffee 1994).
Heightened anxiety about food safety enabled producers to commodify
characteristics such as local, traditional, or craft-made as a way of building trust (Arce and Marsden 1994; Marsden 1992; Thevenot 1998).
Even the politicized desire for what Bell and Valentine (1997) call "ethical foods," from range-fed beef to Fair Trade coffee—the very stuff that
Belasco (1989) once termed the countercuisine—were incorporated into
efforts to capture superprofits (by First World and multinational actors)
in a rapidly "globalizing" economy.[6]

California growers were not immune to these happenings. As such,
most of the post-1980s growth in the organic sector was driven by conventional growers converting to organic production. In part, they were
simply responding to changes in consumer tastes and concerns and the
mediation of this demand by key buyers. But they were also driven by
push—or supply-side factors. These factors can be grouped into two
overarching categories: one encompassing this logic of value seeking, the
other incorporating a changed regulatory environment affecting agriculture.[7] This chapter details these driving forces of organic agriculture's recent expansion by recounting the perspectives of growers who converted.
It begins with an overview of the nature and timing of growth.

THE NATURE AND TIMING OF GROWTH

In terms of numbers, the original organic movement was minute.[8] The
first organic certification program, organized by the Rodales, identified

TABLE I. GROWTH IN CALIFORNIA'S ORGANIC
SECTOR, FOR YEARS AVAILABLE

| | CCOF | | | CDFA | | |
Year	No. of Growers	No. of Acres	Average No. of Acres per Grower	No. of Growers	No. of Acres	Average No. of Acres per Grower
1973	56[a]	—	—	—	—	—
1986	164	4,964	30.3	—	—	—
1987	213	7,268	34.1	—	—	—
1988	244	13,938	57.1	—	—	—
1989	310	22,666	73.1	—	—	—
1990	402	36,310	90.3	—	—	—
1991	493	43,870	89.0	—	—	—
1992	511	52,113	102.0	1,159	42,302	36.5
1993	488	49,121	100.7	1,129	40,571	35.9
1994	528	50,409	95.5	1,372	45,070	32.9
1995	NA	54,604	NA	1,427	46,258	32.4
1996	497	58,468	117.6	1,475	54,768	37.1
1997	648	70,213	108.4	1,533	67,826	44.2

SOURCES: 1973 CCOF data: Steffen, Allen, and Foote 1972; other CCOF data: CCOF 1986,
1987, 1989, 1990, 1991, 1993, 1994, 1995, 1997, 1998; CDFA data: Klonsky and Tourte 1998;
Klonsky et al. 2001.
NOTES: CCOF data represent only *certified* acreage and growers; up to 100 percent more are
pending certification at certain times.
After 1990, CCOF figures include small amounts of out-of-state acreage.
After 1990, significant amounts of CCOF acreage were pasture or fallow (around fifteen thousand per year), and many wine grape growers certified but did not register (which was technically
illegal). CCOF acreage exceeds CDFA acreage because of these and other discrepancies in reporting
(see Klonsky and Tourte 1995 and 1998 for other caveats on the data).
[a] This figure comes from the original Rodale certification program. The CCOF archives made
available to me had no membership lists prior to 1986.

fifty-six certified California organic growers in 1972 (Steffen, Allen, and
Foote 1972).[9] CCOF was founded in 1973, evolving directly out of this
program, so it began with a similar base. Approximately one hundred
more growers trickled in during the following decade. The first major
leap in CCOF membership took place in 1986, followed by another jolt
in 1988 (see table 1). According to Mark Lipson, an early staff member
of CCOF, these two surges directly corresponded with the Aldicarb and
Alar scares, contributing to a quadrupling of certified organic acres in
two years (Schilling 1995).

The next growth surge involved an expansion of grower numbers,
upon implementation of the California Organic Foods Act in 1991. Prior
to passage of the COFA, small market gardeners had no reason to certify if their sales were local and direct, even though there was no alter-

native mechanism by which to mark themselves officially as organic. The registration option allowed by the COFA greatly expanded the official count, for it encouraged such growers and others to enter the formal sector at little cost. The first-year data were collected and aggregated under the COFA (1992–93); 1,159 growers registered as organic growers, representing a fivefold increase since 1988. Yet, only 45 percent of growers were certified, 91 percent of which were with CCOF (Klonsky and Tourte 1995). While it is tempting to extrapolate from this percentage to inflate the number of growers and acres prior to implementation of the law, the fact is that many growers "discovered" themselves to be organic under the relative ease of registration.[10]

In the early 1990s, there was another period of growth, this time driven by expansion of some of the major growers, many of whom had been pioneers in the organic sector. As table 1 shows, average acreage increased considerably. In fact, CCOF's top five growers farmed well over ten thousand acres combined in 1995 (CCOF 1995b). The commodities showing the most dramatic increases in acreage at the time were salad mix, wine grapes, and cotton (Klonsky and Tourte 1995), all of which were dominated by a handful of growers. This rapid growth is corroborated by reports of the *Natural Food Merchandiser,* which reported persistent increases of more than 20 percent in organic sales in the years between 1989 and 1994 (Mergentime and Emerich 1995), although these figures represent nationwide retail sales, which really is a horse of a different color.

After the first year of state-collected data (1992–93), however, growth flattened. In fact, one-third of registered growers dropped out in the second year of reporting, to be replaced by almost as many new registrants and an additional 348 the third year, 1994–95 (Klonsky and Tourte 1998b). Klonsky and Tourte attribute this hiatus to the diminishing of two important incentives for early entry: first, to register in the state program at its inception, when only a one- year transition period was required; second, to get in on the high prices that were bandied about at that time. Nevertheless, this high rate of turnover has since become a pattern, suggesting that many new growers find organic production to be more challenging than expected. As for CCOF, their grower numbers flattened when registration became an option and other certifiers started to compete with CCOF for market share, although CCOF acreage continued to expand.

After 1996, there was another growth spurt in California, this time driven by a large influx of citrus, avocado, and date growers. Growth in acreage, however, was largely constituted by more traditional commodity crops used for processing ingredients, such as onions, tomatoes, rice, and safflower. In addition, fresh vegetable growers continued to test the waters of organic farming, as they had in the decade previous, but resisted wholehearted entry. In other words, growth in general tended to be crop dependent and often halting. To understand these uneven patterns of growth, then, we need to give a closer look at the causes of these conversions.

PULLED BY DEMAND

In the broadest sense, post-1980 growth in the organic sector was demand led. This is not a claim of unfettered consumer sovereignty but instead is based on two observations. The first is that there was a high degree of consumer involvement in constructing organic markets. Marketing surveys (Hartman Group 1997; Moe and Scharf 1997; *The Packer* 1996) and limited academic research (Byrne et al. 1991; Goldman and Clancy 1991; Jolly 1991) have documented a die-hard group of consumers who actively sought organic products. This group was further delineated by a marked geographic differentiation in buying patterns for organics, with some localities supporting several marketplaces with a full line of organic products compared with others having no organic markets to speak of. While this is partly a reflection of the hesitance of retailers to supply organic products in certain regions, unusually strong markets in places such as Berkeley and Santa Cruz suggest a strong subcultural element that cannot be explained solely by income-based market segmentation. More significant, consumers' overwhelming response to the USDA's 1997 proposed federal rules indicates unusual involvement in support of an industry.

Yet, these die-hard consumers of organics did not alone make up the expanding market for organic foods. After all, many in this group were shopping at health-food stores and cooperatives in the 1970s. A much larger group of consumers began to buy organic foods in the late 1980s, triggered, in part, by the Aldicarb and Alar scares but also influenced by broader trends. Young urban professionals—the so-called yuppies—learned of organic food at high-end restaurants and brought home many of the tastes they acquired. The 1980s had also signified the coming of middle age to the post–World War II baby boomers (with considerable yuppie overlap), who were now bearing children of their own and particularly attuned to issues of food safety. This generated demand for baby food, convenience meals, and "healthy" children's snacks. Finally, the diffusion of environmental ideas moved many baby boomers to seek "cleaner" products as a vehicle of environmental action (Katz 1998).

Growers were keenly aware of these changing sensibilities. Asked why they had converted to organic production, many responded with comments like "I'm just giving the consumer what she wants" and "Demand is out there." Consumers were especially influential to growers who sell in direct-marketing venues. For, in certain farmers' markets, consumers came to expect organically grown food, putting those without organic credentials at a distinct disadvantage or, worse, giving them incentive to lie. The experience of having consumers turn up their noses and walk away upon hearing that a product was not organic persuaded more than one grower to attempt organic production. In a few instances, the personal nature of the direct-market transaction encouraged growers to convert, lending, as they felt, both opportunity and incentive to deliver a better product.

Nonetheless, these transactions do not fully capture how demand translated into growth in the sector. What was truly crucial to this growth was the rise of a group of new intermediaries who both generated and expressed demand. Among them were major organic producers who sold others' products, a handful of organic wholesalers and distributors, and the natural food supermarkets. Together they evolved into an organic industry, although many of these key players sprang up from the organic movement.

Some were growers who became industry leaders by the historical accident of growing flagship commodities such as salad mix (Coke Farms, Star Route Farms). Others aggressively pursued growth strategies while the industry was in its infancy. Either way, they faced relatively untapped markets and became strikingly profitable as demand began to surge, allowing them to amass capital for reinvestment. Initially, these early innovators of the 1980s, also including Pavich Family Farms, Lundberg Family Farms, Jacobs Farm, and the now defunct TKO, expanded their own production in California. As the sector became more competitive, their objective became market share. At that point, they found it more lucrative, and less risky, to pursue growth by bringing new growers in through "cooperative arrangements" and/or expanding into Mexico, Arizona, and even South America as traders. Several mostly organic fruit packers and a handful of new-to-organic conventional handlers also expanded this way. The most significant aspect of this type of expansion is that most of these operators chose to bring conventional growers on board, preferring to work, as one buyer so bluntly put it, with professional growers rather than hippies.

The case of Earthbound Farms/Natural Selection Foods illustrates this growth trajectory in a dramatic way. Earthbound began when Myra and Drew Goodman, self-ascribed hippies who met at the University of California at Santa Cruz, moved to Carmel Valley in 1984 and started growing their own organic berries and lettuce. At first they sold to area restaurants like Chez Panisse; then they came up with the idea of bagging their lettuce mixes for roadside stands and eventually supermarkets. By 1989, Earthbound was so large the Goodmans needed a warehouse in Watsonville, and it continued to grow at a rate of at least 50 percent a year until 1995. "But the Goodmans had to grow beyond their organic roots in order to keep up with demand," a 1996 article said. Quoting Drew Goodman, "About 80–90% of the buying public doesn't care if spring mix is organic and want it cheaply as possible. . . . Now we're seeing you can't sell organic lettuce at market prices; you lose money on every box" (Barnett 1996). Meanwhile, in December 1995, Mission Ranches, a conventional operator, bought Riverside Farms, which was then a thousand acres. Earthbound and Mission joined forces to create Natural Selection Foods, marketing nonorganic salad mix under the Riverside Farms banner and organic mix under the Earthbound moniker.

Still having more market potential, even in organics, thereafter Earthbound Farms/Natural Selection Foods expanded through a series of partnerships with some of the largest conventional vegetable growers in the Salinas area, including Growers' Vegetable Express and Tanimura and Antle. Some of these growers were interested in establishing an organic line; many others started growing organically at the behest of Natural Selection. Earthbound also expanded geographically, with at least sixteen hundred acres in production in Baja California, where they began to grow off-season lettuce and tomatoes; they continued to grow their market share by buying out or contracting with some of their erstwhile competitors. Eventually, they became the biggest distributor of specialty lettuce salads in the country and certainly the largest organic "farm" in the world in terms of crop value. Another marketing alliance formed in 2000 with Rainbow Valley Orchards, a mainly organic packer, put them in the citrus, avocado, and tropical fruit business, too.

While Earthbound and other lesser companies have brought growers in, generating demand in that way, their influence has been nothing compared with that at the retail level. In this regard, the most significant development has been the burgeoning (and consolidation) of the "super-naturals," health food supermarkets that carry a full line of grocery items (e.g., Whole Foods and Wild Oats), as well as the major distributors and processors that supply them. Organic sales in this format continued to see 20 percent growth in overall revenues during the 1990s (Smith 1998). These retailers have been pivotal in developing the organic food system because they have provided product screening, in-depth product information, and topical education and have generally pretended to act on the consumer's behalf (Marsden and Arce 1995). In that way, they have raised more generalized interest in organic food. Because they require a full line of grocery items to stock their stores, they have also deepened demand for all kinds of end-products beyond heightening demand for fresh produce. A whole generation of processed organic foods, from cereal to salsa to frozen food, has been developed with these stores in mind.

Although product displays describing or even picturing a grower's operation have become common in these stores, suggesting that the retailer works closely with the grower, in practice these retailers have come to rely almost exclusively on traditional wholesaling and distribution as their operations have become ever more complicated. So the distributors and wholesalers who have supplied these stores have stimulated demand for intermediate goods, provided by other processors, packers, and so forth, and, in turn, have created the demand (usually on a contract basis) to which growers have responded. Although many of the necessary ingredients have been obtained from other states, especially grain-based products, California growers have provided virtually all of the organic rice, raisins, figs, and tomatoes, and much of the safflower, apples, citrus, and vegetables for processed products.

Accordingly, most large-scale contract growers I interviewed were brought into organic production by these intermediary buyers. Being primarily market-takers, a few growers were happy to find that organic buyers offered contracts, whereas they often sold conventional crops on the spot market. Thus, they did not see their entry into organic as particularly risky, nor did they expect to see superprofit rewards. Many rice growers converted upon SunWest's introduction of a new organic line. Many tomato growers got started when asked to grow processing tomatoes for Muir Glen, the largest organic tomato processor in California.[11]

The case of SK Foods, which came into organic production in a particularly indirect way, demonstrates this sort of ripple effect of the organic industry. Owned by an heir of one of the largest cotton empires in

California, the company restructured several times in the early 1990s. Supplying tomatoes to various processors as one of its diversification ventures, newly formed Salyer American decided to build its own tomato processing plant in Lemoore (Kings County) in 1989 (Morris 1991). Still struggling, in 1995 the company sold off the rest of the cotton operation of 33,000 acres and $40 million in crop value to Boswell, the largest farming operation in California, with 130,000 acres, and the Salyer's historical competitor. Since the sale did not include the fresh produce operations in Salinas or the tomato processing plant, the siblings divided these operations among themselves (Lloyd 1995). SK Foods eventually became involved with organic processing and production when its owners were approached by Muir Glen to do bulk processing for organic clients. As a company representative told me, "We are totally customer driven. . . . We didn't do it for the money per se, but because our clients asked us to." But after rigging and certifying the processing plant, they went into organic production themselves, as a way to ensure enough supply for clients when needed.[12]

The widespread conversion of small fruit orchards and vineyards was also buyer-led.[13] In this case, however, most of the affected growers have been gentleman farmers, characterized so by their lack of dependence on farm income and their preference for permanent crops requiring limited management. Many of these growers live on subdivided ranchettes (i.e., one- to five-acre parcels with nominal agricultural activity), where they receive the tax benefits of agricultural land, the amenities of rural living, the income potential of selling the land at a future date, and a supplementary income on the side. One enclave of such growers is in the Sebastopol area of Sonoma County, where the remaining Gravenstein apple orchards are relics of a previous agricultural era when several processing facilities still operated in the area. Gerber (of baby food fame) was the last to close in the early 1980s. After that, the only available sales outlets were the smaller processors, who used this oft-neglected fruit for producing vinegar, juice, and applesauce, and a couple of handlers who were brokering larger deals with outside buyers. When the handlers and processors became organic as the only way of getting any value out of the product, so did those from whom they buy.[14]

A much larger group of newly converted gentlemen growers operates in southern California, in the inland areas of Ventura County (e.g., Ojai and the Santa Paula Valley) and the northern portion of San Diego County. Few of these growers have had an active interest in managing their orchards or selling their fruit, and most hire management compa-

nies or contract with fruit packers to do so. Operating primarily in Riverside and San Diego counties, a handful of avocado and citrus packers
coaxed many of these small orchardists to become organic. Being too
small for Sunkist or Calavo, the major cooperatives, these gentlemen
farmers have had no real options for selling their fruit other than through
these organic packers. Moreover, these packers, with their promises of
premiums, have provided the only hope of making any return, given the
highest per acre irrigation costs in the state. As above, this buyer-led system has been wrapped up in the search for value, the second major driving force in the growth of organics.

PUSHED BY SUPPLY

On an aggregate basis, the 1980s farm crisis had relatively mild effects
on the California agricultural economy because of the high percentage
of production in specialty crops. Yet the crisis was devastating for certain commodity crop growers. The demise of cotton production, especially, was both a cause and a symptom of farm-level restructuring as
prices fell, farmers became overburdened with debt (especially because
mortgage debt was directly related to land in production), and government commodity support programs came to require acreage reductions
(Villarejo 1989). Commodity supports were further retracted as part of
the 1990 farm bill (Le Heron 1993), and in 1996 Congress decided to
phase out crop deficiency payments and acreage planting restrictions altogether (Orden, Paarlberg, and Roe 1999). Well into the 1990s, cotton
farmers continued to sell off land to shore up their cash positions
(Thompson 1998).

By the 1990s, even California's specialty crop growers felt the effects
of heightened international trade in fresh fruits and vegetables. Encouraged by international lending institutions as a structural adjustment
measure, many Third World countries had begun to export tropical
fruits and counterseasonal vegetables into First World markets. Chilean
exports proved especially damaging to California growers; because of
shared climatic conditions, Chile's exports competed directly with California's most valued crops, such as table and wine grapes. With NAFTA
and the decline of the peso, Mexican exports began to compete as well,
most strongly with California crops in the areas proximal to Mexico,
where the climate is similar, so Mexico's lack of restrictions on labor
costs, production practices, and marketing are felt to be particularly
damaging to California growers (Wells 1996). Meanwhile, the produc-

tion of other erstwhile specialty crops shifted to new, lower-cost regions. Such was the case for the once-thriving apple industry in Sonoma County, much of which was replaced by that in Washington State, and southern California citrus production, which moved inland to the Central Valley or Arizona.

Concurrently, many farm families experienced a drastic reduction of what once were very large family holdings. Some had outright sold their land, either for debt relief or because income received in the sale provided a better living than farming (or, in a few cases, because the land was condemned by cities for urban development). A lack of progeny—or a lack of interest among progeny in taking over the family business—also contributed to the sell-off of farm land for commercial purposes. Others had individuated holdings for tax purposes, personal family dynamics such as divorce, or, in some cases, deliberate avoidance of the acreage restrictions of federal reclamation law.[15]

All of these factors caused farmers to rethink what crops they grew and how they grew and sold them. For some, falling prices encouraged them to reduce their input use to save on the costs of doing business. Consequently, some experimented with organic techniques on their conventional farms and found it possible, even easy, to farm without proscribed inputs, at least in certain crops. One grower claimed that "having witnessed a balanced system," he saw "no turning back."

Many of these growers, though, turned to higher-value crops in search of a better return on less land or to keep up with land values, which recovered from the 1980s crisis faster than prices. The organic designation was but one way to generate value, along with growing conventional crops that are relatively scarce or carry other symbolic attributes such as exoticness, luxury, or environmental friendliness. The kiwi boom of the early 1980s was one of the first in this contemporary wave of specialty food production. Hoping to capture the superprofits associated with high-value crops but stay with something they knew, citrus growers moved into varietals such as blood oranges and Meyer lemons; apple growers, into the new Asian varietals such as Fujis; and rice growers, into exotics such as basmati, arborio, and wild rice (which, of course, is not really rice).

So, beginning in the mid-1980s, the quest for higher-value production became the most common motivation for attempting organic production. One grower saw others, as he put it, "pulling the handle," as if the money to be made were as easy as winning at a slot machine. Other growers described their entry in subtler terms: "Going organic is the only way a small farm can survive." "We saw an opportunity for a niche." "We were attracted to the prices they [buyers] were offering."

Particularly in the western and southern parts of the Central Valley (Kern, Tulare, and Fresno counties), where cotton once was king, organics were a road out of cotton production. This was clearly the case for Danny Duncan, who came from a conventional cotton growing family. In the early 1980s, his Kern County farm was doing so poorly that he began looking for a niche market, fearing that he would lose the land his father had owned since 1946. "We were looking for things to grow on a smaller scale that had a higher return and [could] possibly save the family farm." Duncan entered into organics in 1984, planting 10 acres of lemon grass for Celestial Seasonings tea company. By the third year, he had 200 acres in organic production, and by the fifth (1989), his whole farm, which he then named Cal-Organic, was "free of synthetic chemicals." At one point Cal-Organic was the largest organic farm in the world in both sales and acreage (2,560 acres) (Fost 1991). But eventually, Duncan began to grow for an even larger grower-shipper, and in 2003 he sold the company to Grimmway Enterprises.

Complementing their changes in cropping strategies, many growers chose to alter their marketing arrangements. Even larger growers (with sales over $1 million) became involved in direct marketing as a way to capture a larger share of their crop value. Some growers started selling at the farmers' markets with this explicit objective and were drawn into organics as a secondary effect (through consumer demand expressed at such markets). Many medium-sized fruit and vegetable growers (with sales of more than $100,000 and less than $1 million) began marketing directly to retail for the same reason and were remarkably successful as long as they delivered a high-quality product with near-perfect cosmetic attributes. Of course, this strategy is generally limited to those in fresh-market products and is extremely management intensive.

Whatever the initial draw, many growers actually entered into organics because they encountered a relatively risk-free environment for conversion, specifically one that minimized the up-front investment costs. In other words, they were not necessarily interested in organics, but ease of entry allowed them an early cash-in on the high value that organic production then enjoyed. This group of growers, many of whom with sales well above $1 million, explained their involvement as an "opportunity that presented itself." Normally, organic certification requires that land be free of prohibited substances for three years before crops are marketed as organic. Crops are sold at conventional prices during the transition period, but costs generally increase and yields usually plunge, so that growers initially operate at a significant loss.[16] For all intents and purposes, then, transition should be treated as an amortizable investment. However, these growers avoided most, if not all, of the investment costs. As mentioned earlier, some entered into organic production when the COFA was first implemented and required only a one-year transition. A few entered as a condition of a lease or a business transfer on already converted land. Some growers brought in by buyers were able to negotiate deals to mitigate the risk of the transition. One such grower acquired a custom farming deal for the entire transition period, wherein the buyer, a very large all-organic grower-shipper, paid the grower to grow alfalfa with a guaranteed profit margin.

Another set of growers portrayed themselves as innovators in explaining their entry into organics, including some who had fully converted and some whose commitment remained with conventional production. Claiming to be "aggressive," "always trying new things," or "wanting to see what works," these growers seemed to choose early innovation as a rule, to experiment with, learn, and adopt the technologies that were going to keep them at the top of the game. Such a strategy is necessary to reap the superprofits that supposedly exist when new technologies first come into play, although in this case they were striving to capture value through the pricing mechanism rather than through increased labor productivity (cf. Cochrane 1993).

The hardest to characterize are growers who claimed that, at some turning point, organic production seemed "a natural." This applies to the dozens of mixed growers, who were growing certain crops organically and others conventionally. In these cases, growers chose to convert only those crops that were easy to grow organically, either because pests were limited for that crop or allowable materials were effective (such as those for grapes). Easy-to-grow crops generally entail cost reductions, giving growers the benefit of even the smallest organic price premiums. While some just saw a chance of relatively risk-free entry, others were drawn by organic ideas. Growers in this latter group often spoke about a particular biophysical condition that lent itself to organic production, such as access to an isolated area that was free of common pests or otherwise already under biological pest control. One large-scale grower operating as an investment trust tried organic production on a plot of land by the chicken house, which could not be treated with pesticides in any case. Thus, this group of growers was also responding to a changing climate of pesticide regulation.

TURNED BY PESTICIDES

In the United States, there is little question that one long-term effect of New Deal agricultural policy is that it encouraged monocropping and high-input use to maximize yields per acre (Le Heron 1993). Subsidies encouraged further intensification, and growers were given little flexibility to integrate agroecological precepts. In marked similarity to dust bowl history, the 1980s crises of overproduction created some political space for an ecological critique of this sort of agriculture and of the state support that encouraged it (see, e.g., Beeman 1995; Worster 1979, 1994). This engendered a few new government programs, including the Conservation Reserve Program, which took marginal land out of production, and the modestly funded sustainable agriculture research and extension programs. Food scares also called into question both the safety and necessity of certain practices, especially insofar as most intensifying practices and inputs contribute to overproduction. Such was the case from Alar, to bovine growth hormone, to offal as feed (implicated in mad cow disease) and more recently in much of the controversy surrounding genetically engineered plants. Perhaps most significant for California's agriculture, widespread public recognition of "the pesticide treadmill" and its concomitant public health and environmental costs normalized ideas of alternative pest control technologies, from integrated pest management (IPM), to genetic engineering, to organics.

The current system of pesticide regulation originated with the 1947 Federal Insecticide, Fungicide, and Rodenticide Act (FIFRA), which mandated instructional labels on containers of pesticides and was administered by the USDA.[17] Amendments to this and the Federal Food, Drug, and Cosmetic Act created a basic regulatory framework of risk-benefit analysis, albeit no simple, agreed-upon system has ever existed to make such assessments (National Research Council 1987). The original regulatory mandate was further complicated by the 1958 Delaney clause, which established a zero-exposure, zero-risk standard for *processed* foods grown with oncogenic pesticides. Yet, for all of its strength, the Delaney clause effectively created a separate standard for fresh as opposed to processed foods (National Research Council 1987) and did not address other sorts of toxicity, such as endocrine disruption.

The first major challenge to this framework came from none other than Rachel Carson, who many call the progenitor of the modern environmental movement. Yet, her immediate impact on pesticide regulation was limited. To be sure, DDT was banned in 1972, but in *Silent Spring,*

Carson mentioned many other equally deleterious chemicals that remained allowable for years to come. And regulators failed to heed her warnings that certain pesticides were likely to have cumulative and interactive effects. Upon its inception in 1970, the EPA was given responsibility for determining which pesticides were allowable and at what tolerances. The EPA took a more active role in regulating agricultural chemicals than the USDA had, but its regulatory capacity was still limited. To this day, it has not caught up with the reregistration process required by amendments to FIFRA for chemicals that were previously grandfathered in (Steingraber 1997).

In the California arena, pesticide regulation has faired no better. Despite California's reputation as environmentally progressive, pesticide regulation has been noticeably lax, in no small part because its specialty crop farmers are particularly dependent on pesticide use. The Department of Pesticide Reform, which is part of the California Environmental Protection Agency, is funded by taxes on pesticide sales. This is the agency responsible for registering and regulating pesticides in California as well as collecting data on pesticide use. While pesticide reporting can be very onerous for farmers, creating a disincentive for their use for that reason alone, the department has otherwise done little in the way of enforcement (Liebman 1998). For example, registration of methyl bromide, a contentious fumigant (widely used in both preplant and postharvest operations), has been repeatedly extended under considerable pressure from the farm lobby (Gunnison 1996).[18] According to a 1997 report by Californians for Pesticide Reform, not only did California use 25 percent of all pesticides in the United States on a volume basis, but also pesticide use actually increased in the 1990s (Liebman 1997).

In other words, until the mid-1990s, regulatory incentive for growers to shift away from chemical agriculture was minimal, with the availability of substitutes for those chemicals that had been regulated out of existence and extensions for those about to be banned. The 1996 Food Quality Protection Act (Public Law 104–170) changed all that, at least in the eyes of growers. Created to replace the Delaney clause, which focused only on cancer-causing chemicals, the FQPA established tolerances for pesticide residues, covering all food uses of pesticides and taking into account multiple and cumulative effects as well as effects on children, according to a new standard of "reasonable certainty of no harm." In effect, the FQPA permitted chemicals that would eventually have been banned under the Delaney clause and, as opposed to Delaney's "zero tolerance," reinforced old norms of risk assessment (Wargo 1998). Nevertheless, in 1999 in the first action taken under this law, the EPA banned the use of methyl parathion on all fruits and many vegetables and limited the quantity of azinphos methyl that could be used on foods common to children's diets. It was expected that the EPA would disallow several other organophosphates thereafter, although much of this progress has been put on hold with the current Bush administration.

Even though it is arguable that this round of regulation was too little, too late, the fact is that growers responded to this new climate of pesticide regulation. Particularly during the 1990s, growers across the country began to seek alternative strategies for pest and disease management, one of the major justifications for their adoption of some of the new biotechnologies (Economic Research Service 1999). Similarly, many growers entered into organic production in this new climate of pesticide reform.

Some growers were not convinced of the dangers of pesticides but were driven by a fear of having their "tools taken away." Growers who specialized in one or two crops and had specific inputs on the regulatory chopping block were especially motivated this way. Such was the case for Bakersfield-based Grimmway Enterprises, which became the largest vegetable producer in the country (*American Vegetable Grower* 1996), growing mainly carrots. Grimmway became involved in organics when it bought out competitor Yurosek and Sons in 1995. Of Yurosek's seven thousand or so acres, eighteen hundred had already been converted to organic production at the time of the purchase, allowing a quick and easy way for Grimmway to gain expertise. As a company spokesperson said, "We want to be proactive about alternative methods of growing, especially before California says we can't use many of the chemicals we are already using. . . . I'm not necessarily a fan of organics, but I admit to being uneducated. When I see statistics showing strong danger, I may well become a fan. Right now I do not see that conventional farming does harm." Although Grimmway since expanded its organic acreage, "whether [it] will stay with organic for the long haul depends on profitability."

Similarly, a few conversions took place to minimize what can be onerous pesticide reporting. Gallo and other winegrowers moved to organic production for this reason and also because of the relative ease of growing grapes organically. Many did not remain in the organic program, however, because wine cannot be sold as organic unless sulfites are eliminated from the wine-making process, and they did not want to be subject to the regulation that organic itself entails (Fisher 1991). Nevertheless, for a time Gallo was the largest organic farm in the United States, having converted six thousand of its ten thousand acres of wine grapes to strictly organic production (Zwerdling 1993). This suggests that pesticide regulation has had an indirect effect on pesticide use, at least in some crops, despite the discouraging statistics to the contrary.

Growers also responded to a changing cultural context of acceptability. During interviews, I commonly heard somewhat perfunctory justifications such as, "I would rather not be around those chemicals" and "pesticides are bad for the environment." Nevertheless, many growers converted to organic production out of explicit concern with the costs, liability, and inefficacy of pesticides. Some were simply looking at ways to reduce costs in a competitive environment by reducing pesticide use. A few mentioned the liability issues related to pesticide exposure, particularly when their farms were close to residential zones.[19] A few interviewees even expressed regret at exposing their workers to pesticides, though this was not foremost in most growers' minds. At the very least, the California Food and Agricultural Code (sec. 12981), which restricts worker reentry into sprayed fields, awakened growers to the potential of employee-led suits. And many growers became attuned to the ecological concerns around pesticide use, particularly insofar as pesticides upset predator-prey cycles on the farm, sometimes even exacerbating their pest control problems.

Operations that were under relatively little financial pressure were particularly amenable to experiments in pesticide reduction. This is how a handful of large farms, operated as trusts, limited partnerships, or various other tax shelters (as well as residential real estate worked by gentleman farmers), converted to organic production. These farms never represented a major source of income for their absentee owners, yet became actively managed in the late 1980s when the tax reforms of 1986 no longer allowed passive write-off. As urban investors seeking a place to sink money without necessarily making a return, owners found it easy enough to square their investment with notions of sustainability. Such was the case of Hopeton Farms, a 2,200-acre ranch, east of Merced, which was acquired in 1979 in a property exchange and owned by a partnership of three absentee families. Before the tax reforms, the ranch had been largely neglected. Thereafter, the owners hired one of their existing (urban) employees to run the farm and turn it into a profit-making business. They replanted significant amounts of acreage, so that by the time of the interviews they had 2,036 acres of almond trees (a quarter-million trees!) along with 65 acres of walnut trees in production.

The manager explained to me that although they had continued to farm the almond trees conventionally (in that they were not enrolled in the organic program), their involvement in the business had caused them to become "more skeptical of the use of chemicals," especially when they realized their pest control adviser worked for a chemical company. For that reason, they had enrolled some acreage in the BIOS program. Impressed with those results, they had gradually enrolled more acreage and eventually put all of their walnuts into organic production in a separate area they felt was particularly suited to it.

Finally, a startling number of growers converted to organic production out of personal experience with the risks of pesticide use, when they themselves, friends, or relatives became sick or developed cancer, causing them to question the necessity of the inputs they used. A San Joaquin Valley grower of several generations lost his father and two aunts to cancer. Once having used "every trick in the book" when diagnosed with malignant melanoma himself, he decided "to make a lot of changes and think about what [he was] doing." He is now very active in the organic movement. While the links between cancer and pesticide exposure are hotly contested, as documented by Proctor (1995), the most decisive conversions—those that are seemingly permanent and thorough—have nonetheless been motivated by these sorts of personal experiences.[20]

In sum, the early legitimacy of organic farming created an important space for erstwhile "hippie" farmers to reach a broader clientele. Having reached a level of acceptance, some of these growers went on to play an important normative role by exemplifying alternative modes of food provision. Some of the early innovators, following an entirely different path, began to develop an industry, helping to generate the demand to which conventional growers responded. In that way and others, growth in the organic sector during the 1980s and 1990s was not driven by a sudden transformation of grower attitudes, counter to the suggestion of the opening epigraph of this chapter. Although some new entrants were beginning to question agribusiness as usual, growers' decisions to convert did not turn on a newly found critique of agricultural industrialization for the most part. To the contrary, growers wanted to cash in on the value that was generated by this new niche market, or they reacted to a changed regulatory climate not of their own making. Indeed, by their own admission, some new entrants into organic production were "dragged in kicking and screaming." As a consequence, growth in the organic sector necessarily transformed the character of organic *farmers*. At the very least, the sector became dominated by those who converted to organic production. The question is how such growth affected the character of organic *farming*, a topic to which we turn in the next chapter.

CHAPTER 3

Organic Farming

Ideal Practices and Practical Ideals

On the drive back to Boise, I thought about why Heath's farm remained the exception, both in Idaho and elsewhere. Here was a genuinely new paradigm that seemed to work. But while it's true that organic agriculture is gaining ground, few of the mainstream farmers I met considered organic a "realistic" alternative. . . . Heath's type of agriculture doesn't leave much room for the Monsantos of the world: organic farmers buy remarkably little—some seed, a few tons of compost, maybe a few gallons of ladybugs. That's because the organic farmer's focus is on a process, rather than on products.

Michael Pollan, "Fried, Mashed, or Zapped with DNA?"

Between 1987 and 1997, the beginning year of this study, approximately seventeen hundred California growers entered into organic production for the first time, and the amount of acreage in organic production grew more than tenfold. Many entered not because of any particular ties to the organic movement but because they felt compelled to change the way they farm or were lured by high prices and the promises of buyers. Whether they approached opportunistically or were pulled along, this sort of growth was unimaginable ten years prior. On the surface, then, it would appear an astounding success on the part of the organic movement.

Yet, to presume that such rapid transformation would not affect how organic agriculture is practiced would be folly. With their arguably more tepid motivations and their background in conventional agriculture, converted growers brought a different set of structures and practices, some of which instantiated the very qualities that organic agriculture is supposed to counter. Indeed, a sizable percentage of these new organic growers continue to grow some, even most, of their crops conventionally (again, I refer to these as mixed growers). Nor can it be assumed that the earlier movement growers, or "all-organic" growers, were not affected by these changes or, for that matter, that their practices ever conformed to the organic imaginary. In this light, this chapter examines what organic agriculture actually looks like in California in relation to how it is imagined. I begin with the more structural features of the sector, then move to practices, and end with grower motivations.

STRUCTURES

As we have seen, organic growers are often portrayed as small-scale family farmers on freehold land, a characterization that draws from the agrarian populist strains of the organic farming movement. At first glance at the organic sector, scale, ownership, and land tenure—the structural foundations of agriculture—conform to this agrarian populist ideal. As one measure of scale, Klonsky and colleagues (2001) reported a median organic farm size of five acres in 1997, drastically smaller than the typical Californian farms that Carey McWilliams ([1935] 1971) termed "factories in the field." Median gross sales, arguably a better measure of scale, were eight thousand dollars that same year.[1] Similarly, organic production seems to be the terrain of the family farmer. The Organic Farming Research Foundation makes much of the 1997 statistics compiled from respondents to their survey of U.S. certified growers: 72 percent were sole proprietors, 15 percent were family partnerships, and 6 percent were corporations (OFRF 1999); in California, 66 percent were sole proprietors, 17 percent were family partnerships, and 7 percent were corporations (OFRF, personal communication, 1999). Along the same lines, my study found a substantial proportion of landownership among organic farmers; only 13 percent of those interviewed were tenant farmers.[2]

Unfortunately, these statistics, which imply a wealth of small farms, do not do justice to portraying the sector. Statistics compiled by Klonsky and colleagues (2001) describing the distribution of revenue among farms of different size show that gross revenue from organic operations is highly concentrated. In 1997, for example, over half of the value of organic production was captured by 2 percent of organic growers—those who grossed over $1 million annually from their own crop sales. This statistic does not even count sales of others' crops. Hardly aligning with the Jeffersonian imaginary of like-sized farms, these data demonstrate a major imbalance in market share and further suggest a symbiotic relationship between large and small farms.

Even more important, the state-collected data that are the basis of Klonsky and Tourte's statistical study are very misleading, for they include only the organic portion of operations that may also have had conventional acreage.[3] If OFRF's national survey is at all representative, approximately one-quarter of all organic growers have mixed operations (OFRF 1999). Data I collected from pesticide use permits (see appendix) show that some of these mixed operations may be operations of very large acreage. To give the reader a sense of the magnitude of this problem, I identified six operations with over twenty thousand acres that had from thirty to five hundred acres in organic production. These include American Protection Industries, operating as Paramount Citrus Association; Cadiz International, operating as Sun World/Superior Farms; Harris Farms; and farms held by the Abatti, Gill, and Salyer families.[4] At the time of the interviews, because some of these growers were not even selling all of their organically grown crops as organic, they were placed in the very smallest-scale category in the statistical survey of Klonsky and colleagues (2001). These misleading data are just the tip of the iceberg; other large-scale conventional growers who were dabbling in organic production similarly are treated as smaller-scale growers in their survey. In short, the sizable proportion of organic farming done by large-scale conventional farms is buried within these statistics.[5]

Nor do the truly small-scale farms that populate the organic sector live up to the meanings with which they are imbued. Most of the 79 percent of organic growers with sales under $50,000 were not full-time growers or at least did not receive their primary income from farming, contributing to this remarkably low median farm size compared with California's conventional farming operations. Some were working farms that provide a modest living, but the vast majority were fruit orchards and backyard gardens on residential real estate, providing their owners with tax breaks (write-offs, agricultural property taxes) and inconsequential income. Only organic farms midsized in sales—say, in the range of $100,000 to $1 million per year (which makes them quite large by census standards)—came close to the ideal: viable economically and, often, remarkably independent.[6] Significantly, many of these growers identified themselves as small farmers.

In short, the California organic sector is extraordinarily bipolar in its structure, with a veritable oligopsony (i.e., a small group of buyer firms) at the top. At the time of my study, there were a dozen or so pioneers in the California organic industry that had drawn a substantial proportion of market share. These included Pavich Family Farms, Bornt Family

Farms, Lundberg Family Farms, Eco Farms, Rainbow Valley Orchards, Purepak, Cal-Organic, and Earthbound Farms/Natural Selection. All but two were conventional growers who had converted to organic production early on. The exceptional two (Eco Farms and Earthbound) moved backward into handling "ecologically grown" conventional crops as a way to sustain growth in the business.[7] Significantly, all of these players were handling crops of other growers, substantially adding to their revenues. In addition, a handful of conventional firms had enthusiastically entered into organic handling, including Grimmway, Missionero, Capurro & Sons, and Victor Packing. After interviews were completed, this upper end of the California industry consolidated even more, with several of the pioneers combining forces with or contracting to others.

The issue of farm ownership is similarly misread. As it turns out, the structure of farm ownership in the organic sector is almost identical to that of California as a whole. In 1997, only 6.5 percent of all California growers were organized as corporations, that is, with the vast majority existing as sole proprietorships or as family partnerships (Department of Finance 1997).[8] Almost all small farms are organized as sole proprietorships, but even the larger ones organized as corporations tend to be closely held family corporations (S corporations). Grimmway Enterprises, the largest vegetable grower-shipper in the United States, is, in fact, a family corporation. As a rule, there are very few corporations that are *not* closely held in the California crop-farming sector and only a handful of publicly held corporations.[9]

What is most remarkable in terms of ownership within the organic sector is not the predominance of the family-owned farm but, rather, the lack of alternative ownership structures. Of the 1,533 registered growers in 1997, only 17 were not-for-profit organizations. Of these, nine were run as independent NGOs, with research and education constituting part or all of the mission, five were affiliated with colleges or universities, and one was part of a detention facility. That leaves two that claimed to be collectives or cooperatives—a far cry from the alternative food delivery institutions that spawned the organic sector in the 1960s.

Finally, patterns of tenure in the organic sector also roughly parallel those of California's agriculture as a whole. According to the 1997 Census of Agriculture (USDA 1999), 13 percent of California growers are tenant farmers, the same percentage that were tenant farmers among those I interviewed.[10] That said, I did find higher rates of landownership for all-organic growers than for mixed growers.

The preponderance of landownership among all-organic growers is not

surprising given the number of small-scale back-to-the-landers who populate the sector. Many of these all-organic growers are first-generation
growers who by necessity started farming in California's interstitial spaces:
the small valleys, hillsides, and other unlikely spots, often on less-than-
prime farmland, and many were the first to bring this land into crop production. To this, add growth from residential real estate holders and gentleman farmers, who by definition own their own land but for whom
farming is an avocation.

Leasehold arrangements are much more prevalent among those growers who converted to organic production from substantial conventional
operations. Many in this group are descendants of multigeneration farm
families whose land has been divided among numerous family members
over time. Although these growers may have inherited (or bought out)
some of the family holdings, many of them have felt their holdings to be
insufficient, forcing them to lease land. They also tend to farm in the
prime agricultural zones, where there are other historical and economic
reasons for particular tenure arrangements.

The higher proportion of tenancy among mixed growers also reflects
the higher proportion of large growers in that category. In fact, once we
control for size, there are no other substantial differences between growers who are all-organic and those who are mixed. In my sample, 97 percent of growers with ten acres or less owned or mainly owned their
farms, whereas only 47 percent with more than a thousand acres owned
or mainly owned the land they farmed. Large-scale vegetable growers
have come to prefer leases in a high-cost land market to maintain flexibility (FitzSimmons 1986; Leibman 1983), as do those involved in commodity crop production for the processing market. Only large-scale operations farmed by the original settlers, held primarily for investment
purposes and/or devoted to perennial crops, tend to be owned. Nevertheless, since organic conversion entails an investment similar to that of
perennial crops, most mixed-tenure growers with any intention of staying with organic production put their organic operations on owned land
or at least on land with longer-term leases.

AGRONOMIC PRACTICES

Agroecology, "the science of sustainable agriculture," provides the putative scientific basis of organic farming.[11] According to Miguel Altieri,
the central principle of sustainable agriculture is the minimization of energy and resource use by recycling resources within the farming system

or at least within the local region. From a technical viewpoint, the basic components of such a system are: (1) the use of cover crops, mulches, and no-till practices as soil- and water-conserving measures; (2) the promotion of soil biotic activity through the regular addition of organic matter such as manure and compost; (3) the use of crop rotations, crop-livestock mixed systems, agroforestry, and legume-based intercropping systems for nutrient recycling; and (4) the encouragement of biological pest control agents through biodiversity manipulations and the introduction and/or conservation of natural enemies (1995, 92).

To what degree do organic farmers conform to this agroecological ideal—organic agriculture's most central claim? Not to the extent one might think. As part of this study, growers were assessed on the degree of adoption of agroecological precepts (with slightly different criteria for annual and perennial crops) and assigned an aggregate rating (see appendix). A rating of 0 was assigned to growers if they were in obvious violation of organic codes and practices; a 1 was given to those who took no affirmative steps but merely replaced disallowed inputs with allowable organic inputs; 2 through 4, to those who attempted to put some of these principles into practice; and 5, to those who managed the entire operation *by design* with minimal outside inputs and maximum attention to processes (see Hill 1985).

As shown in table 2, the modal rating was a 2, suggesting that many growers rely on what Rosset and Altieri (1997) have called an "input-substitution" strategy to manage their organic program. Nevertheless, there were noticeable differences between mixed growers, who disproportionately achieved a 1 to 3 rating (about 96 percent of those interviewed) with a modal rating of 2, and all-organic growers, who achieved a 2 to 4 rating (about 94 of those interviewed) with a modal rating of 3. (When further disaggregated to those who had always been organic, the modal rating went up to 4, or 41 percent in that category.) Likewise, 90 percent of growers in the two largest-scale categories received ratings of 1 to 3, while 90 percent of growers in the two smallest-scale categories received ratings of 2 to 4.

In many cases, the half-hearted adoption of agroecological principles, particularly among mixed growers, simply reflects a lack of commitment. Yet, there are formidable obstacles to whole-hearted adoption. The case of cover crops is illustrative in this regard. Cover crops are annual or herbaceous plants that are not grown for harvest but rather to fill gaps in either time or space when cash crops would leave the ground bare (Altieri 1995). Planted sequentially between cash crops, they are supposed

TABLE 2. AGRONOMIC PRACTICES, RATINGS BY GROWER TYPE, 1998–99

	Total		Ratings from Least to Most Agroecological										
			0		1		2		3		4		5	
	N		n	%	n	%	n	%	n	%	n	%	n	%
Type														
Mixed	67		1	1.5	10	14.9	40	59.7	14	20.9	2	3.0	0	0.0
All-organic	77		0	0.0	1	1.3	20	26.0	29	37.7	23	29.9	4	5.2
Sales[a]														
<$100,000	43		0	0.0	1	2.3	14	32.6	17	39.5	9	20.9	2	4.7
$100,000–999,999	38		1	2.6	2	5.3	13	34.2	10	26.3	10	26.3	2	5.3
$1,000,000–9,999,999	45		0	0.0	6	13.3	19	42.2	14	31.1	6	13.3	0	0.0
>$10,000,000	18		0	0.0	2	11.1	14	77.8	2	11.1	0	0.0	0	0.0
TOTAL	144		1	0.7	11	7.6	60	41.7	43	29.9	25	17.4	4	2.8

[a] Sales include all aspects of operation, not just crop value.

to restore fertility, increase biomass, and reduce soil compaction and erosion. Beyond the benefits they offer to soil, they also help in moisture retention, weed control, and if they are flowering, are useful for pest management by creating beneficial insect habitat. Depending on the need, many growers use a combination of species in their covers, ranging from the leguminous nitrogen fixers (e.g., bell beans, vetches), to the more biomassive (e.g., sudan grass), to the more flowery. Cover crops are usually mowed and left as "green manure" or disced in; rarely are legumes harvested.

For cover cropping to work in vegetable systems, any given piece of land must be without a cash crop for at least four months out of the year. Even the best intentioned growers have difficulty ensuring this sort of fallowing, hindered both by the organizational complications of rotating different blocks in and out of production and by the economic costs of having land out of production. Thus, besides those growers who plant only one cash crop per year anyway, growers who most often reach the ideal of having every part of the farm in cover during one point in the year farm on cheap or fully subsidized land (by inheritance or outside support) and/or farm very intensively. The rest see cover crops as a luxury (particularly in areas where water is expensive) or claim that cover crops cause more problems than they solve. Some of these latter growers squeeze in as many cash crops as possible.

A similar situation exists for compost, organic farming's most symbolic material. The purpose of compost is to recycle agricultural waste back into the system, so that a minimum of energy and nutrient transfer occurs away from the farm, aside from the food produced. In an ideal system, compost is composed of crop residues, livestock manure, and organic household waste. It is supposed to be "cooked" for a few months' duration to stabilize nutrients, neutralize pesticide residues, and kill weed seeds and pathogens (CCOF 1998b). In practice, few farms meet the ideal of on-farm composting. First, only a handful of farms integrate livestock into their production system; at best manure is purchased from nearby dairies or chicken farms, where livestock have been fed nonorganic grain, treated with antibiotics, and so on. Even then, not all growers cook or properly age such manure, and tree crops are often fed with so-called raw manure. Mostly, the ideal is extraordinarily difficult to meet, because composting is land extensive itself and necessitates bringing in material to make sufficient compost. As one grower presented it, "With the amount of land, water, and monitoring it takes, making compost is like growing another crop."

Accordingly, large-scale mixed growers are particularly inclined to rely on input substitution. Few plant cover crops because of the expense; instead, they use the controversial sodium (or Chilean) nitrate and other purchased fertility inputs. Those tied to production contracts also do large-acre plantings of single crops, for even a minimal temporal or spatial rotation would entail operating at a loss or developing additional markets. While they may release predator insects via helicopters, implementing a biological pest control of sorts, they never plant noncash crops to act as trap crops, beneficial insect harbors, or fertility enhancements.

Yet, some growers do not fully implement agroecological principles simply because they can get away without them. They are dubbed by others as organic by neglect because they do not actively manage their organic operations. They often market their crops to processors, where qualities such as cosmetic perfection are less important. Or they grow crops that are particularly easy to grow. The legality of the controversial sulfur dust to control bunch rot makes raisin grapes one of the easiest crops to grow organically, even on a relatively large scale.

Many (but not all) growers who started off in organic production more actively incorporate agroecological practices, although not always to an ideal. Some are particularly innovative in their approach, using the latest in organic techniques, such as bug vacuums, plastic mulches, and microbial inoculants, but remain input dependent. In contrast, some of the smallest-scale all-organic growers are able to integrate a full range of highly labor-intensive design elements into their farming systems, mainly because they operate as hobby gardens. It is rare, however, for a professional farm (i.e., one that supports at least one household's livelihood) to come close to the agroecological ideal, where external inputs are minimized and the farm operates in a "balanced" and "self-regulating" manner. Growers who integrate livestock, intercropping, and/or intense mosaic cropping designs with a high degree of on-farm input development are few and far between, although some clearly work in that direction.

Those professional farms that come close to the agroecological ideal are almost always organized as subscription farms. Although they occasionally rely on allowable "natural" pesticides or purchased compost, their otherwise integrative production style is very much intertwined with their marketing strategy. Direct marketing, through subscription boxes and farmers' markets, requires as diverse a crop mix as possible, with the timing of harvest smoothed so that an array of choices is always available to the buyer. At the same time, such diverse (and ecologically conscientious) operations are also strikingly intensified. Their productivity is enhanced by having their own greenhouse, a market for harder-to-sell (and grow) winter crops, and systematic rotational systems, including cover crops.

LABOR PRACTICES

Those who posit organic farming not only as an environmental movement but also as one for social justice imply that the movement includes the concerns of rural workers. Although farm labor concerns were deliberately shunted aside in the political construction of organic rules, as will be discussed in chapter 6, organic production might still differ from conventional in several ways in regard to labor. For one, organic production arguably requires more careful attention in the field. This applies to more than just the so-called artisanal production of certain crops (e.g., baby vegetables); in an organic system, all crops must be handled in compliance with organic regulations. A second difference, related to the putative cropping styles of organic production (e.g., sequential cropping and multicropping), is the need to spread labor more evenly throughout the year. A third is that growers might have a stronger ideological commitment to improve the conditions of farm labor insofar as they see themselves as part of a larger social movement. If these hold true, one would expect to find, *inter alia,* labor recruitment strategies that secure worker commitment, more year-round and permanent employment, and improved remuneration all the way around. Perhaps growers would even adopt a pro-union stance and make efforts to restructure typical relations of agricultural production.

The use of labor contractors, for example, is arguably anathema to the maintenance of an ongoing, committed labor force. Yet, the use of labor contractors is quite common in organic production, as shown in table 3, largely having to do with established patterns of labor recruitment in the prime agricultural regions.[12] Mixed growers rarely employ separate crews for their organic parcels, so whatever they do in conventional production carries over into organic. While all-organic growers tend to be more cautious of their use of labor contractors, knowing their workers need familiarity with organic rules and techniques,[13] a surprising number, particularly those with cropping systems that have a short harvest period, do not think twice about recruiting their labor force this way.

Nor do most organic growers provide full-time year-round employment for the majority of their employees, also seen in table 3. Large

TABLE 3. LABOR PRACTICES, BY GROWER
TYPE, 1998–99

	All-Organic		Mixed		Total	
	n	%	n	%	n	%
Use of Labor Contractors						
Never	53	67.9	23	34.8	76	52.8
Occasionally	12	15.4	27	40.9	39	27.1
Routinely	13	16.7	16	24.2	29	20.1
Year-Round Employment						
Family only	8	10.4	1	1.5	9	6.3
None	28	36.4	7	10.8	35	24.6
1–25% of workforce	17	22.1	32	49.2	49	34.5
26–75% of workforce	13	16.9	23	35.4	36	25.4
Over 75% of workforce	11	14.3	2	3.1	13	9.2
Pay and Benefits						
Minimum	21	43.8	36	69.2	57	57.0
Above minimum	19	39.6	14	26.9	33	33.0
Unusual	8	16.7	2	3.8	10	10.0

growers use contractors; small growers do not have the volume, relying instead on casual labor. Yet, there are marked differences between mixed and all-organic growers. More all-organic farms than mixed are managed solely with family labor, but those few farms that do provide year-round employment for at least 75 percent of their workers are almost all solely organic farms with diverse crop mixes, particularly subscription farms.

As for remuneration, the need for workers' care and commitment, along with more job stability, potentially reduces their vulnerability so they can demand higher wages. In turn, growers might be ideologically inclined to offer more wages as part of their political engagement. Nevertheless, wages remain low in the organic sector, with 57 percent of those interviewed paying the minimum wage. Although some growers at least recognize that workers' pay is insufficient ("you can't pay them enough"), few actually manage to pay wages of more than $7.50 an hour, far below what several municipalities have established as a living wage. Again, of the few growers that offer substantially higher pay and/or benefit packages are in the all-organic category.

When organic growers are considered together, it is clear that only a handful have systematically worked toward improved labor practices. Those that have experienced some success with this are, with few exceptions, the ultradiversified farms whose cropping and direct-marketing strategies fundamentally alter the organization of production. Sequential cropping strategies substantially smooth labor demands and allow workers to be involved in a number of different tasks. Therefore, fewer people are employed, but they can be employed for all or most of the year. Flipping typical racialized labor arrangements on their head, seasonal work in these situations tends to be done by white interns (often at less or no pay), with Latinos receiving the more secure jobs.[14] Moreover, a high ratio of sales per acre, a product of significant intensification and a direct-marketing focus, gives these particular growers the capacity to pay somewhat higher wages.

It is nevertheless striking that ideological proclivities have not led more organic growers to construct alternative labor relations. Although a few organic growers are sympathetic to the cause of agricultural unionization—indeed the first UFW strawberry contract was signed by an organic farmer in Santa Cruz County, the only existing union contract for an organic operation and the only strawberry contract—most maintain the air of the *patrón,* claiming to treat their workers as family and boasting about worker longevity, echoing the rhetoric of conventional growers. At best, organic growers take pride in exposing their employees to less toxicity and providing more year-round employment. One deeply committed organic grower expressed anger at people questioning how much he pays labor. "We do the best we can given the prices. People should be willing to pay more for their food. . . . Agriculture is getting a bad rap for labor but conventional agriculture deserves it with the pesticide exposures and short-term labor influxes. With the program we do, we can provide year-round jobs." Finally, no California organic farms are operated as employee-owned collectives, although a few are nonprofit organizations, illustrating how unquestioned the social relations of production remain.

MARKETING PRACTICES

Tied to the bioregionalist critique of agricultural industrialization, claims about the locality of organic markets abound in organic discourse. From an agroecology perspective, "exporting" food too far from the farm is energy intensive and defies the ideal of recycling energy on or near the

farm, including the energy metabolized by eating. Besides the environmental benefits, more attenuation in marketing arrangements may benefit growers. Such arrangements allow them to exert greater control over
what and how they grow and to capture a higher proportion of crop
value. Direct marketing, in that way, becomes part of the discourse of
saving the small family farm and also a strategy for regional development. As for consumers, direct-marketing arrangements are supposed to
produce knowledge and, hence, trust in their food supply.

So, to what extent do organic growers adhere to this bioregionalist
ideal? In certain respects, regional food provision is flourishing, as evidenced in the unprecedented growth of farmers' markets. In California, there are well over three hundred ongoing certified farmers' markets (California Service Agency 1997). These markets provide an
important sales outlet for organic farmers. As shown in table 4, 24 percent of growers in this study sold at farmers' markets, and 35 percent
of the all-organic growers did. Farmers' markets are a particularly important venue for small and medium-sized growers, who otherwise experience more difficult access to usual marketing arrangements.[15] In
California, restaurants are also an important group of buyers. While
high-end restaurants are known to "forage" at some of the best markets, most restaurants set up direct relationships with specific growers
to supply them. Restaurant buyers are fairly particular about what
crops and varietals they desire, however; they also exact high standards
of quality, which often put the grower at considerable risk. Table 4 also
shows that many growers sell directly to retailers, and, in fact, much
of the food sold to regional distributors stays within the region, given
the existence of a substantial home market for organics in California.[16]

In terms of marketing control, two-thirds of the growers interviewed
in this study handled their own marketing, meaning that they actively
participated in sales activities beyond arranging contracts. Significantly,
78 percent of the all-organic growers did their own marketing compared
with 52 percent of the mixed growers, a difference that increases with the
exclusion of raisins (a common organic product that is federally regulated and almost exclusively sold through packers). In part, the percentage is lower for mixed growers because many were coaxed into organic
production by buyers. The difference may also point to a greater degree
of freedom and profit potential among organic growers or, in less rosy
terms, undeveloped and more uncertain markets for them. Many of the
smallest growers, for example, do not even bother marketing their crops
in any but the most casual ways.

TABLE 4. MARKETING PRACTICES, BY GROWER TYPE,
1998–99

	All-Organic		Mixed		Total	
	n	%	*n*	%	*n*	%
Export (internat'l.)	11	14.1	14	20.9	25	17.2
Fresh export (internat'l.)	5	6.4	4	6.0	9	6.2
Contract	28	35.9	46	68.7	74	51.0
Wholesale	36	46.2	29	43.3	65	44.8
Direct to retail	37	47.4	24	35.8	61	42.1
Farmers' markets	27	34.6	8	11.9	35	24.1
Restaurants	9	11.5	5	7.5	14	9.7
Subscription	6	7.7	0	0.0	6	4.1
On farm	10	12.8	5	7.5	15	10.3
TOTAL	78	—	67	—	145	—
TOTAL OWN SALES	61	78.2	35	52.2	96	66.2

NOTE: Categories are not mutually exclusive; growers are counted for each marketing outlet used.

At the same time, much organic produce, like all California produce, is shipped throughout the United States and, as also seen in table 4, exported internationally. Export produce crops are primarily citrus, dried fruits, and nuts. The 17.2 percent figure for total exports is actually understated, for many growers were unaware of the final destination of the products they sell to packers and shippers.[17] Furthermore, if the 1999 OFRF survey holds true for California, on an acreage basis 80 percent of organic product was sold through wholesaling, with handlers/brokers being the most common outlet (34 percent). Even the largest grower-shippers were involved in some sort of wholesale arrangements, although they can presumably make up for the various handling fees and other extractions in sheer volume of sales. Nonetheless, this is a far cry from the control and immediacy that is assumed to be intrinsic to organic markets.[18]

For most growers, marketing practices are not a "choice" independent of other factors. Marketing both shapes and is shaped by crops grown, personal networks, and, ultimately, production practices. Less desirable and/or less perishable crops tend to be sold in bulk to packers and processors, often considerably decreasing growers' profits. In some cases, handlers share revenue and selling expenses on a percentage basis. In most cases, the terms are more beneficial to them than to growers. Either the grower gets a small remainder after the handler pays selling expenses and takes a cut, or, as in the case of processing ingredients, the grower gets a tonnage price set in advance by the buyer. Consequently, large-acre growers specializing in contract production for processing markets make their income through economies of scale, especially because many "commodity crops" can be machine harvested. Still, large-acre, all-organic growers tend to do their own sales more often than mixed (or conventional) growers of the same size. For some, this has come as a matter of necessity, arising from undeveloped markets. For others, it has involved an explicit decision made with the realization that it was the only way to retain more production value.

For the most experimental farms, direct marketing is the crucial component of the operation. Some sell a portion of their high-value crops to wholesalers, but the majority of sales occur through farmers' markets, farm stands, and subscription operations. In the last case, member-subscribers agree to participate for a specified amount of time and, for a weekly or monthly fee, receive a box of food every week. To entice customers to join and stay, these growers offer a wide variety of produce and continual supply. Therefore, this method of marketing works only with farms large and well-managed enough to maintain healthy and varied rotations. Most of them willingly integrate livestock, not only because of its agronomic benefits, but also because of the opportunity to offer subscribers a well-rounded market basket, containing eggs or even goat's milk. In other words, there is a synergistic relationship between this sort of marketing and the agroecological ideal, even though subscriptions are not the only, or even the most lucrative, sales outlet. In general, subscription farms garner the most devoted customers, who so trust the growers that some subscription growers are not certified organic, and others have dropped the organic designation altogether.

In sum, the marketing strategy that holds the most promise (other than for the large grower-shippers themselves) is direct sales of fresh produce in regional markets, a strategy which is most faithful to the organic dogma. It is most often followed by the midsized growers and a few microgrowers who sell to restaurants from which they receive extraordinarily high margins on a small volume of crops. For these growers, organic farming can seem a panacea, indeed. Yet, the strategy also depends on an expanding market and/or highly committed consumers, because growth in production volume is starting to exert competitive pricing on these growers. In any case, on an acreage basis, most of organic production is being funneled into an increasingly oligopsonistic industry structure—albeit sometimes on a concessionary basis—with marketing controlled by a small group of intermediary firms for any given commodity or group of commodities. Although larger growers who sell to these firms are brought in with attractive prices, they are still reduced to making their money on volume, not a particularly easy task with organic production. The many small apple, citrus, date, and avocado growers who sell to packers have virtually no bargaining power and are lucky to make any profit at all.

IDEOLOGICAL DISPOSITIONS

Perhaps the most all-encompassing claim made about organic agriculture relates to the internal processes of organic growers themselves—specifically, that they are motivated by different values from those of conventional growers, even that they operate under a different "paradigm" (see Beus and Dunlap 1990, 1994; Allen and Bernhardt 1995; Chiappe and Flora 1998; cf. Jackson-Smith and Buttel 1998). If they no longer operate in explicit opposition to "the food system," organic growers are thought to strive to provide alternatives to conventional food delivery. The flip side of this claim is that conventional growers seek only to make money and are ignorant of or flagrantly disregard other concerns.

More than one interviewed grower attacked the organic/conventional divide as a false dualism, noting that organic agriculture is constructed on deliberately created barriers, promoted, as one grower said, by "a very verbal and articulate cohort of hobby farmers." Such dualistic thinking also ignores how motivations evolve with differing degrees of individual agronomic and financial success or with regard to the changes that the organic sector undergoes.

There is no question that organic growers who began their career with organic farming—primarily first-generation farmers—identify most strongly with the notion of organic agriculture as a social movement, as compared with those who descended from farming families. It is also true that smaller growers more often voice social movement ideals, and it is virtually axiomatic that larger ones are more business-oriented. In addition, those who have farmed organically for a longer time tend to be more committed than those who are neophytes.

Yet, given the number of growers who do not fit these characterizations, we should take them with a grain of salt. A surprising number of small growers in this study became involved in organic production solely to reap value from residential real estate or down-sized farming operations. Many of these growers expressly doubt the validity of or-

ganic precepts. For example, a small fruit grower, who said he was told
he could get more money from his grove if it were organic, supposed organic agriculture to be the equivalent of saccharine or margarine in its
food-faddist origins. Likewise, growers who have been organic farming
for years can be quite cynical about their involvement. One large-scale
commodity crop grower and part owner of a chemical distribution company had been growing organically since the late 1970s, having started
out as a contract rice grower for macrobiotic-oriented Chico-San. Despite such longevity with the organic industry, this grower produced organically only when he could get a lucrative contract. As he said, "Some
are into it for the concept; I'm into it to make money."

Nor can it be presumed that all-organic growers are necessarily advocates. A two-hundred-acre fruit grower fell into organic while on the
verge of farm foreclosure. Not being able to afford inputs at the time, he
discovered that he could do without them. For him, organic production
kept him in business. Yet, as he put it, "I'm not out to save the world; I
just happen to grow organic food. . . . We are about feeding people organic food for a profit. . . . Hell, my politics are way to the right of center." Even one of the oldest organic operations in California—listed as
a Rodale certified grower (in Steffen, Allen, and Foote 1972)—claimed
to farm organically primarily because it was a very profitable niche market. Other than her appreciation of organic techniques, she defied stereo-
types of the organic grower and, in particular, was adamantly opposed
to the rhetoric against genetically engineered organisms (GEOs) that was
then starting to emerge in the organic movement.

More typical are mixed or converted growers who fall somewhere in
the ideological middle. Some who were attracted to organic agriculture
primarily for business purposes eventually found other reasons to farm
organically. Some became concerned with the ecological degradation or
safety risks associated with conventional production, and others became
cognizant of some of the agronomic benefits, such as improved soils, from
certain organic farming practices. Even growers who came in early on
"only for the money" realized the importance of the integrity of the organic name as a key to their success and eventually were convinced of the
integrity of organic production in ecological terms. One such grower
noted how he had increasingly bought into the organic philosophy over
time. Although organics used to represent a challenge of new practices and
economic promise, he had come to realize that it is a practical way of farming. A like-minded grower, noting that all his decisions are market-
driven, claimed he did not know of any grower who would not be 100 per-

cent organic if it were economic, a truism if there ever was one. Yet, many
of these growers remain economically tied to conventional agriculture in
ways that have made them cautious entrants, although they claimed to incorporate as many practices as they can in their conventional fields.

By the same token, some well-entrenched in the organic community
are ambivalent about their movement roots. A sales manager for one of
the largest all-organic operations (who had been involved in conventional agriculture much more recently than the company he worked for)
was blatantly patronizing about the small growers who had been formative in developing the sector. "A serious grower can't be a part-time
picker with overgrown sideburns and expect to compete," he said.
"There's a place in organic for mom-and-pop operations if they would
school themselves and have ambition and desire for excellence. . . .
Those guys are screaming now; they thought they had niche in market
and now they are resentful." The context for his vitriol was that this
company had been involved in a series of expansion-oriented deals in
which it was simultaneously curtailing buyer relations with small growers. Although short on social vision, the company had a five-year plan to
be "totally self-sustaining and earth friendly," hoping to incorporate on-
farm recycling, alternative fuel use, and even livestock operations into its
way of doing business. (Soon after my interviews, the company became
a contract supplier for another, even larger organic grower-shipper.) Of
the all-organic megaoperations that had moved into conventional production as a way to sustain company growth, one justified the shift as a
broad move toward sustainable production; another claimed to be
merely apolitical, having been involved with organic production because
of personal inclinations but not necessarily as a company philosophy.

Even among those who consider themselves ecological farming advocates, their motivations are not as visionary as one might think and, indeed, are often quite singular. Some I spoke with were more impressed
with soil quality; others were more concerned about pesticide use. A few
were also farm activists, involved in agricultural land preservation issues
or rural development generally. Yet, only a small number of growers
claimed to be involved in organic production for an alternative or radical vision (usually well-articulated), whether centered on lifestyle, personal health, social justice, or, in one case, "practical Christianity." Fly-
ing in the face of organic agriculture's putative historical roots, even fewer
had adopted a systemic critique of the agrofood system. Nevertheless, of
the handful of growers who had combined political vision with actual
farming, almost all were subscription farms. By adopting this model, they

at least hoped to address working conditions, equitable food access, and grower security, along with the more conventional goals, as it were, of organic production: ecological farming and healthy food delivery.

Taken together, few organic growers see organic farming as a means to alternative institution building, although many are explicitly distrustful of the worst of conventional agriculture. More significant perhaps, even dyed-in-the-wool all-organic movement growers are becoming less ideologically radical and are adopting practices they might have otherwise shunned. With a handful of buyer firms controlling market share—with the organic sector looking a lot like an oligopsony—a few players are able to set prices and effectively limit how production is carried out. Moreover, the rapid growth these firms generate is bringing competition that had heretofore been absent in the organic sector. Consequently, even those who are external to this industry structure are being pushed into capitalist decision making as the industry grows and changes.[19] No matter how committed they feel to organic farming qua social movement, they increasingly have to weigh their political goals against their livelihoods. In that way, they are caught up in a deeper logic of agrarian capitalism, particularly as it has evolved in California. The next chapter more closely examines these forces of agricultural industrialization in California and how they have affected the organic sector.

CHAPTER 4

California Dreaming

California's Agro-Industrial Legacy

> In no other state has farming so quickly lost its traditional character and become an established industry as in California. Today, "farming" in its accepted sense can hardly be said to exist in the State. The land is operated by processes which are essentially industrial in character. . . . To understand how farms have become factories in California, it is necessary to trace the rise of typically capitalist patterns of industrial operation in California agriculture.
>
> Carey McWilliams, *Factories in the Field*

Michael Pollan's 2001 exposé of the organic-industrial complex in the *New York Times Magazine* has generated increased awareness of what some are now calling the corporate takeover of the organic food system.[1] As chapter 3 showed, the sizable presence of agribusiness-like firms in the organic sector has transformed the structure of the sector. Their entry has also shaped the way organic agriculture is practiced, for conventional agriculturists' habits die hard. Yet, this transformation was not the doing of conventional agribusiness per se. Nor is it the case that agribusiness entry was intended to subvert the organic sector. Instead, the pioneers of the organic industry have grown and expanded to become effectively agribusiness themselves, drawing in these conventional firms with them. Along the way, the upper echelon of the sector has consolidated significantly.

Although such prima facie evidence of agribusiness participation and intra-industry consolidation is cause for concern, I argue that the focus on the presence of "big" players is off the mark. For the problem with agribusiness is its legacy of social and ecological exploitation rather than its scale of production per se. Additionally, such an analysis elides how all growers become subject to agribusiness logic, no matter what their intentions. In other words, California's agribusiness legacy runs much deeper than the particular firms through which it operates. So, to understand the mechanisms by which organic agriculture has ceased to live up to its imaginary, we need a deeper understanding of processes of industrialization in agriculture.

To that end, this chapter begins with a fairly theoretical discussion of innovation in capitalist agriculture and its effects on land values. The chapter continues with a brief review of California's agricultural history, to illustrate the formative and, in some respects, unique ways in which agricultural industrialization has proceeded in California. It then returns to the question of land values in California, which are unusually high not only for the degree of agricultural innovation that has taken place in the state but also for the more widespread effects of commercial development. Ultimately, these land values shape what can be grown and how, making all growers subject to the logic of agribusiness—and real estate speculation.

THE DYNAMICS OF CAPITALIST AGRICULTURE

When [agricultural mechanization] does not lead to the
decline of the small farm, the industrialisation of agriculture sets the seal on the small farmers' dependence
on the factory, the sole buyer of their products. They
become fully subordinated to industrial capital, and
their farming is directed solely to meet its requirements.

Karl Kautsky, *The Agrarian Question*

Recent work in the sociology of agriculture has focused well-deserved attention on the processes of consolidation in food processing and retailing and, to some extent, in on-farm production itself (e.g., Heffernan and Constance 1994).[2] John Ikerd (2001), one of the darlings of the sustainable agriculture movement, posits that specialization, standardization, and centralization are the key processes in agricultural industrialization, making even farm production equivalent to factory production. Carey McWilliams ([1935] 1971) once referred to this sort of agriculture—mistakenly, I believe—as factories in the field. The presumption is that scale economies are at work, squeezing out less capitalized growers and leaving food production to a small class of agrarian industrialists, a process crystallized in the well-known maxim of "get big or get out." While the growth of large-scale corporate farms represents an important aspect of agricultural change, particularly vis-à-vis livestock production, this analysis does not fully inform the processes of industrialization that I wish to interrogate, nor, for that matter, does it describe those that have the most far-reaching effects for organic agriculture.

Agricultural Exceptionalism

The central problem with the blithe equation of industrial agriculture with manufacturing is the failure to consider the unique aspects of food systems and how they shape the ability to generate value for producers (Fine, Heasman, and Wright 1996; Fine 1994; Goodman and Redclift 1991; Goodman and Watts 1994). Although the notion of agricultural exceptionalism has become the focus of an intense academic debate, in my mind there is little question that these exceptions have great explanatory power for the uneven industrialization of agrofood systems. These can be summarized in three categories.

One unique aspect of agriculture is that food systems are fundamentally dependent on biophysical production, to the extent that much of the value received in the market is created by biological processes. An apple is worth more than a seed. Yet, biological conditions can impose constraints on food production. Plants and animals are always vulnerable to the risks and uncertainties of weather, pests, diseases, and decay, among other things. Plants and animals also take time to grow, and their growth is often spurred (or hindered) by seasonal changes. In that way, the rhythmicality and seasonality of many biological processes limit the extent to which food production can be controlled or sped up (Kautsky [1899] 1988; FitzSimmons 1986; Goodman, Sorj, and Wilkinson 1987; Mann 1989).

A second uniqueness of (food-oriented) agriculture turns on eating. Besides medicine, food is the only commodity that consumers literally consume and, indeed, must consume. Because food is ingested, the biological processes of hunger, palatability, toxicopathy, and metabolism always impinge on what is eaten, in what quantities, and how (Fine 1994; Goodman and Redclift 1994). Thus, food must be grown in accordance with human digestive functions, albeit these functions have evolved with different food availability. At the same time, food and eating are awash with symbolic content. Food is a key medium through which cultural meanings are reproduced and performed, and food itself always has symbolic content (Beardsworth and Keil 1997; Bell and

Valentine 1997; Bourdieu 1984; Douglas and Isherwood 1996; Warde 1997). The absolute necessity of eating for social reproduction provides a ready-made market for food products, albeit a constrained one because of upper limits to appetite and outside limits to palatability. Taste, in turn, at times reflects intractable cultural taboos and at other times one of the most clear-cut realms of individual agency. In short, both the biological and symbolic aspects of food set up contradictory imperatives for producers of food.

The third unique aspect of agriculture is that land is the major medium of production, an input that is inextricable from the production process and plays a role far more important than the passive spatial role land plays in industrial production (Benton 1989). Its unique, unsubstitutable qualities create all manner of perversities for a neoclassical economic calculus. For example, although land can be devalued and even severely degraded, it is indelible; it rarely loses all value, unlike socially produced commodities that are used up or made obsolete (Harvey 1982). It is also what Polanyi (1944) called a fictitious commodity, one bought and sold in the market but not produced by human activity. Most significant, its fixity and scarcity makes it appropriable and monopolizable in the form of private property (Kautsky [1899] 1988; Fine 1979; Mann 1989). All of these aspects of land give it special social meaning, widely understood as a fundamental basis of livelihood and, in the American imagination, the basis of independence.

One assured effect of the interaction of these three factors within a capitalist framework is systematic overproduction. The propensity for the overproduction of food derives, in part, from its low demand elasticity. Aggregate demand for food does not tend to expand with increases in income or decreases in price (Cochrane 1993). In other words, people do not buy significantly more food if they become wealthier or if prices drop, because there is only so much one person can eat. In effect, the introduction or promotion of a new food simply "cannibalizes"—that is, displaces—another. On the supply side, farmers tend to stay in business even in the face of dim economic prospects. In particular, freehold family farmers can survive at the margin, by foregoing their own profits in the interest of holding on to their land (Friedmann 1978, 1980; Bonanno 1987). So, competition does not necessarily squeeze out least-profitable enterprises. In addition, the biology of crop production, involving long periods between planting decisions and harvest (Mann 1989; Pfeffer 1983), constrains farmers' flexibility to respond to market signals. It is very difficult to alter cropping strategies upon discovery of a glut in any given year; it is impossible with permanent crops. Finally, because there are few technological barriers to entry (the new agricultural biotechnologies being a groundbreaking exception), it is hard to establish a monopoly position in agriculture (Barham, Bunker, and O'Hearn 1994; Markusen 1985). Farmers are essentially price-takers, especially when faced with crops about to perish.

Innovation in Agriculture

In this light, we can better understand the driving force of innovation in agriculture. It is not only to generate economies of scale, which are not always present in agriculture in any case,[3] but also to overcome some of the obstacles thrown up by agriculture's exceptional characteristics, including the propensity for overproduction. Innovation in capitalist agriculture has thus taken three main forms, what I will call intensification, appropriation, and valorization. The first two correspond with two different notions of industrialization; the third does not necessarily entail industrialization, indeed can be quite the opposite. Let us examine each in turn.

Intensification is broadly characterized by efforts to speed up, enhance, or reduce the risks of biological processes (see Boyd, Prudham, and Schurman 2001 for a sustained analysis). Obvious "improvements" on biology range from growth hormones to high yielding varieties to chemical pest control to ripening agents. Yet, fertility enhancements that reduce or eliminate the need to fallow are also included here, because they allow more production from a piece of land—a sort of spatial intensification. Even some nontechnical innovations in labor control can be considered intensification by this definition, for example, the use of vulnerability to ensure a timely and compliant labor force come harvesttime (see Thomas 1985; Wells 1996). Such innovations make agriculture more like industry: more predictable, continuous, and flexible, and less risky (Goodman, Sorj, and Wilkinson 1987).

Efforts to minimize the role of nature nevertheless remain imperfect. To be sure, the very scares that have riveted contemporary attention to agriculture have arisen out of ill-fated attempts to enhance biological processes. Bovine spongiform encephalopathy (BSE)—or mad cow disease, as it is commonly known—is a product of feeding cow by-products to cows in an effort to produce more protein. Moreover, intensification only adds to the problem of overproduction. At introduction, early innovators enjoy surplus profits based on improved productivity. As others jump in, price competition ensues, causing rates of profits to fall, until marginal returns are very low (cf. Cochrane 1993; Schumpeter 1939; Storper and Walker 1989). This process that Schumpeter termed "creative destruction" in respect to industrial innovation is even more pronounced in agriculture, where there is little opportunity for price fixing, minimal demand elasticity, and a tendency for farmers to stay in business when they are failing.

Agricultural innovation has also taken the form of extracting value from others, or *appropriation.* Opportunities for more predictable profit making can be found in discrete activities that can be removed from the rural setting and put into factories, either at the input end or the processing/marketing end, so there is increased participation in food production by industrial players (Goodman, Sorj, and Wilkinson 1987).[4] This is essentially Kautsky's ([1899] 1988) notion of agricultural industrialization—a relational one.[5]

Whether such industrialization is led by nonfarm industry moving into these activities or by well-capitalized growers moving up the ranks, the result is the same. Eventually other growers become dependent on purchased inputs (e.g., seeds, tractors, fertilizers) as well as on intermediate buyers. In effect, the labor value farmers add (as well as value extracted from nature) is shifted to nonfarm industry (Fine 1994; Mooney 1983). Contract farming is an extreme form of this sort of exploitation; like sharecroppers, farmers own the means of production but are essentially propertied laborers, hired hands on their own land (Watts 1993; cf. Wolf, Hueth, and Lison 2001). By this definition, industrialization does not always mean that farms get larger. Yet, the ability for industrial capital to commodify farm processes does appear to be limited, perhaps leaving some value for farmers to glean. Organic farmers bank on these limits, albeit rarely consciously.

The third aspect of innovation, *valorization,* is about seeking value through the realm of consumption. Here, innovation turns on finding new ways of enhancing the desire for the product itself as opposed to intensifying the creation of value or extracting value from others. Brand-name marketing is a classic sort of product valorization, but valorization has also taken the form of growing or creating products that are valued for their scarcity and/or exoticness. Either way, valorization often involves the assertion of some sort of monopoly position. Those who are successful at valorization may be able to reap superprofits—or *economic rents,* as I will refer to them hereafter—profits above and beyond the "normal" rate of return. For farmers, the movement from so-called commodity crops to specialty crops exemplifies this form of innovation, although when too many farmers follow this strategy and specialty crops become commonplace, the purpose is defeated.

In the contemporary period, valorization is increasingly based on claims that the product is made or grown in a particular way. Especially as the processes of intensification and appropriation approach their end game, valorization appears the more lucrative avenue. Often, the value added is the assurance that one or both of these other two processes are not happening. Such is the promise of organic production: that crops are grown in accordance with nature and that value stays with the farmer (the second being the less common claim). Yet, this promise elides another dimension of agricultural innovation, which is its effect on land values.

Land Values as Nexus

All of the aspects of innovation discussed thus far have a certain futility to them, as newly gained value is always vulnerable to competition. Because of systematic overproduction (as well as expectations of cheap food), the treadmill effects of intensification are particularly harsh. Yet there is another reason for farmers to intensify to the limit of existing technologies. This last tendency is largely located in the nature of land markets, which are "sticky" and optimistic. In short, land values both anticipate the future and lock in the past.

In the language of real estate economics, the selling price of a given piece of agricultural land should approximate the present discounted value of the expected future income from that land. The present discounted value is the sum of probable future receipts from that land adjusted for the interest one would receive on a fixed investment held for the same period. In other words, land is capitalized (i.e., assessed) on the basis of future revenues but with the recognition that a dollar today is worth more than a dollar a year from now because of inflation. For a farmer, future income is a function of both the market value of the commodities to be grown and the productivity of land; for a landlord, future income is simply rent, a function of farmers' income.[6] Either way, then, current agricultural land values reflect common expectations of what can be grown, how fast, and how much.

Because land values incorporate future expectations, the potential to reap more profit from a piece of land exerts upward pressure on land values in the present (Shoemaker 1989, 43). Yet, when prospects are dim—

when, for instance, commodity prices are low—land values do not necessarily fall in proportion. So, for instance, U.S. agricultural land values increased 75 percent in real terms (adjusted for inflation) between 1947 and 1987, at the same time that real agricultural commodity prices declined 60 percent (Shoemaker 1989, 43). In this case, much of the difference was made up by increases in productivity, yet the nature of these improvements—increased dependence on purchased inputs—effectively shifted value to off-farm capital and thereby decreased farmers' share of agricultural output relative to land values.

Finally, when land becomes fully commodified, that is, traded with ease in capital markets, it becomes a vehicle of speculation, especially vis-à-vis future *commercial* development. Land prices start to reflect the capitalized value of the highest *possible* income, or what is commonly referred to as highest and best use (Harvey 1982, 368). Effectively, agriculture is forced to compete with other land uses and/or to act as a holding place for future development. What the USDA calls urban influence has had a significant effect on farmland values; during 1994–96 the value of farmland that was not urban-influenced was $640 per acre, while urban-influenced land was valued at $1,880 per acre (Blank 2000, 4).

The point is that land values act as routers of sorts. Although they do not exactly determine agriculture, they take signals from all spheres that affect agriculture, from technological development to consumer taste to land use planning, and create a single, if imperfect, index of expectations. Thus, innovations that improve productivity, whether changes in the rate of labor exploitation or intensification of biological activity, are capitalized into land values.[7] So are high-value cropping regimes, especially those with monopoly characteristics.[8] For farmers, then, the necessity to make payments to land capitalized at its highest and best use exerts tremendous pressure to adopt those technologies or cropping systems that maximize value per acre, creating a daunting treadmill effect. As we shall see, no other place better exemplifies this phenomenon than California, the land of value.

CALIFORNIA'S AGRO-INDUSTRIAL LEGACY

The history of California agriculture is an exemplar of agricultural modernization. All three innovative processes—intensification, appropriation, and valorization—have defined California agriculture, but with a particular twist: California had a capitalist agriculture from the get-go.

These processes, then, were not tendencies that passively shaped the transition from a peasant or family-farm tradition (cf. Goodman, Sorj, and Wilkinson 1987); they were strategies actively employed by a class of business farmers to address periodic crises of overproduction. As George Henderson puts it in *California and the Fictions of Capital*, patterns unfolded recurringly; however, they were "not simply the successive addition of crops to California's repertoire, but the strategic emplacement of the 'new' to absorb the losses of the 'old' " (1999, 8).

The question, then, is whether organic agriculture was ever truly outside this logic or, to the contrary, whether it represents another case of the new absorbing the losses of the old. This can be answered only in historical perspective. To that end, I employ the notion of crop regimes to suggest that each crisis was resolved differently but invariably involved new sorts of cropping patterns and new sorts of practices.[9] For reference purposes, table 5 is a schematic of these crop regimes, and table 6 shows the most valuable crops at different points in time. The narrative, however, will focus on the processes of intensification, appropriation, and valorization contained within each.

The Basis of Exceptionalism: Bonanza Farms

The gold rush provided a jump start to the region's economy. The high productivity of the widely accessible placer mines and the high wages of the quartz mines placed wealth in the hands of many, which, in turn, created demand for basic mining equipment, transport, foodstuffs, and other consumer goods (McWilliams 1949; Rodman 1988). The home market for grains, beef, and truck crops that developed directly out of the mining economy was the nascence of California agriculture. The first farms in California, besides the soon-to-be-defunct mission ranches, were situated en route to the gold-filled hills.

Mining did more than develop a home market for basic commodities. Although the mines were financed in large part by eastern mercantile capital, much of the mined wealth stayed in California to be amassed in banks in San Francisco and reinvested in a burgeoning multisector regional economy (Walker 2001). Some of these reinvestments took the form of real estate speculation. Thus it was gold rush money that was used to buy up and disenfranchise Californio holdings on the original Spanish and Mexican land grants, reclaim the vast "swamp" lands and other federal lands that had been removed from the Homestead Act, and create the early bonanza cattle ranches and wheat farms. So what was

TABLE 5. CALIFORNIA CROP REGIME HIGHLIGHTS

Primary Period	Bonanza Farming 1850–80	Specializing 1880–1920	Consolidating 1920–80	Value Seeking 1980–?
Typical crops	Wheat, cattle	Citrus, grapes, stone fruit	Cotton, sugar beets, rice, lettuce, processing tomatoes	Strawberries, premium wine grapes, kiwis, organic anything
New lands	Sacramento and San Joaquin valleys	Southern California, east side of San Joaquin Valley, smaller periurban valleys (e.g., Santa Clara, Sonoma, Napa)	Imperial Valley, Salinas Valley; postwar: west side of San Joaquin Valley	Interstices, rolling coastal valleys
New irrigation	Dry-farmed	Irrigation colonies, irrigation districts	American Canal, centrifugal pump, Central Valley Project, State Water Project	None
Scale	Huge: ≥20,000 acres not unusual	Subdivision: many 10- to 80-acre fruit farms	Polarization: new lands, larger scale	Higher value per acre: acreage reduction
Ownership	Absentee-owned by San Francisco business elites	Sharecropping, tenancies by Japanese and	Leasehold arrangements on vegetable land	Mexican tenant farmers, urban investors, "gentlemen farmers"

		European immigrants, speculative purchases by professionals		
Labor	Short supply: white "tramps" and Chinese	Oversupply: systematic exploitation of non-white immigrants	Labor conflict, Braceros, rise of UFW	Demise of UFW; increased reliance on undocumented immigrants
Marketing environment	Exported abroad	Growers' cooperatives	Vertically integrated grower-shippers; contract farming	International competition, strength of retail, direct marketing
Agroecology	"Mining the soil"	Pest control with arsenical compounds, some biological control	Intensification: end of lease clauses requiring fallows; postwar: DDT, petroleum-based fertility	Antipesticide climate but increased use of pesticides; very intense land use

TABLE 6. TOP FIFTEEN CALIFORNIA CROPS AT KEY POINTS

(In thousands of dollars)

1910		1940		1960		1980		2000	
Hay	42,187	Cattle/calves	102,014	Cattle/calves	514,721	Dairy	1,771,383	Dairy	3,703,920
Dairy	19,083	Dairy	67,128	Dairy	382,711	Cattle/calves	1,438,667	Grapes	2,836,313
Cattle/calves	18,589	Hay	40,164	Cotton	311,056	Cotton	1,389,342	Nursery	2,247,256
Barley	17,185	Oranges	39,353	Hay	177,086	Grapes	1,215,585	Lettuce	1,484,115
Oranges	12,952	All vegetables	38,960	Eggs	166,875	Hay	723,316	Cattle/calves	1,266,985
Cotton	11,744	Grapes	30,357	Grapes	131,761	Nursery	498,005	Tomatoes	951,030
Grapes	10,847	Cotton	26,519	Oranges	110,453	Tomatoes	490,310	Cotton	898,263
All vegetables	6,887	Plums/prunes	15,662	Tomatoes	108,008	Almonds	487,320	Flowers/foliage	841,914
Eggs	6,717	Dry beans	14,171	Potatoes	79,988	Rice	423,612	Strawberries	767,306
Dry beans	6,517	Barley	13,895	Lettuce	76,554	Flowers/foliage	395,907	Hay	730,422
Wheat	6,324	Sugar beets	11,778	Turkeys	71,078	Lettuce	382,563	Almonds	681,649

Plums/prunes	5,474	Walnuts	10,909	Barley	70,258	Eggs	370,165	Broccoli	536,757
Potatoes	4,879	Peaches	10,639	Rice	57,528	Wheat	357,945	Chickens	471,081
Peaches	4,574	Sheep	10,411	Prunes	53,515	Chickens	229,177	Avocados	362,118
Sugar beets	4,321	Chickens	10,071	Sugar beets	—	Oranges	224,548	Carrots	346,731
Total value of top 15 crops	178,280		442,031		2,311,592		10,397,845		18,125,860
Total value of all crops grown	—		—		3,164,865		13,539,000		25,509,829
% value of top 15					73.0		76.8		71.1

SOURCES: Economic Development Agency 1961, 1981; National Agricultural Statistics Service 2002; U.S. Bureau of the Census 1910, 1950.

exceptional about California agriculture was not only that it was made up of large landholdings early on, rather than having first been settled and developed by a class of smallholders; more significant, it was capitalism de novo (Leibman 1983; McWilliams 1949; Walker 2001).

The period between 1850 and 1870 was a time of rapid and expansive land acquisition led by what had come to be the biggest names in California finance, as well as Henry Miller, who had made his first fortune in meatpacking in south San Francisco. Some holdings extended into the hundreds of thousands of acres; Miller's neared 1.25 million at the time of his death, and the Southern Pacific Railroad once held over 11 million (Henderson 1999). The 620 largest farms in 1872 averaged 22,000 acres each (Gates 1975). What emerged, then, was an extraordinarily polarized landholding structure, which was only somewhat abetted when specialty crop production got under way some two decades later. Much of this land was planted to wheat, which was enjoying a strong export market. Perfect for absentee landlords, wheat production required little labor, and it also worked well as a dryland crop if timed with the routine winter flooding of the Sacramento Valley. Early wheat production, however, was an extensive form of agriculture, with little done to improve outcomes.

The Shift to Specialty Cropping

The first major crisis to hit California agriculture was the international glut of wheat production in the late 1890s. Declining prices first squeezed out smaller producers; then wheat production became more difficult altogether because of nutrient-depleted soils. Consequently, the bonanza holdings were devalued. Rather than farm the land themselves, these large landholders subdivided or leased their land to a large group of new growers, many of whom were newly arrived immigrants. Using their expertise, most went into specialty crop production, especially fruit growing.[10] Another road to smaller-scale fruit growing involved participation in one of the irrigation colonies, backed by either private land speculators or the Southern Pacific Railroad (Henderson 1999).

Many of these latter new orchardists, particularly in southern California citrus, were not "dirt farmers" or recent immigrants but merchants and professionals who defined themselves as businessmen or "growers" (Moses 1995; Stoll 1998). As Henderson (1999) points out, fruit production was too capital intensive to be done on a large scale at the time, given the considerable up-front investment for a tree to come into production. The capital these businessmen brought, along with cheap credit, is what allowed specialty cropping to take hold, albeit on a small scale. Yet specialty crop production, with the high prices it yielded when crops were sold, created a push on land values that further undermined the grain economy (Leibman 1983). Although field crops were hardly entirely forsaken early in the new century, as shown in table 6, the shift away from them was the first step in valorization as a fix for overproduction.

The early successes of the fruit industry were dependent on the confluence of many factors, not only irrigation, easy credit, and immigrant expertise, but also innovations in marketing (Rhode 1995; Stoll 1998; among others). Most important were the various ways in which "natural" obstacles of distance and durability (Friedmann 1993a, b) and the lag between production time and labor time (Mann 1989) were turned into opportunities, such that time and space were effectively compressed (Henderson 1999). Such was the case with innovations as seemingly disparate as the canneries, the refrigerated cars of the Southern Pacific, and the various cooperative marketing arrangements for fruit growing. Although such innovations etched a dependence on distant markets, that dependence was no less pronounced during the wheat boom. What was different in specialty cropping, as Stoll tells us, was the way in which businesses expanded: growers expanded not so much by buying land as by investing in packing sheds and lithographed labels.

Commodity specialization proceeded apace, the result of a high degree of commodity specificity coupled with the scale economies of collective marketing. Horticultural production, especially, quickly became organized around commodities, often reflecting the dominion of commodity-specific growers' organizations, marketing boards, and other intermediaries. Those who were able to establish a brand name won early control, and growers scaled up and "diversified" through distribution, the Earl Fruit Company/DiGiorgio and Cal Pak/Del Monte being prime examples (Stoll 1998).[11] By the 1920s, the small-scale fruit growers that had started to emerge circa 1870 had been brought under the total control and discipline of packers (whether cooperatively owned or private), so that landholding per se ceased to be the source of power and profits within the fruit industry. This establishment of powerful buyer organizations exemplified appropriation on a wide scale.

There was, of course, another critical factor in specialty crop production. Whereas wheat production (already mechanized) could be accomplished with little labor, so that the minuscule and itinerant labor force that existed up until about 1880 was adequate, specialty crops were labor intensive and required a reliable and plentiful labor force, yet one flexible enough to be dismissed at harvest's end. The problem was solved on the backs of various ethnic groups who were recruited to work in California's fields but were made politically vulnerable through immigration policy and racial discourse, both of which reinforced their marginality (Almaguer 1994; Henderson 1999). By squashing the political power of the most vulnerable immigrant groups (and violently interceding in their strikes), the state kept wages low and laborers moving in accordance with the needs of growers (Daniel 1981; Mitchell 1996; Thomas 1985).

Thus began a reciprocal relationship between high-value produce and cheap labor. And since land became capitalized on the basis of high-value horticultural production and low wages, growers had to keep their labor costs low to stay in business, reinforcing these exploitative labor patterns (Daniel 1981). Yet, growers themselves were victims of surplus extraction by finance capital and vertically integrated marketing companies. In that way, growers came to have a "contradictory class position" as both exploiters and exploited.[12]

The final critical factor in specialty crop production was advancement in pest control technology—a major factor in intensification—led by the University of California. Specialization brought uncontrollable insect infestation and weed introductions, which also posed a problem for interstate commerce (Sawyer 1996). The University of California had started playing a major role in plant protection beginning in 1875, when Hilgard, the founder of the College of Natural Resources, identified phylloxera in grapes. At first, Hilgard and his colleague, Dwinelle, introduced resistant varieties, but by 1886 Hilgard had developed Bordeaux mixture, a combination of copper, sulfur, lime, and water, to control fungi. But the coddling moth proved troublesome too, and the university started to recommend large-scale spraying with arsenical compounds as early as 1890, with the knowledge that chemicals were less harmful to plants (!) when suspended in water (Smith 1946).[13] Alongside its efforts to promote insecticidal sprays, the University of California had the only department of biological control in the country.[14] Yet, "far from offering a noble, environmentalist alternative to industrial-scale farming, biological control developed within an agricultural science establishment dedicated to all-out production and maximum profit" (Sawyer 1996, xxiii). For, as Sawyer argues, the purpose of early pest control was not only to maximize production but also to keep prices high through aesthetic appeal (valorization). For a long time, the one indubitable success of the Division of Beneficial Insect Investigations was controlling cotton-cushiony scale on oranges, which was solely a cosmetic problem.

The larger point is that this blip of fruit farming from 1890 to 1920 or so, as Stoll (1998) describes it, was small farming done by a capitalist class. Irrigation had been promoted as a way to make good on the agrarian dream of small family farmers, but it was never successful in that regard (Daniel 1981; Henderson 1999; Hundley 1992; Pisani 1984; Worster 1985). To the contrary, irrigation created the conditions for the more industrial style of farming that was beginning to emerge in the 1920s and was solidified by the 1930s, by pointing the way to the economies of scale to be gained from lower per unit production and consolidated marketing (Stoll 1998).

Consolidation and the Reemergence of Agribusiness

In the face of massive overproduction, the 1920s and 1930s were a time of integration and consolidation. Landholdings repolarized during this period, for the number of farms under fifty acres increased, effectively creating a class of part-time farmers, at the same time that the middle dropped out and the number of farms over a thousand acres also increased (Jelinek 1979). Undoubtedly, the vertical integration strategies of Cal Pak, DiGiorgio, and other processors kept small fruit farms alive, if not wholly viable.

With the expansion of irrigation meanwhile, new commodity crops such as cotton, rice, and sugar beets were introduced to California agriculture. Production of these crops was organized on a particularly large-scale basis, given the low per acre revenues and clear economies of scale in production.[15] They were also federally supported crops, so cotton and sugar beets were in the top fifteen of California's highest value crops from 1910 to 1970, after which sugar beets dropped out (see table 6).[16] Mechanical harvesting of these crops increased productivity, also contributing to intensification. All told, the amount of irrigated acreage nearly doubled from 1909 to 1945 (Jelinek 1979), and many areas gained a second growing season.

World War II facilitated even more growth in California agriculture, and consolidating trends continued. First and foremost, the population of the state expanded tremendously, and the postwar economic expansion created a healthy market for basic commodities such as beef, dairy, and poultry (Jelinek 1979). Between 1950 and 1982, the number of milk cows increased by 57 percent, although the number of dairy farms dropped considerably when dairy farmers started to practice intensive drylot dairying (Gilbert and Akor 1988).[17] Since these dairies purchased their feed, a healthy market for forage crops was maintained as well. Yet, the primary locus of expansion was in vegetable production.

A series of technological developments facilitated this expansion of vegetable production. Improvements in refrigeration and marketing had already enabled lettuce, melons, tomatoes, and dates to be grown in the southeastern part of the state, overcoming seasonal and agronomic obstacles (Henderson 1999). Then, the petrochemical technologies that were developed during the war broadened the farmer's repertoire of both fertility management and pest control and brought the widespread use of DDT. Fertilizer use increased twentyfold between 1940 and 1980 and, in 1980, 112 million pounds of pesticides were applied, mostly sulfur and petroleum distillates but also synthetics (Scheuring 1983, 27). In effect, land already in production could be made to work harder and faster, yielding several crops per year. These chemical technologies, together with extended "cool chains" (Friedland 1994b), made vegetable cropping for a national market possible, and the coastal areas of the Salinas Valley, Santa Maria, and Oxnard along with the Imperial Valley became the nation's primary vegetable producing region. Imperial Valley broccoli and cauliflower acreage, for example, increased from five hundred to fifteen thousand acres between the early 1970s and 1987 (Martin 1987, cited in Wells 1996).

In terms of industry structure, agribusiness firms were happy to integrate vertically while maintaining flexibility in production through, for instance, leasing land and contract farming (Leibman 1983). In the coastal areas in particular, subcontracting to provide specialty services (e.g., irrigation, transplanting, harvest labor) and to moderate supply instabilities—the latter of which FitzSimmons (1986) refers to as "capacity subcontracting"—became the dominant form of organization. At the same time, multinational corporations began to control that economy by marketing the crops of smaller growers, whose decisions were specified in marketing contracts (FitzSimmons 1986, 338). Thus, observes Leibman (1983), after World War II the direction of California agriculture was not necessarily to latifundia-style farms, although they became quite large by national standards; instead, grower-shippers, marketing agents, processors, and other consolidators assumed increased importance in a food system based on the marketing of highly perishable and delicate fruit and vegetable crops to increasingly distant markets (see also Friedland, Barton, and Thomas 1981; Friedland 1994a, b; Wells 1996).[18] In vegetable production, in other words, intensification, appropriation, and valorization worked together.

Nevertheless, specialty cropping—now increasingly based on vegetables—continued, from 1945 to 1980, to depend on the cheap labor of those who had been racialized and marginalized, providing an invisible sort of subsidy to agriculture.[19] During the war and postwar period, this subsidy was made more explicit in the form of the Bracero program, in which the U.S. and Mexican governments allowed for the importation of contract workers (see Wells 1996). The program was justified on the basis of a shortage of harvest workers, but the real reason for such shortages was growers' refusals to pay higher wages. The program was terminated in the 1963, but it had the long-term effect of stymieing collective efforts among workers to raise wages, for it institutionalized a pattern of displacing dissent with the employment of a more vulnerable group (Jelinek 1979; Thomas 1985) or reconfiguring the very nature of the employment relationship, as Wells's study of strawberry sharecropping makes clear. That is, even the highly visible successes of the United Farm Workers union were short-lived, eclipsed by a new wave of undocumented immigration from Mexico (which employers encouraged) and the political construction of piece work as independent contracting (Wells 1984, 1996).

The Search for Value

As discussed in chapter 2, the worldwide farm crisis of the 1980s had relatively mild effects on California. Wells (1996) observes that California has been relatively impervious to crises because of its dedication to fruit and vegetable crops. Specialty crop growers neither depended on government commodity supports, nor were they as vulnerable to world market price swings, because the very nature of the fresh commodity gives it a strong home market. So, as Wells (1996) points out, in the farm crisis year of 1986, fruit and vegetable crops actually increased in value by 12.3 percent while field crops declined by 18 percent (from California Department of Food and Agriculture 1987).

Still, in 1980, a full 45.5 percent of California's crop value remained in crisis-vulnerable field crops and livestock. Dairy, cattle and calves, hay, and cotton, were four of the top five crops, and together accounted for almost 40 percent of all crop value (see table 6). Likewise, some specialty crops in California had become so common that they had taken on the character of commodity crops (e.g., processing tomatoes, oranges, almonds, etc.). Some of these erstwhile specialty crops had started to see competition from cheap imports when the global fresh fruit and vegetable trade began to unfold (Friedland 1994b). And though they had not been directly subsidized through commodity programs, they had certainly benefited from the technical support of the University of California, in addition to state-supported irrigation. So these crops, too, were subject to the crisis of overproduction, worsened by the indirect subsidies they had received.

Nonetheless, just as Henderson (1999) notes for an earlier era, the fix was underway before the crises fully took hold. It involved intensification of production as well as valorization, when a new round of specialty crops replaced commodity crops.[20] As can be seen from the percentage distributions in table 7, vegetable production began to grow in importance in the period between 1960 and 1980, as production of nursery and flowers did. In the same period, field crops dropped in value and then recovered to near their prior level, and the value of fruits and nuts increased only a little. Hence, the relative ascendancy of horticultural crops was at the expense of livestock.

Beginning in the mid-1980s, the reorganization of California agriculture to yet more nonstaple crops intensified. In a five-year period, land in cotton, rice, and wheat declined by over seven hundred thousand acres, nearly offset by increases in vegetables, fruits, and set-aside acreages.[21] Cotton dropped from third place to seventh place in terms of crop value from 1980 to 2000. As discussed in chapter 2, many of these cotton farmers started growing vegetables. By 2000, lettuce, tomatoes, broccoli, and carrots, all of which benefited from partial mechanization of the harvest in response to strong labor organization in those crops, were solidly in the top fifteen (table 6). Strawberries had seen ebbs and flows of production since Japanese truck farmers first arrived, but they had always been a local and short-seasoned crop. Advances in technology, including varietal development allowing year-round production, underlay a 1990s strawberry boom that brought strawberries into ninth place on California's top fifteen in 2000 (Wells 1996). Meanwhile, oranges, long a workhorse of specialty agriculture, dropped out of the top fifteen. Although grapes had been an important crop since the late 1880s, they emerged as the highest-value crop in the 1990s, largely driven by the boom in wine production, only surpassed by dairy. Finally, by 2000, nursery and flowers represented nearly 11 percent of crop value (table 7).

TABLE 7. CALIFORNIA CROP VALUES, BY SECTOR

(in thousands of dollars)

	1960		1970		1980		1990		2000	
	$	%	$	%	$	%	$	%	$	%
Vegetables	401,911	12.7	699,266	15.7	2,326,000	17.2	3,560,880	18.4	6,665,373	26.1
Fruits and nuts	614,431	19.4	878,735	19.7	2,883,200	21.3	5,060,665	26.2	7,308,327	28.6
Field and seed	810,163	25.6	860,495	19.3	3,274,100	24.2	3,257,224	16.9	2,478,081	9.7
Nursery and flowers	85,176	2.7	227,425	5.1	907,100	6.7	1,908,974	9.9	2,788,959	10.9
Livestock	1,253,184	39.6	1,790,167	40.2	4,148,600	30.6	5,515,159	28.6	6,269,089	24.6
TOTAL	3,164,865	100.0	4,456,088	100.0	13,539,000	100.0	19,302,902	100.0	25,509,829	100.0

SOURCES: Economic Development Agency 1961, 1971, 1981, 1991; National Agricultural Statistics Service 2002.

What does not show up in the aggregate numbers is the growth of exotics, crops that heretofore had been extraordinarily precious or completely unknown. Beginning with the early 1980s kiwi boom, many orchardists started to experiment with exotic fruits or switched to more unusual varietals, such as Asian apples and blood oranges. Basic vegetables became equally exotic, and unusual varieties were (re)introduced: sugar snap peas, Yellow Finn potatoes, Belgian endive, Brandywine tomatoes, fava beans, and so on. Not uncommon to the process of valorization, the delicateness and perishability of these crops entail more labor intensity, because it is for these very qualities that many heirloom varieties were shunned in an earlier era of agricultural industrialization.

Accordingly, new production relationships have been forged around these newly valorized crops. Strawberry growers have always been quite small on an acreage basis, averaging around thirty acres, not only because strawberries require intensive management and close supervision of the harvest, but also because high per acre sales make such small farms economic (Wells 1996). Labor is by far the largest component of production costs, and besides rent, most other costs (for transplants, chemicals) are variable. As such, undercapitalized growers have entered into strawberry production en masse. Financed by shippers, who control postharvest and marketing, growers themselves have operated on a small margin and most strongly felt the squeeze of price fluctuation, so that, indeed, unionization could put them out of business (Bardacke 1999).

In contrast, owners in the wine grape business are relatively wealthy. While the wine industry was previously very concentrated, with two firms sharing about 50 percent of the output (Gallo and United Vintners), the boom that began in the 1970s was led by a polyglot of entrants, including "Coca-Cola, many European firms, large landowning operations, tax-shelter investors and speculators, and wealthy individuals indulging enological impulses giving rise to the phenomenon of 'boutique wineries' " (Friedland 1984, 230). For farmworkers, however, job security has worsened with the heavy reliance on labor contractors. Labor contractors are most often used when farming systems are highly specialized and marketing takes place in lump transactions, creating extremely punctuated field labor requirements.[22]

Finally, many of the new exotics are grown by backyard gardeners, residential real estate holders, and other small entrepreneurs who have found they can make a living growing these high-value vegetables, often organically, on small pieces of land. They tend to employ labor in the most sporadic of ways, hiring friends, neighbors, and interns when needed, and relying on a good deal of self-exploitation (i.e., not earning revenues equal to the cost of their own labor).[23]

What is unprecedented about these crops is the way consumption forces have driven their growth. In the case of strawberries, their extreme delicateness and perishability would seem an undeniable drawback were supply considerations paramount, even though the riskiness of fresh strawberry production has been somewhat mitigated by new technologies and the ways in which labor has been constructed around the characteristics of the strawberry, as Wells (1996) rightly shows. Nevertheless, such growth might not have been possible without the central positioning of fresh fruits and vegetables in current thinking regarding the optimal diet.[24] Premium wine came of age in conjunction with the many other demographic and cultural changes that have affected American food tastes. These include increased prosperity among a younger and more experimental population (the so-called yuppies), the internationalization of the economy and the cross-cultural exposures that have accompanied it, and a newfound sophistication among American lifestyles (Eysberg 1990). Many of the new exotics have been positioned as more luxurious and tasty "vanity foods," with symbolic attributes of class, place, healthy living, and sensual experience constructed into the commodity (Cook 1994, 236). Indeed, many of these new crops have been popularized by restaurateurs.

The other important similarity about these newly valorized crops is that small producers can compete and even thrive with only a few acres in production and little capitalization. This has given rise to a sense that high-value crops can lead to a rural renaissance, a sense that many share. Nevertheless, their prospects for the long run are unclear. Both the wine and strawberry industries were on the verge of oversupply in the late 1990s (Thompson 1998); market gardeners, for their part, were beginning to complain of the volatility of having a great year selling a new crop after which they were met with a rash of competition in that crop the following year.

The fundamental problem with exoticized foods is that they depend on production flexibility to keep ahead of rapidly changing tastes, especially insofar as novelty and scarcity themselves contribute crucially to taste. Yet, it does not take long before an exotic food becomes ordinary and loses much of its value (witness kiwis). Therefore, if high-value produce is the making of a new crop regime, it is one that is extraordinarily prone to crises of overproduction. And labor remains as contingent as ever, if not more so.

THE VALUE OF LAND IN THE LAND OF VALUE

The evolution of California agriculture, particularly in terms of intensification and valorization, can be witnessed in its land values. Average agricultural land values are substantially higher in California than those in the rest of the country (USDA, n.d.). Values started to diverge at the end of the nineteenth century, when specialty fruit production came into play (Agricultural Research Service 1958; Pressly and Scofield 1965). Irrigation development generalized the shift from extensive grain crops to intensive horticultural crops, which itself contributed to an increase in the value of agricultural land (Leibman 1983; Worster 1985, 1992). Furthermore, since irrigation district assessments were levied on the basis of crop potential, irrigation effectively compelled farmers to grow the most profitable crops (Jelinek 1979, 66).

Land values started to soar again in the 1960s, when technological development enabled mass, year-round vegetable production. Particularly in the prime coastal zones, land became capitalized on the basis of several crops per year. In effect, alternative production practices that depend on rotations of marginal-value crops, as is critical in most "sustainable" systems, ceased to be economically viable. A telling example occurred in the Salinas area. Until the mid-1950s, customary leases there required fallowing and green manuring. By the late 1970s, growers had gained the upper hand in lease conditions, so that rents no longer met the costs of land purchase; effectively, these practices of good stewardship were snubbed (FitzSimmons 1986, 342). By the 1980s, however, land was so valuable that landowners could make a living leasing out land. Consequently, virtually all prime vegetable land was available only on a lease basis from farm families of yesteryear, whose rental prices demanded intense crop rotations.

So what, if anything, has this latest round of valorization done to land values? Good evidence suggests that it has contributed to this spiraling of land values. Where strawberry production replaced fruit orchards and row crops, strawberry land has become some of the most expensive of all agricultural land, reflecting the unparalleled per acre crop value of this production. In fact, pockets of strawberry production remain in places that are otherwise rapidly urbanizing (e.g., Irvine, Oxnard), suggesting that, at least for a while, strawberry rents can compete with development for "highest and best use." Where premium wine grapes were planted, the effect was extreme. In 2000, premium wine acreage rose to $140,000 per acre in Napa (Burnham 2000)—the highest ever—reflecting, in this case, the monopoly rent of a Napa Valley designation. Clearly, these levels of assessment preclude the profitable production of other crops, much like the effect of peaches on wheat a century before.

Two other aspects of California land values have played into the problem. One is their relative immunity to economic downturns. For instance, one of the proximate causes of the 1980s farm crisis nationally was that land values became too high relative to commodity prices, causing many farmers to default on their debt, effectively devaluing land devoted to particular commodities (Strange 1988). Although the California agricultural economy experienced the same downturns as elsewhere then, as well as in the 1890s and 1930s, the troughs were not nearly as steep or prolonged (Blank 2000). California's relative immunity to this devaluation speaks not only to the area's privileging of specialty crops and the apparent cohesion of the landowner-farmer alliance but also to good old-fashioned California boosterism. From early on, real estate speculation was a driving force of the California economy, often preceding industrial development (Davis 1992; Henderson 1999). In such an economy, rising land values are the surest signal of success.

The unflagging optimism embodied in 1980s land values points to the other important aspect of California agricultural land values: the constant pressure of commercial development. Rapid and unplanned economic development, along with an entrenched politics of exclusion, has contributed to the sprawl that has characterized California urbanism (Pincetl 1999). It also has added a premium to agricultural land. According to agricultural economist Steven Blank (2000, 4), the urban influence on agricultural land values has affected only 17 percent of all U.S. acreage in general but almost all of California's harvest acreage.

According to census figures, the state lost nearly nine million acres of total farmland between 1955 and 1992, a decline of about 24 percent in total acreage (figure 2 in Medvitz 1999, 16). Much of this land was lost to urban expansion, with many farmers selling out at premium prices and others forced out by increasing property taxes (Jelinek 1979, 89). Yet, during this same period overall farm output did not decline, because new technologies increased yields and crop turnover (Medvitz 1998). In fact, the 1997 Census of Agriculture showed that California agriculture continued to experience growth despite urbanization, and farmers were harvesting more *cropland* than ever before. In effect, acreage in pasture, some of which was being urbanized, was also being converted to intensive crop production. Orchard acreage increased 336,000 acres in just five years (between 1992 and 1997), reaching the highest total in history, and the vegetable harvest was up 19 percent in that period. There was also more intensification in dairy; fewer producers were managing more animals on less pasturage (CIRS 1999). And those who farmed in the most developed areas did, indeed, farm very intensively (i.e., several crops per year) on smaller, often fragmented pieces of land.[25]

Growers subject to the effects of real estate pressure on land values have little choice but to leave farming altogether or find ways to increase crop value, either by intensification or by identifying opportunities for some sort of premium. According to farmland preservation advocates Daniels and Bowers, the best way to protect farmland is to make farming more profitable, through locally organized farmers' markets, community-supported agriculture projects, and niche marketing of specialty crops (1997, 19). To be sure, in Sonoma County, where hay farming has become highly uneconomic given urbanization and the restructuring of dairy, high-value market gardening continues to be attractive, competing as it can with wine grape production in terms of per acre value and meeting the requirements of what has become one of the strongest land preservation measures in the country (see Sokolow 1998).[26]

In this light, it is worth considering what some of the other efforts in land conservation have added to the picture. The Williamson Act of 1965, California's premier land conservation measure, was intended to give farmers incentives to hold on to farmland. Farmers who enter into Williamson contracts have their property taxes assessed at a reduced rate if they agree to use the land for agricultural purposes for ten years. Although half of California farmland was in Williamson contracts during the 1990s (Daniels and Bowers 1997), much of the acreage enrolled in the program was in areas not particularly threatened by development (Sanders 1998). More problematic, this preferential assessment often has been used as a tax break for hobby farms and ranchettes, or pure speculation, allowing landowners to hold on to land cheaply until it increases in value (Daniels and Bowers 1997). Zoning laws have had similar effects. Most agricultural zoning is based on minimum lot size, which prohibits the subdivision of parcels below the minimum acreage, making the effectiveness in terms of farmland preservation highly dependent on minimum lot size. With small minimums, parcels are likely to have a higher per acre value, for they become relatively attractive to urban refugees and hobby farmers (Daniels and Bowers 1997).[27] Finally, conservation easements, which allow growers a tax deduction, have been used primarily to protect several thousand acres of vineyards in Napa, Monterey, and Sonoma counties, most of which are owned by wealthy gentlemen farmers (Sokolow 1998; Vink 1998).[28]

In short, development pressure on farmland has had three main effects. It has affected the structure of agriculture by reducing the number of farms and increasing their crop and land values (Jelinek 1979). It has reconfigured the geography of farm production by minimizing economically marginal land uses, shifting lower-value production to less landcompetitive regions and inviting production that carries a certain aesthetic to greenbelts and genteel exurbs, largely to the benefit of wealthy landowners. Most important, it has ratcheted up the necessity of growing high-value crops, and very intensively, for those farmers who care to remain in business. This last aspect, in particular, has intersected with organic production in important ways.

ORGANIC LOGIC

Notions of a rural renaissance suppose that organic growers operate outside the punishing logic of conventional agricultural production. Although there might have once been such a heyday for organic agriculture, these days organic growers are faced with ever more competition as the sector expands. Like all growers, they face a dynamic that is difficult to subvert. To survive, they must compete as nominally capitalist enterprises, at the very least making payments to land, labor, and inputs and earning returns that ensure their own reproduction unless they receive other sources of income. Some of these "factors" are more elastic than others, but land as the defining feature of agricultural production is essential; there must be payments to land, whether in rents or in mortgage debt, unless growers are subsidized by past generations.

Land values, though, reflect past rounds of intensification and valorization. With values capitalized on past profitability, all growers become subjected to the logic of faster crop turnover, careful pest management, and continual cash cropping, to name a few. This is the main reason that agroecological patterns of agricultural production have not radically changed in organic production. The fact that growers are so squeezed also contributes to the taken-for-grantedness of existing labor relations, increasingly the crucible of organic agriculture.[29] Even the most well-intentioned growers have trouble radically reconfiguring farm-work to the point that the more conscientious ones have become visibly defensive about "the labor problem." Although those with highly di-verse, intensive, direct-marketing operations can make some economic space for better and more stable remuneration, they are still constrained by payments to land (in the form of mortgage or rent), illustrating a con-tradictory class position in the most classic sense.

In short, payments to land effectively reinforce preexisting patterns of agricultural production. For this reason, as well as from habit and for convenience, organic growers tend to replicate many aspects of conven-tional production. Yet, as we are about to see, visible regional distinc-tions occur in the way organic agriculture is practiced. Such variation points to an additional influence of California's agrarian past.

CHAPTER 5

Organic Sediment

A Geography of Organic Production

There are many landscapes. There is no one California.
Philip Fradkin, *The Seven States of California*

The development of California agriculture has been punctuated by crises, out of which new strategies have emerged to resolve the contradictions in profit making that led to these crises in the first place (Lee 2000). As with all economic restructuring, most of these innovations have reconfigured existing production relations, creating new ways to extract, appropriate, or add value among classes of people and, in the case of intensification, between people and nature as well. Yet, as geographer David Harvey has insisted (e.g., Harvey 1982), economic restructuring is also fundamentally spatial. Particularly since agriculture is land-based production, restructuring not only responds to the changing requirements of profitability vis-à-vis the social division of labor (Massey 1984); it also responds to land itself, as a productive asset that can be revalued (i.e., improved or degraded) by human labor, natural occurrence, and changing structures of tenure (Benton 1989; Marsden et al. 1993).

In California especially, the resolution of crises has often involved new lands coming into production or the reconfiguration of existing agricultural lands through, for instance, subdivision, consolidation, and rezoning. Accordingly, the shifting crop regimes discussed in chapter 4 involved not only temporal changes but also spatial changes, many of which were formative of new agricultural regions. The value-seeking regime that arose in the last part of the twentieth century has been no different in this regard. Market gardeners specializing in unusual crops have carved up some of the last arable spaces. Strawberry production, which happens to fare best with sandy, well-drained soils, was established on many coastal hillsides. There is little need for tractors in any case when production involves so much hand labor. Since premium wine grapes do best with some coastal cooling, vineyards supplanted vegetables to some extent in the temperate coastal valleys, but mainly production was expanded on land that was fallow, in pasture, or previously dry-farmed.[1]

So too did the shift toward organic production involve a visible transformation of the landscape and a new set of social relations. As "back-to-the-landers," experimental gardeners, and other sorts of rural visionaries, the first growers to call themselves organic were cultural and political outliers, in keeping with the "antiestablishment" politics of the era in which California organic agriculture was born. Spatial isolation was part of this ethic and, as it turned out, a good agronomic strategy for dealing with pests. Thus, many of the first organic farmers took to occupying the interstitial spaces of agriculture: the small valleys, hillsides, pastures, and suburban backyards, in effect, opening up new spaces of production.[2] Outside the usual peregrinations of migrant labor, these growers had to be more creative in how they organized work as well. In their recruitment, for instance, they often relied on personal networks and creative advertisement (e.g., appealing specifically to organic gardeners rather than farm laborers). They also employed more white interns.

But again, the more recent growth in organic production has largely involved conversion of land that was already in production, with both long-time organic growers expanding their operations and conventional growers altering theirs. As an important consequence, there are significant variations in the ways organic agriculture is practiced, variations that do not necessarily parallel the simple distinctions among mixed, fully converted, and always-organic growers. Rather, they are largely regional, reflecting another aspect of California's agrarian past. The purpose of this chapter, then, is to explore this regional differentiation within California's organic sector. It begins with a discussion of the underlying causes. Then, to illustrate the character and extent of this differentiation, it focuses on six regions and how organic agriculture has come to look in each of those regions.

EXPLAINING REGIONAL DIFFERENCE

Regional difference within California agriculture is fundamentally historical. One of the ways California's historical geography has influenced organic production is in the scale of operations, which has been shaped by the unique circumstances under which various agricultural regions were developed. For example, some of California's largest landholdings in the prime coastal zones were derived from the original Spanish and Mexican land grants of pre-Anglo California. Most of these vast holdings were once held by a Mexican elite, who used them to run cattle for the tallow and hide trade. Although Anglos eventually wrenched control of these valuable lands from the extant Californios and went on to subdivide them, many of the holdings remained relatively large.[3] In contrast, agricultural land on the east side of the Central Valley and in southern California was developed largely by land speculators. Grabbing huge tracts of land from the public domain by various means, they gambled on the future by bringing irrigation and rail transport to these areas, then sold off the land in small parcels to newly arriving fruit growers (Henderson 1999; Leibman 1983).[4] As a consequence, holdings in these areas remained relatively small. So even though scale is a changing characteristic of farms, always affected by the dynamics of accumulation, some element of historical embeddedness is involved. When conventional growers who farm on these lands convert to organic production, they pass these legacies on to organic production.

Crop specialization, another regional outcome of California's agrarian past, has been even more significant to organic production, for it bears more closely on actual production practices. Broadly speaking, cropping conventions always have been sensitive to existing patterns of farm size, tenure, water rights, and so forth. Nonetheless, as Stoll (1998) argues, single crop specialization became much more prevalent with the advent of fruit growing. From the outset, fruit growers cultivated only those varieties suited to specific local climatic and soil conditions. Research and extension services quickly became crop specific as well. But crop specialization was fortified when these small growers found they had to produce enough of any one commodity to be a player in the market. Thereafter, intermediate buyers gained control of the market, and since many of them specialized in one or two commodities, they reinforced a more generalized system of regional specialization for almost all commodities.

Reciprocally, farming systems became finely tuned to the requirements of these commodities. Even the characteristics of regional labor markets and tenure relations developed around commodity particularities.[5] In effect, any given commodity specialty developed into a coherent ensemble of production, labor, and marketing practices that growers learned and passed on (Friedland 1984; also see Storper 1997 on evolutionary economics). The point is that such patterns are not necessarily unbundled when growers move into organic production (cf. Morgan and Murdoch 2000). Indeed, despite the agroecological ideal of polycultural production, most newly converted organic growers continue in the one or two crops they know best, borrowing on the social ties and competencies they have already developed.

Arguably, then, there is a degree of path dependence brought to organic farming. Yet, even those growers who attempt to do things differently are limited by the extent to which regional cropping systems have been sedimented into land values. California agricultural land values are relatively high in general. However, land values for different crops and regions are dramatically different, a result of crop specialization as well as uneven commercial development pressures.[6] For example, in 1999 the price of rice land in the Sacramento Valley hovered around twenty-five hundred dollars per acre, while field crop land in the San Joaquin Valley was valued at around forty-three hundred dollars per acre. Yet, orchard land in the San Joaquin was nine thousand dollars per acre, reflecting the investment of perennial crops. In the southern California citrus belt, land values were even higher (around sixteen thousand dollars per acre), because much agricultural land simultaneously serves as residential real estate. Finally, land values for truck and vegetable crops on the Central Coast averaged twenty-seven thousand dollars per acre (Cal ASFMRA 2000).[7] As we shall see, the causes of such high land values for the Central Coast are multiple in origin. Again, high land values surely affect what can be grown profitably, pushing organic growers to match, if not exceed, the highest-value crop mix for that region.

Besides the variegated influences of California's agrarian history, the other major basis of regional variation lies within the geography of the organic movement itself. Within California, there is a good deal of unevenness in institutional and cultural support for organic production. Some growers have had much greater access to programs that provide technical support for organic production, for example. Since many of these programs are based around the Santa Cruz and Davis areas, growers in those areas are much more likely to incorporate state-of-the-art knowledge of organic production. Different cultures of expectations tend to develop at the regional scale as well. Because of the relative smallness of the organic sector, organic growers in an area usually know and influence one another. Many even do business together. These dense networks tend to establish regional norms for organic production. Finally, strong cultural differences occur among those urban regions that are the primary markets for local agricultural production. In general, the San Francisco Bay Area has been much more supportive of political radicalism and countercultural movements than southern California has and, therefore, has tended to provide a deeper market for alternative producers. In short, following organic ideals has been easier in some regions than in others.

SIX REGIONS

To illustrate fully the distinctive ways in which organic culture has intersected with other regional influences requires a more fine-grained examination of the regions and the growers who represent them. Table 8 lists the regions explored in the course of this study. These regions were devised to best reflect similar histories and cropping regimes.[8] (Map 2 shows these regions; the number of interviews conducted in each region can be found in the appendix.) By comparing the number of organic producers in each region during the year of interviews (1997–98) and the first year that data were collected (1992–93), the table gives a sense of growth in each region. The rest of this chapter focuses on six key regions, briefly describing important aspects of each region's history and geography, its influence on organic agriculture, and the practices of a typical organic grower there. Table 9 presents these six typical organic growers in matrix format. Though their descriptions are based in ethnographic data, they have been fictionalized to protect anonymity, making each one more a composite of several growers in that region.

West Valley

The Central Valley, made up of two main watersheds, is one of the most famous agricultural regions in the world.[9] It is fed by the spring run-off of the Sierra Nevada, which once made an "inland sea" in the late spring, until various private and public water projects took on the dual tasks of flood control and farmland irrigation. This particular region is situated on the western slope of the more southerly San Joaquin Valley, where water has been more problematic; there is a rain shadow effect from the coast ranges, and the area is out of range of the snow-melt-fed rivers coming out of the Sierra. Early homesteaders in this area practiced dryland grain farming. Growers began cotton farming in this area around 1910, just when the southern United States was experiencing its worst

TABLE 8. STUDY REGIONS

| Region | Counties Included | Producers in Organic Sector | | | | |
| | | 1997–98 | | 1992–93 | | % Change |
		n	%	n	%	
Cascade-Sierra	Amador, Butte, Calaveras, El Dorado, Inyo, Lassen, Modoc, Mono, Nevada, Placer, Plumas, Sierra, Tuolomne, Yuba	56	4	48	4	17
Far North	Del Norte, Humboldt, Shasta, Siskiyou, Trinity	68	4	65	6	5
North Valley	Butte, Colusa, Glenn, Sutter, Tehama, parts of Sacramento	145	9	112	10	29
North Coast	Lake, Marin, Mendocino, Napa, Sonoma	276	18	231	20	19
Solano-Yolo	Alameda, Contra Costa, Solano, Yolo, parts of Sacramento	67	4	50	4	34
Central Coast	Monterey, San Benito, San Mateo, Santa Clara, Santa Cruz	148	10	105	9	41
West Valley	Kern, Kings, parts of Fresno, parts of Merced	136	9	105	9	30
East Valley[a]	Madera, San Joaquin, Stanislaus, Tulare, parts of Fresno, parts of Merced					
South Coast	San Luis Obispo, Santa Barbara, Ventura	128	8	109	9	17
Southwest	Los Angeles, Orange, San Diego	412	27	276	24	49
Desert Valleys	Imperial, Riverside, San Bernardino	97	6	58	5	67
TOTAL		1,533	100[b]	1,159	100	32

SOURCES: Klonsky and Tourte 1995; Klonsky et al. 2001.

[a] I felt it was important to distinguish the two Central Valley regions because of their distinct histories, crop specializations, and organization of production. Because some Central Valley counties span west to east (and these statistics are based on county-level data), it was impossible to represent both regions statistically.

[b] This column does not add to exactly 100 because of rounding.

pest problems. When demand increased during World War I, these California cotton growers accelerated production. "King Cotton" was to become the mainstay of the southern San Joaquin Valley, even though it relied heavily on reworking the natural waterscape.

The cotton economy was first enabled by private ownership of the Tulare and Buena Vista lake basins and the electric pump (Reisner 1993; Worster 1985). With the depletion of groundwater and consequent saltwater intrusion, farmers increasingly relied on the centrifugal pump for

TABLE 9. TYPICAL GROWERS IN SELECTED STUDY REGIONS

Region	West Valley	East Valley	South West	Central Coast	North Coast	Solano-Yolo
Grower description	Third-generation family farm managed by 3 brothers	Second-generation farmer of Armenian descent	Retired aeronautics engineer	First-generation farmer with urban roots	Part-time market gardener; also has professional job	Partnership of 3 unrelated individuals
Acres/layout	2,000: many noncontiguous parcels	240: 2 contiguous parcels	3: grove part of residential real estate	200: 3 noncontiguous parcels	5: 2 acres in crops; 3 in rolling pasture (not marketed)	120 acres: 2 parcels
Approximate annual sales	$2,000,000	$300,000	$15,000	$1,200,000	$30,000	$500,000
Tenure	Mainly leased, many leases from family members	Owned; inherited	Owned free and clear	Leased	Owned, residential mortgage	Part leased, part owned with ag credit
Crops	Cotton, onions, garlic, tomatoes, alfalfa	Raisin grapes	Oranges, avocados	Lettuce, chard, radicchio, squash, peppers	Heirloom tomatoes, herbs	50 different fruit and vegetable crops, eggs
Extent of organic/how long	200 organic acres; 6 years	All organic; transitioned 12 years ago	Only oranges are organic; 2 years	Always organic; 15 years farming	Always organic; 5 years farming	Always organic; 10 years farming
Organic knowledge acquisition	Hired organic consultant	Advice from certifier	Intermittent advice from packer	Apprenticed at UCSC agroecology program	Trial and error; organic farming magazines	Have strong ties to sustainable ag community; trained interns work on farm

(continued)

TABLE 9. (*continued*)

Region	West Valley	East Valley	South West	Central Coast	North Coast	Solano-Yolo
Production practices	Plant in 40- to 80-acre blocks; use allowable organic substitutes	Cover crops middles, provides additional fertility inputs; uses sulfur dust	Uses mushroom compost, no sprays, mows weeds	Plants in 4-acre blocks, rotating blocks; uses innovative, high-tech organic techniques: bug vacuums, plastic mulch, drip irrigation, compost (makes own), some cover crops in winter	Makes own compost, mulches with straw, uses flowering plants for insect habitat	Plant in small blocks and constantly rotate; purchase compost from supplier; sow cover crop every block every year; use chickens for fertilization and pest control; use non-crop plants for pest control; occasionally use oil, soaps for pest control
Labor arrangements	Do mechanical harvesting; have own crews but occasionally use contractors for hoeing	2 year-round employees take care of vineyards; uses labor contractor for 3-week harvest	Does own grove management; packer picks fruit	Uses transplanting and labor-contracting services, has small in-house crew	Uses family, friends, and neighbors for harvest	Hire all labor in-house; most are year-round employees, some summer interns
Marketing	Various marketing contracts, some forward contracts	Sold to packer at price set by Raisin Bargaining Assoc.	Packer picks and sells fruit at per box rate	Markets, packs, and ships own produce	Does direct sales to restaurants	Sell through CSA and farmers' market; wholesale some high-value commodities

(*continued*)

Why organic	Buyer asked them to grow some organic; are concerned with water usage and agricultural runoff so attracted to some organic methods; but hearts are with conventional and don't want to flood the market	Became organic with gradual discovery that grapes need little management, although has always been concerned with the safety of pesticide use	Packer convinced him to grow organic to be able to earn a return; to his knowledge, has never eaten organic food	After getting college degree, started off as a small hippie farmer and then sold salad mix to restaurants; sits on boards of several organic organizations; thinks organic crucial for environment	Is strong advocate for local, small-scale production for local markets; thinks provision of nutritious delicious food is important political act	All have been active in sustainable agriculture; see direct marketing of organic food as way to save family farm
Certifier	QAI	FVO	none or QAI	CCOF	none	CCOF

deep drilling to a dangerously fallen water table. The ensuing ecological and economic crisis of water table depletion led to the Central Valley Project, a Promethean plan to move water from Lake Shasta, in the Far North region of California, across the Sacramento Delta, which spills into the San Francisco Bay, and down the arid San Joaquin Valley. Although its inception was in the 1930s, the project was not substantially completed until the 1950s. Through technicalities, farmers largely evaded the circumscriptions of the Federal Reclamation Act, which limited the allowable number of irrigated acres to 160, and continued to pump groundwater using deep turbine wells. On the heels of the Central Valley Project came the even more fantastic State Water Project, which moved water from the Feather River in northeastern California to the southwestern parts of the San Joaquin Valley (and eventually into southern California) through a series of dams, pumping stations, and canals (Hundley 1992). Despite the goal of eliminating pumping, the effect was an expansion of production into the most marginal west side of the Central Valley.

This region is also a well-known territory of large-scale agribusiness. The landholdings are some of the largest in the state, in part as relics of the Miller and Lux agricultural empire but, more important, as a result of irrigation development. Much of the land developed under the Central Valley Project is individually owned by individual members of various families for technical compliance with reclamation law but is managed as a single unit. The infamous Westlands Water District of Fresno and Merced counties—where unacceptable levels of selenium have poisoned waterfowl by the thousands—sustains a handful of growers who have several thousand acres apiece. The State Water Project, designed to elude all federal acreage restrictions, guaranteed an incredible subsidy to some of California's largest corporate farms, many of which are held by oil companies (Hundley 1992; Worster 1985).

Because land here is very salinated and water is not cheap, this land is last to go into production and first to go out when prices fluctuate. Consequently, there are few permanent plantings here. Besides cotton, growers have traditionally planted commodity crops such as sugar beets, wheat, and alfalfa.[10] Accordingly, growers here were highly affected by the 1980s farm crisis, when prices fell and commodity subsidies were withdrawn. Since then, they have devoted more acreage to carrots, onions, garlic, and processing tomatoes. Yet, because of the hot, dry weather and marginal soil, there is little opportunity for multiple crops per year. Instead this area is increasingly used as a site for one (occasionally two) annual crops for Salinas-based grower-shippers seeking to provide year-round vegetables. West Valley growers who work with the grower-shippers typically follow three-year rotations, mixing these vegetable crops with their usual commodity crops.

Many growers in this region have experimented in organic production, and some are continuing to put acreage into organics. A few, such as Cal-Organic, once the largest organic grower in the state, have wholly converted. While hardly part of the organic subculture of northern California, some of these growers have nonetheless become active in sustainable agriculture initiatives, driven, in part, by having constantly to defend farming in the Westlands district. Still, many others of these growers are economically tied to conventional agriculture in ways that make them cautious entrants.

Thus, a typical West Valley organic grower (often a corporation or partnership) continues to keep significant amounts of acreage in conventional agriculture (albeit applying a few techniques gleaned from organic agriculture). Although the company will occasionally sell conventional crops on the spot market, it grows organic crops only with a specified contract, offered by one of a handful of organic processors or grower-shippers. Economically tied to these contracts, the company plants in large-acre blocks of single crops, because even a minimal temporal or spatial rotation would entail operating at a loss or the need to develop additional markets. The particular inclination is to rely on input substitution because of state-of-the-art knowledge of its efficacy, acquired from hired consultants. Cover crops are rarely planted because of the irrigation expense; instead, controversial sodium (or Chilean) nitrate and other purchased fertility inputs are used. Predator insects may be released via helicopters, implementing a biological pest control of sorts, but noncash crops are never planted to act as trap crops, beneficial-insect harbors, or fertility enhancements. As for labor needs, most of the crops are mechanically harvested, and other work, such as hoeing, is usually arranged through a labor contractor, as is typical in that area.

East Valley

The East Valley region encompasses the eastern part of the San Joaquin Valley, situated on the alluvial soils deposited by the several rivers that drain the Sierra Nevada. Much of this area was brought into production earlier than the West Valley, made possible by localized irrigation solutions, including private appropriations, speculator-driven irrigation colonies, and the Wright Act, which established irrigation districts (Pisani 1984). It immediately became a center of specialty-crop production. Having come into production when many of the large landholdings were subdivided (circa 1870s and 1880s), the area hosts a high degree of landownership, and farms are generally smaller (Leibman 1983). Both characteristics contribute to the continued dominance of permanent crops. Almonds and grapes are the most significant crops grown here, with an increasing amount of acreage devoted to wine grapes for bulk wines. Figs, walnuts, and citrus are grown throughout the region, and stone fruits are grown toward the delta of the Sacramento and San Joaquin rivers. Merced County is also a center of sweet potato production.

The substantial number of organic growers in the area reflects the many conversions of raisin vineyards. Grapes are relatively easy to grow organically, and since sun-drying them erases most cosmetic problems, it is an easy decision to convert wholly to organic production. Several fig growers have converted for the same reason. In contrast, the fresh fruit and nut orchardists in the area have converted because they have received some technical and moral support. The protracted conversion of peach and almond orchards, particularly in Merced County, is largely due to the work of the Biologically Integrated Orchard System (BIOS) project, because many growers prefer the gradual approach of integrated pest management to deal with typical orchard pests. An organic almond packer with close associations with one of the international organic certifiers has also been instrumental in bringing growers into organic production. In addition, a handful of sweet potato growers have partly converted to organic production, although their efforts are more suspect, as we shall see in chapter 7.

Nevertheless, the most typical organic grower in this region is a raisin grape grower. Armenian in origin, like many of the growers in the Fresno area, the typical East Valley grape grower profiled in my study has secure tenure that derives from inheritance, his family having been one of the first to plant vineyards there. This grower is happy to sow a cover crop between the rows. Not only does he have access to cheaper water; he also knows this crop provides habitat for beneficial insects. This, along with the legal though controversial use of sulfur dust to control bunch rot, makes the decision to grow raisin grapes organically a "no-brainer." In fact, with raisin and wine grapes, organic production is often easier and cheaper than conventional production. Although this grower is convinced by organic methods, if faced with a more difficult crop he might not be so sanguine.

Especially because conventional raisins have faced considerable decline in demand, marketing arrangements reinforce his decision. He is bound by a federal marketing order that established the member-run Raisin Bargaining Association. The association sets prices at harvesttime to which all two hundred or so members must agree. Included in this pricing mechanism is a guaranteed organic premium. So, even though raisins are handled by one of several packers in the valley, these handlers have fewer opportunities to prey upon growers, although conflicts have arisen in regard to what is considered organic. The other aspect that has made organic raisin growing easy is the absence of pressure on the grower to alter his labor practices. Like most everyone else in the area, he maintains a small year-round crew for thinning and pruning but uses a labor contractor for harvest because of its much narrower temporal window.

Southwest

What remains in agricultural production in the Southwest area is for the most part the last vestiges of the southern California citrus belt that arose in the 1880s. Developed by the Southern Pacific Railroad and promoted through its booster magazine, *Sunset,* much of this land was originally sold to in-migrating professionals and merchants, who went into orange growing as a business (Moses 1995). Since World War II, most of the orange groves have been razed, with housing and shopping centers taking their place, although some groves remain on residential real estate.

In the 1970s, new groves of citrus and avocado were planted on the often-steep hills of north San Diego County to take advantage of some of the tax incentives offered through California's Williamson Act. Most of these "farms" are located in areas such as Escondido, Fallbrook, and Pauma Valley, more or less rural areas within commuting distance of urban jobs. Most of the land here was purchased explicitly for residential real estate or as an investment, with the aim of subdividing it in the future. Current zoning restrictions, including two- to four-acre lot minimums, keep groves standing and minimally acting as "landscaping." Irrigation water, however, is extremely expensive in this region, so that many such orchards are neglected. In addition, two major buyer's cooperatives dominate the market for conventional produce: Sunkist, the brand name of what was originally founded as the California Fruit Growers' Exchange, which buys citrus fruits, and Calavo, which buys avocados.

Paradoxically, this largely urban and politically conservative region has the most organic farms in the state, although the parcels themselves are very small, usually in the two- to three-acre range. In 1997, San Diego County alone had more registered organic growers than any other county, representing 25 percent of the state's growers (Klonsky et al. 2001). Most of these growers are citrus growers; only a few vegetable growers are in the region, operating on land that is extraordinarily hard to come by. The groves simply bestow tax benefits and supplemental income to an area rapidly undergoing suburbanization. The reason so many are organically managed is that the citrus and avocado packers dealing in organic produce actively recruit growers to organic production, knowing that Sunkist and Calavo will not buy from the smaller farms. However, according to several growers, the organic packers promise decent prices and then use the grading process to ratchet prices down. One of the reasons they have growers so tethered is that the latter have no substantive ties to the organic industry. One packer was able to withhold proceeds from a group of neighboring growers for five years, under the guise that they could not be paid until they were fully organic, when, in fact, conversion takes three years!

So, although the typical Southwest all-organic grower has fully converted to organic production, he is not a strong adherent of agroecological techniques or philosophy. A retired aeronautics engineer by profession, he bought the land on which his groves sit for his retirement residence. Unlike the professional approach taken by his West Valley counterpart, he tends to be "organic by neglect," managing as little as possible. The mushroom compost he uses is of dubious legality, since mushrooms often contain substantial pesticide residues. The weeds he mows offer some of the benefits of a cover crop, but he would never plant a real cover crop because of the irrigation expense. Organic, to him, means not spraying. Meanwhile, the packer handles the fruit-picking labor, in effect acting as a labor contractor.

Central Coast

The temperate region of the Central Coast, cooled by fog and ocean breezes during the summer but rarely seeing frost during the winter, is the most important vegetable-growing region in the country. As an agricultural region, it was opened around 1900, when the Spreckels family opened up three different sugar beet refineries (Jelinek 1979). For a long time, sugar beet production in the Salinas Valley was carried out by tenants and smallholders who contracted to the refineries. Many also grew grains and beans, and a few grew truck crops (i.e., annual fruits and vegetables), often doing their own marketing. Still, truck crops did not become important to the region until the end of World War II, when demand for vegetables mushroomed (FitzSimmons 1986).

After the war, the Central Coast led the way in intensifying innovations (e.g., the use of petroleum-based fertilizers and transplanting to allow speedy crop turnover, intensive spraying, "cool chain" shipping), all of which built upon the region's natural advantages for vegetable production (e.g., cool, foggy summers). According to FitzSimmons (1986), industry restructuring proceeded apace with intensification: smaller growers lost their ability to manage in an intensified environment, not least because truck farming requires more operating capital. Many of these erstwhile independent farmers ended up on forward contracts. Meanwhile, larger growers shipped their own produce and began to ship for others, prefiguring the grower-shipper arrangements that dominate today. The opportunity to market vegetables year round then attracted outside investment of large international firms, such as United Brands and Coca-Cola, aided by the attraction of new vineyards as tax-loss investment in the 1970s. By 1978, specialty crops dominated the economy (fresh vegetables, wine grapes, and nursery and seed). More important, an industry structure had evolved so that multinational corporations dominated the economy by leasing land they farmed and marketing the crops of smaller growers whose decisions were specified in marketing contracts (FitzSimmons 1986, 338). Today, the industry structure in this region parallels Silicon Valley, with an elaborate network of subcontracting for all sorts of agricultural services, including seedling grow-out, laser leveling, irrigation, pesticide applications, harvest labor, and post-production handling. Marketing is primarily done through powerful grower-shippers, who bring all sizes of growers into various contract relations.

In Monterey and San Benito counties, the main crops grown along the coast are lettuce ("green gold"), broccoli, celery, cauliflower, and artichokes, and further inland peppers and tomatoes are grown. Additionally, the northern part of Monterey and the southern part of Santa Cruz counties (in the Watsonville area) are heavily planted in strawberries, one of the highest-value crops in the state, typically grossing more than twenty-five thousand dollars per acre. A good deal of wine grape acreage also covers the benches of the Salinas Valley. In other words, the Central

Coast specializes in highly valorized crops, valued for their "freshness," healthiness, and/or luxury.

Therefore, a key characteristic of this region is high land values, reflecting both the degree of intensification and the market value of crops grown here. Land values are so high in prime coastal zones that landowners can earn a living by leasing out their land, freeing them from the necessity to farm. As the manager of one very large Salinas farming operation said, "If you own land around here, you don't have to farm it." Consequently, there is little turnover of land, and most growers are forced to lease it. In addition, future urban development is imputed into the price of much of the land in the region. Yet, in areas where there is significant real estate pressure on land, leasing can be an advantage, for lease prices are generally computed solely on the basis of expected agricultural revenues.

Many of the organic growers in this area got their start on salad mix, some as small-scale consolidators and others as component growers. Already a major restructuring of organics has taken place in this area having to do with TKO's unprecedented success and then demise, and later Missionero's and Earthbound Farms/Natural Selections' explosive growth. Because of the latter's work alone, San Benito County has the highest *proportion* of organic acreage of any county in the state. Many of the original growers in the area have since diversified into other vegetable crops, including unusual varieties. While some contract to the grower-shippers, many attempt to do their own marketing in an effort to retain more value (and meet costs to land). Until recently, there was little organic strawberry production because of the industry's dependence on methyl bromide. However, beginning in the late 1990s, growers found ways to avoid fumigation, creating an influx of organic strawberry production. The plurality of organic growers in the area are in Santa Cruz County, which has a very high number of growers for a small semiurban county, instantiating its role in the genesis of the organic farming movement. Many of these growers are direct marketers.

Altogether, the counties in this region host about 10 percent of the organic growers in the state and, in 1997–98, had 17 percent of the state's organic acreage. This same year, however, the region claimed 23 percent of organic sales in the state (Klonsky et al. 2001), again demonstrating the high value of crops grown in this area, in addition to the capacity to harvest multiple crops on the same acreage within a given year. In other words, despite being a center for the organic movement, organic production is still highly intensified.

Thus, my study's typical organic grower in this area, while very committed to the organic movement, is a serious, professional grower. He may be a college graduate in the liberal arts who started farming expressly to act on his environmentalist sentiments. He is extremely innovative in his approach, having been schooled at the University of California's agroecology program in Santa Cruz. Yet, he is also very input-dependent in his employment of bug vacuums, plastic mulches, and microbial inoculants. A committed user of compost, he cannot afford to put all his land under cover crop every year, not wanting to take land out of production in an area where land values are capitalized on several crops per year. He is also a tenant, realizing he has little choice but to lease if he wants to take advantage of the long growing seasons, fertile soil, and ideal soil conditions for his high-value crops. Since he farms year round, he typically keeps a permanent crew for more skilled work, but he also employs labor contractors in peak periods for specialty jobs such as transplanting or harvesting.

North Coast

North of the San Francisco Bay Area and noticeably wetter than southern California (although still arid in the summer), the North Coast was one of the first agricultural regions to come into production. Agriculture was never practiced on a huge scale, however, because a high proportion of the land is not arable, particularly as it reaches north into redwood country. In its valleys, this area was historically planted in grapes and pome fruits. In addition, Mendocino County was a major hops-growing region until Prohibition. Northern Marin County and southern Sonoma once had vibrant dairy and egg industries because of the good pasturage provided by the rolling oak woodlands.

Today the region encompasses one of the premier regions in the world for growing wine grapes, with land values in the Napa and Sonoma areas reflecting the monopoly conditions of a French *terroir*. Napa, Sonoma, and Mendocino counties continue to expand their wine production. In twenty-five years, Sonoma County, for example, doubled the acreage dedicated to vineyards, 20 percent of which was planted in the latter portion of the 1990s (Podger 1999). Moreover, because of the renown of the Sonoma and Napa appellations, total crop value continues to grow disproportionately to acres in production. In 1997, for instance, Sonoma County's farm gate value increased 30 percent from the previous year on the basis of not only record tonnage of wine grapes but also the highest ever average price paid for wine grapes (Thompson 1998). Meanwhile, once-flourishing apple and pear orchards, especially in the Sebastopol area of Sonoma County, have since been subdivided into two- to three-acre residential parcels. And although the area still holds dairy and chicken farms—mainly in the Petaluma area—and a burgeoning organic milk industry, some of the hay farms have turned into high-value market gardens, as have many of the little pastures nestled among the rolling hills. With strong ties to the so called foodie culture of the San Francisco Bay Area, this area can best be described as the urbane countryside, bringing forth such goods as Sonoma lambs, free-range chickens, craft-baked bread, goat cheese, culinary herbs, and heirloom tomatoes.

The large number of organic growers in this area is made up mainly of wine grape growers who have converted to organic production, particularly in Sonoma and Mendocino (as opposed to Napa) counties. A couple of winemakers, Fetzer being the most notable, have encouraged those with whom they contract to make the conversion, although little wine is marketed as organic.[11] Also a few dozen organic apple growers sell their oft-neglected apples to one of a few handlers who specialize in organic apple juice, applesauce, and apple cider vinegar, in a style similar to the Southwest region's citrus growers. Finally, there are several vegetable growers in this area, including the pioneering Star Route Farms as well as smaller market gardens.

Because small-scale market gardeners also typify the Far North region, not discussed here, the typical grower described here in the North Coast could be found in that region as well. In many respects, she most conforms to the organic imaginary. She is a particularly urbane back-to-the-lander, who purchased the once-cheap rolling pasture on which her farm sits for its beauty and seclusion as well as for its ample space to support her organic gardening interests. She is active in the organic movement and has a well-articulated vision, saying, for example, "it is dangerous not to know where your food comes from." In addition, her very small farm—say, two acres—comes closest to the agroecological ideal. She is able to integrate many design elements, borrowed from her extensive readings of organic philosophy and technique. Since her farm was carved out of a space that had not previously been brought into agricultural production, she is situated where beneficial habitat is ample. In addition, she has plenty of water to grow winter cover crops, plants only one cash crop per year, being limited by heavy winter rainfall and a colder climate, and is too far away from primary farming regions to source expensive fertility inputs. The farm's microscopic size also allows a very labor-intensive approach. In addition, she does all of her own marketing, catering primarily to upscale restaurants in the San Francisco Bay Area. Her preexisting ties to the gourmet food community enabled her to start a commercial operation, growing to the specifications of chefs. In return, she receives extraordinarily high prices for her herbs and heirloom tomatoes, allowing her to supplement her part-time professional job. She hires her friends and neighbors to perform harvest labor, and she pays an unusual wage, although the work lasts only a few weeks at best. In that way, her farm is not exactly an alternative institution.

Solano-Yolo

Yolo County is the primary agricultural county in this region and lies within the Sacramento Valley, the first area in California to come into agricultural production after the gold rush (sown largely with wheat and hops then). Today, agricultural land in Yolo County is typically planted in fruit and nut orchards as well as rotations of commodity crops such as alfalfa, corn, wheat, and processing tomatoes. The center of Yolo County is the University of California at Davis, one of the two "aggie" schools of the university system but one that has been historically dismissive of sustainable agriculture ideas. The other counties in this region are urban or rapidly becoming urban, so farming is limited to several periurban market gardens and a sizable area where stone fruits are grown on the exurban outreaches near the Sacramento Delta.

This region has been more markedly influenced by the sustainable agriculture movement than areas north and east in the Sacramento Valley. Despite the predilections of the agricultural school, Davis has become a center of organized agricultural activism and programs such as the Biologically Integrated Farming Systems (BIFS), Biologically Integrated Orchard Systems (BIOS), and the university's Sustainable Agriculture Research and Education Program (UC-SAREP), all of which have had an obvious influence on growers in the area. Accordingly, many conventional growers have been experimenting with or wholly converting to organic production. This is also the California center of the growing community supported agriculture (CSA) movement. There are over ten subscription farms in Yolo County alone, far more than any other area in the state. Many are located in the somewhat remote and idyllic Capay Valley, once a thriving agricultural region that was largely abandoned and has since evolved into an alternative agriculture enclave. In defiance of specialized crop production, several growers here plant upwards of fifty crops, including tree crops. Many market directly to a Bay Area clientele, striving to provide a "market basket" of produce at reasonable prices.

Thus, a typical organic grower in this area is a Capay Valley subscription farm, owned by a partnership of like-minded individuals. Fully dedicated to the sustainable agriculture movement, as we saw of subscription farms in chapter 3, their production style is by far the most integrative, very much intertwined with their strategy of direct marketing. And again, the employment of complicated rotations to ensure a constant harvest of crops allows them to provide year-round employment to many of their employees, often at higher-than-average wages. Outside the high-cost land markets, they are the exception that proves the rule.

In short, once growers began to convert to organic production, it simply was not or could not be inserted into the landscape without confronting existing patterns. In effect, it has been layered—to use Massey's (1984) geological metaphor—upon existing landscapes of California agriculture and the social relations they embody, making some adjustments within but rarely transforming structures and practices. This occurs because growers who convert to organic production inherit what are already well-defined crop specializations as well as the entire ensemble of land tenure, marketing arrangements, labor organization, technical support, and so forth, that evolve around these specializations. Yet, the easy replication of commodity specializations is not the only cause. After all, growers can always change what they grow, and many do. The more fundamental problem is that regional land values have been capitalized on the basis of these specializations, constraining what can be grown and by what methods. It is in this way that past regional development so strongly shapes organic futures.

If anything, the exceptions prove the rule. The spatial manifestations of the organic movement's evolution—the move to the margins—have allowed some organic growers to create what effectively are their own regional styles, some of which go against highly entrenched patterns of agricultural production. By and large these growers have been better able to stay true to organic ideals, incorporating more complicated crop rotations, for example. Whether by choice or necessity, some have even altered their labor practices. Being physically located outside the major agricultural labor markets, many have paid higher wages and/or found new ways of organizing work to help recruitment. Finally, many have found or even helped create institutional support for organic production in the form of associations, informal networks, and annual gatherings. Still, aside from those growers who are independently wealthy or have supplemental income, even those on the margins have had to intensify to make payments to land, giving them little space for alternative institution building.

In other words, organic producers assume the trappings of California's agrarian past whether they want to or not. But there is another fundamental problem with organic farming qua social movement, having to do with the centrality of the organic commodity. This outcome was not a necessary one but follows how the meaning of "organically grown" was constructed and institutionalized. Henceforth, being part of the organic movement was defined by upholding the meaning of that commodity and selling it. The next chapter examines how this came to be.

CHAPTER 6

Conventionalizing Organic

From Social Movement to Industry via Regulation

Where in our mission statement do we talk about trying to be liberal, progressive, or universal?

> John Mackey, CEO, Whole Foods supermarkets

Let's not become what we set out to oppose.

> Michael Sligh, Rural Advancement Fund
> International, Organic Regulatory
> Conference, Claremont Hotel, Oakland,
> Calif., August 1997

The emergence of an identifiable organic movement in the late 1960s did not pose a major threat to mainstream agriculture. Thoroughly awash in countercultural idioms, organic farming was, if anything, an object of derision of the mainstream agricultural establishment. As former U.S. Secretary of Agriculture Earl Butz said in 1971, "We can go back to organic agriculture in this country if we must; we know how to do it. However, before we move in that direction, someone must decide which 50 million of our people will starve!" (*Nation's Agriculture* 1971). Not until the farm crisis of the 1980s articulated with increased environmental concern and changes in consumer tastes did political openings arise in support of new approaches to agriculture. Since then, sustainable agriculture programs have blossomed, and the notion of sustainability has gained widespread acceptance. Remarkably, though, it is *organic* agriculture that has become the flagship of sustainable agriculture, despite organic agriculture's deeper countercultural origins, which some have argued were less politically palatable (see, e.g., Youngberg, Schaller, and Merrigan 1993). How is it that organic farming took the mainstream?

The unparalleled market growth in organics rests on its distinction as the only form of alternative agriculture to have substantive meaning in the marketplace. This recognition stems directly from the nature of its institutional support. As part of a broader wave of social movement institutionalization that began in the early 1970s—what some call NGOization (Buttel 1992)—loose associations of organic growers gradually turned into trade organizations and certifying agencies, taking the lead in an otherwise multiconstituent movement. After considerable debate, these organizations began to define "organically grown" specifically as a production standard for farmers (and later processors), not as a food safety standard for consumers and surely not as an alternative system of food provision.[1] Thereafter, the movement evolved into a drive for institutional legitimacy and regulation of the term *organically grown* in the interest of trade. Consequently, the right to claim that any product is organically produced became contingent upon compliance with legal definitions, enforced through an unusual configuration of private and state institutions. This codification arose from multiple intentions, but its greatest success was to open up markets. As such, the drive for regulatory legislation effectively subsumed much of the organic movement into an organic industry.[2]

In the process of codification, many of the more radical goals associated with organics were sacrificed. Broader meanings were narrowed to technical terms, and certifying agencies became institutions of surveillance, competing over the ease and legitimacy of their own individual practices. Both aspects of codification had serious implications for the ways in which organic agriculture is currently practiced. A focus on allowable inputs has minimized the importance of agroecology, enforcement has become self-protective and uneven, and reliance on incentive-based regulation has created a set of rent-generating mechanisms that has profoundly shaped who can participate and on what terms. In that way, the direction organic farming has taken in California is not only the legacy of the state's own style of agrarian capitalism. It is also a product of the movement's own choosing, albeit not all the consequences of its choices were evident from the get-go.

The question addressed in this chapter, then, is how this regulatory framework came to be. To answer it, first I will review the legislative history of organic production. Then I will focus on the evolution of the two mutually constitutive features of organic regulation: organic definitions and standards themselves, and the institutions that create and enforce them. For clarity, they will be treated separately. In chapter 7, I will more fully address the consequences of this regulatory framework.

FROM SOCIAL MOVEMENT TO INDUSTRY VIA LEGISLATION

There is a little invention in organic farming's genesis story. It is true that ideas about alternative farming were once explicitly linked with critiques of, say, processed food and inequitable food distribution. Yet, this stance from the margins was always ambiguous. First of all, the early U.S. movement was largely influenced by the pragmatic Rodales, who were hardly skeptical of capitalist institutions. On the contrary, they were boldly committed to spreading the techniques of organic farming to expand their sphere in the magazine publishing world. Similarly, business-oriented growers such as the California-based Lundbergs, who came under the organic aegis to grow rice for Chico-San (a producer of macrobiotic foods), were present at an early stage. Obviously, they would benefit financially from the expansion of the organic market. Finally, consumers needed to have some assurance that they were actually buying what they thought they were. At a minimum, the claim of "organically grown" meant many different things to many different people; more significantly, occasional cases of fraud put a damper on consumer enthusiasm by challenging the legitimacy of organic claims.

Not surprisingly, the Rodales took the initiative in creating an institutional procedure to address fraud, blaming it on short supplies as well as lax regulation. Consequently, the Rodales offered the first certification program for organically grown food. The criterion they adopted for certification was a 3 percent minimum humus content in soil, verifiable by an independent lab test (Nowacek 1997). Since most of the organic farmers who joined the Rodale program, including the Lundbergs, were based in California (Steffen, Allen, and Foote 1972), the Rodale certification program shortly evolved into CCOF (California Certified Organic Farmers), founded in 1973.

As described by some of its early members, CCOF in the beginning was a ragtag group of about fifty mostly hippie farmers who identified themselves as part of a back-to-the-land movement. There was a strong countercultural element within CCOF and among nonaffiliated organic growers as well, evidenced in the idiom they used in reference to their annual meetings: "tribal gatherings." This idiom was barrier enough to other, less countercultural growers for a long time. In addition, the original CCOF growers were notably resistant to formality; it was not until the late 1980s that CCOF received proper tax status from the Internal Revenue Service and filed its first tax returns. Being primarily a group of farmers, their common interest was in developing, refining, and sharing a set of production practices. It only made sense that these practices be recognized in the market, both to protect consumers from false claims and to create informed access to the growers' products. For these reasons, CCOF members decided to create uniform definitions and standards for those practices and to refine the certification program so that it could adequately verify them (though certification was appreciably more informal than it is today). Their efforts were joined by similar organizations in other states, starting with Oregon Tilth. By the end of 1974, eleven other regional certification organizations had been formed, largely with the support of Rodale's *Organic Gardening* magazine (Nowacek 1997).

Meanwhile, a handful of organic distributors and marketers had begun to pursue recognition in the legislative arena, having most to gain from clear definitions of organically grown food. After a few setbacks, they had their first success in California in 1979, when the first Organic Food Act was passed, to be amended in 1982. The act provided a legal definition of *organic*, but the state explicitly abdicated enforcement, with a clause stating that "no state agency shall have any affirmative obligation to adopt regulations or otherwise to enforce the provisions of the Organic Food Act of 1979" (OFA, 1979, cited in Nowacek 1997).

Over the next decade, bigger and more visible fraudulent uses of the term *organic* necessitated a more proactive stance. In California, one of the most renowned cases was the "great carrot caper" of 1984, in which a vegetable distributor had been found selling large amounts of allegedly organic carrots at a time when no substantial amount of organic carrots were known to be in production. Aiming to embarrass the state for its lack of enforcement, a handful of major organic producers and distributors decided to take the story to the *San Jose Mercury*, despite the risk of calling attention to fraud in the organic market. When the surge in organic demand due to the Alar and Aldicarb scares of the late 1980s saw another set of growers become instantly organic, the CCOF board as a whole voted to take decisive action in strengthening the existing law. These efforts culminated in the California Organic Foods Act of 1990 (COFA), which both established a legal baseline definition of organic growing practices and included enforcement provisions for the first time.

At the federal level, meanwhile, organic agriculture was facing considerable hostility. For example, in 1974 the Food and Drug Administration (FDA) proposed to eliminate completely terms such as *natural* and *organic*, although it satisfied itself with regulations prohibiting any labeling claims that natural and organic foods were superior or more nutritious (Nowacek 1997). The USDA, moreover, forbade any claims that livestock was organically raised, even though many states had already put organic laws on the books.[3] Only when mainstream agricultural experts acknowledged the need for farmers to reduce their reliance on high-cost and/or petroleum-based inputs in the wake of the energy crisis of the mid-1970s and the farm crisis of 1980 did federal regulators begin to raise doubts about the existing trajectory of conventional farming (Youngberg, Schaller, and Merrigan 1993). Yet, as is evident in the weak endorsement of organic farming found in the USDA's 1980 report, federal support for organic agriculture per se was minimal.

According to Youngberg and colleagues, lack of progress in the federal arena owed everything to the connotation of organic farming. "The proponents of low-chemical production techniques," they say, "had seriously underestimated the negative symbolism of organic farming, which had long since been dismissed by conventional agriculture as little more than a primitive, backward, nonproductive, unscientific technology suitable only for the nostalgic and disaffected back-to-the-landers of the 1970s" (1993, 298). In an effort to develop alternative terms, supportive policy makers latched onto *sustainability*, a notion that was already gaining credence in foreign aid circles. They also liked the idea of *low-input* agriculture, a fitting response to the debt and energy crises. Even though these terms were not necessarily compatible, neither seemed as threatening as *organic*, for neither ruled out the use of synthetic chemicals (as organic had). Nevertheless, as Beeman notes, "Defining sustainable agriculture became a cottage industry in itself" (1995, 219), with the eventuality that the debates over meaning dropped diversity, equity, and scale to emphasize economic viability and sustainable profit margins (Youngberg, Schaller, and Merrigan 1993; see also Sachs 1992). Having tempered the concept of sustainability, legislators incorporated it into the 1985 farm bill (the so-called Food Security Act) as the Low-Input Sustainable Agriculture program (LISA), the intent of which was to secure research and extension funds for sustainable and low-input farming. The first congressional appropriation in 1988 marked the beginning of the national Sustainable Agriculture Research and Education (SARE) program. The 1990 farm bill (the Food, Agriculture, Conservation, and Trade Act of 1990) was even more expansive and included a multitude of initiatives dealing with sustainable agriculture.

Nevertheless, LISA and SARE hardly met the needs of a nascent organic industry. So at the same time that sustainable agriculture was being made safe for agribusiness, the first nationwide organic trade group, the

Organic Foods Production Association of North America (OFPANA) formed in 1984. Composed primarily of traditional certification associations and larger producers, OFPANA's stated goal was to develop a national organic labeling law to resolve conflicts in state laws and hence ease trade. From the group's perspective, not only had fraud become more prevalent, but also there were growing fears that the word *organic* would become meaningless, as *natural* had when it was co-opted by the major food companies. Implicitly, OFPANA expected to define *organic* in ways that would continue to give it distinction but at the same time move it into the mainstream.

Yet, the first bill the group helped craft encountered obstacles in Congress, because too many representatives felt beholden to farm commodity groups and chemical manufacturers. The USDA also actively opposed it. Thereafter, OFPANA allied with consumer groups to drum up broader support for organic agriculture, forming a new coalition, temporarily called the Organic Food Alliance, which was headed by the co-owner of the now publicly held Horizon Organic, specializing in dairy products. Subsequently, OFPANA changed its name to OTA, the Organic Trade Association, as it remains today, to reflect that its membership had expanded to nonfood producers and services related to organic production (Mergentime 1994).

The federal law for organic production was passed as part of the 1990 farm bill, largely on the momentum of the Alar scare, suggesting a different justification from LISA's. Named the Organic Foods Production Act (OFPA), it authorized the independent National Organic Standards Board (NOSB) to create standards for organically grown foods. Of important note, the OFPA was designed as an incentive program. In other words, the explicit purpose of designing national standards was to give more backbone to the market premium for organically grown foods by giving organic production definitional distinction without having to devote substantial government resources in the form of, say, subsidies.

Yet, even though the OFPA—largely modeled after the California law—was passed in 1990, its implementation was delayed for more than ten years. The delay started as a struggle between the NOSB, a group largely chosen from among the organic industry, and the USDA, which was to administer the law, because the USDA continued to contest many organic principles. This battle became quite public when the USDA released proposed standards in 1997 that were far afield from expectations. The so-called Big Three (the allowance of genetically engineered organisms, irradiation, and sewage sludge in organic practices) galvanized the most public attention, but there were dozens of other issues that were equally insidious for those who were intimately involved in organic production and marketing. While the final rule is much closer to what the organic industry envisioned, its implementation in the fall of 2002 has undoubtedly opened another chapter in the history of organic agriculture. Among other changes, the National Organic Program (NOP) promises to drastically rework the certification business.

Even before implementation, though, the OFPA had already altered the organic landscape, mainly by strengthening the divide between movement and industry. For those who most vehemently sought a federal law were those engaged in interstate trade, where uniformity of standards is the salient issue, and those who deal with processed food items and livestock, the two areas encompassing most of the unresolved issues, which are quite tangential to fresh fruit and vegetable production. Thus, a federal law was of most direct concern to big producers, processors, and interstate distributors, along with the major certification agencies and organic trade organizations that came to represent them. For those who identified with the organic movement, the federal law represented a huge symbolic loss. It effectively asked agencies that had been most hostile to organic farming to confer it legitimacy, and it forced organic farmers to do business with the very agricultural establishment they set out to oppose. Beyond the symbolic loss, the law created more regulatory burden for those who sell in local and regional markets, which for some is the core of alternative agriculture.

Nevertheless, in the early salad days it was unforeseen that the act of institutionalizing the organic movement would thwart its radicalism. In hindsight, it seems inevitable, particularly insofar as the objective was to uphold a market meaning for a particular set of commodities. For, the purpose of definition making was to distinguish organic products in order to sell them, paving the way for business concerns to take priority.

ORGANIC DEFINITIONS

The Organic Foods Production Act is an organic production act, not a social justice act, not an anti–junk food act.

> Craig Wheatley, Cascadian Farms, Organic
> Regulatory Conference, Claremont Hotel, Oakland,
> Calif., August 1997

Certain members of the so-called organic community are quick to say that organic agriculture is only about production standards. Yet in popular discourse and within the organic community itself, the justification for organic agriculture continues to involve a multiplicity of ecological, economic, and social concerns that reach beyond the farm gate. Many producers and consumers in the organic movement are critical of the industrialization of farming and food provision. The issues they raise range from food itself (e.g., nutrition, microbial contamination, toxicity) to the environment and resources (e.g., water and air quality, soil conservation, energy) to social or humanistic considerations (e.g., ethical treatment of animals). The new agrarianists, motivated by social and economic concerns, invoke the survival of small farms and livable rural communities as a reason for farming organically. Some within the movement express concern with the remuneration and working conditions of food and agricultural workers and equitable access to food, although these concerns are rarer.

Nevertheless, few of these issues were ever addressed in organic standards, at least in the United States. Even before implementation of the federal rule, the definition of organic agriculture promoted by CCOF was as follows:

> an ecological production management system that promotes and enhances biodiversity, biological cycles and soil biological activity. It is based on minimal use of off-farm inputs and on management practices that restore, maintain and enhance ecological harmony. The principal guidelines for organic production are to use materials and practices that enhance the ecological balance of natural systems and that integrate the parts of the farming system into an ecological whole. Organic agriculture practices cannot ensure that products are completely free of residues; however, methods are used to minimize pollution from air, soil and water. Organic food handlers, processors and retailers adhere to standards that maintain the integrity of organic agricultural products. The primary goal of organic agriculture is to optimize the health and productivity of interdependent communities of soil life, plants, animals and people. (CCOF 1998b, 6)

The focus of this particular definition is on farm management principles, although many years of debate were involved in reaching this consensus. Even then, it presents an agroecological ideal that does not easily fit into practicable standards, nor does it make any guarantees about outcomes. Its social agenda is altogether ambiguous.

Although the above definition was adopted by the NOSB, the current legal definition is even more technical, constrained by both the 1990

OFPA and the rule that was finalized in late 2002. According to the federal rule, organic production is "a production system that is managed in accordance with the Act and regulations in this part to respond to site-specific conditions by integrating cultural, biological, and mechanical practices that foster cycling of resources, promote ecological balance, and conserve biodiversity" (USDA 2001). The act itself simply proscribes the use of synthetic chemicals in organic production and handling (with certain exceptions) and bars crops from being sold as organic from land to which any prohibited substances have been applied during the three years immediately preceding the harvest. Its only nod to production processes is that organic products be produced and handled in compliance with an organic plan. How, then, did the definition of organic agriculture come to be so narrow?

Narrowing the Field

When the USDA first released its proposed federal rule in 1997, it generated intense public focus on the politics of defining organic. Amid the furor, the point was lost that this task had always been political. Not just a matter of philosophical jousting, the many other, perhaps less glamorous, fights that occurred along the way had codified organic meanings and shaped organic conventions, all of which had social and ecological repercussions to at least some degree. So although this narrowing was to some extent a by-product of broad processes of legitimation and institution building that came hand in hand with the growth of an industry, it was in the rule making itself that "organic" was deliberately and irrevocably confined.

In practical terms, the task of rule making was to establish enforceable *standards*. Those involved faced the enormous and difficult task of melding contested and sometimes contradictory imperatives into a single standard and bounding the issues to be addressed. The process also involved reducing the issues to principles that were easily measurable and verifiable. In political terms, the imperatives to define standards in ways that protected existing participants but at the same time were transparent and provided incentives to entry were contradictory. *Organically grown* needed to be reduced to a technical term so that anyone could participate, if not necessarily on his or her own terms. So while it may be the case that organic standard setters never intended to incorporate a substantive critique of conventional agrofood delivery, politicized decisions were made many times over that further delimited the social focus of organic agriculture.

In this last regard, two issues in particular were formative. The first derived from the notion that organic farms should be limited to a certain scale, in keeping with an agrarian populist imaginary. At one point, a small group of organic activists introduced the idea of imposing an acreage limitation on those within the CCOF program. Although there was some support for the motion, most board members felt it would discourage larger-scale growers from attempting organic production. Moreover, since some key dues-paying members of CCOF already had over several hundred acres in production, they mounted considerable opposition to such a standard. It is not surprising that the motion was not successful.[4]

The second, more telling issue involved the fate of farmworkers on organic farms. While many growers and marketers insist that farm labor concerns are external to organic philosophy, the organic industry is happy to boast, when it is convenient, about providing a safe environment for farmworkers as one of organic agriculture's benefits. For their part, some consumers choose organic food with the assumption that it is somehow better for farmworkers. In keeping with these assumptions, labor standards were drafted within CCOF at several points but ultimately defeated at the board vote, with the justification that standards should stick to agronomic practices. One CCOF member recalled that labor standards never had much of a chance, since one of the organization's highest dues-paying members had been the target of the United Farm Workers' grape boycott.

CCOF's fundamental position as a growers' organization was made perfectly clear in a legislative battle over the use of the short-handled hoe, which forces farmworkers to stoop when weeding fields. Although this hoe has been banned in California since the mid-1970s, a loophole in the law still continues to allow the use of bare hands. California Rural Legal Assistance and other labor rights groups nearly succeeded in closing this loophole with Senate Bill 587 in 1995, but the bill was opposed by the organic and ornamental flower industries, which argued that such a ban would make obsolete many production practices that are felt to be crucial, such as hand weeding. CCOF (1995a) boasted in its newsletter that its last-minute lobbying was instrumental in defeating the bill.

Other ideas tossed about in organic discourse also received little institutional bite. Although so-called enhanced standards are disallowed in the federal rule, some certification agencies (but never CCOF) used to include support for regional food systems as one of their guiding principles, yet there were no standards to support such efforts. The idea of minimal processing, once a mainstay of the concept of natural foods, became a ruse when all the major certifiers became involved in certifying food processors. Likewise, some certifiers used to give a rhetorical nod to ensuring that producers receive a fair economic return, but their rhetoric was not backed up by enforcement mechanisms.

Principles and Problems

The Material List is emphatically not a recipe for organic farming; a grower who relies primarily on highly soluble mined fertilizers for fertility management and botanical insecticides for pest control may be "organic" within the letter of the law, but cannot be viewed as truly farming organically. They are merely replacing a synthetic treadmill with a botanical one.
                                        CCOF Certification Handbook

Even narrowed to a focus on production, defining exactly what organic production is remained an issue. For crop production, four debates crucially informed this definition: (1) whether organic production should be centered on processes or inputs; (2) whether organic production should guarantee practices or outcomes (and which outcomes); (3) how an allowable organic input should be defined; and (4) how organic growers should be marked off in time and space. Although many of the conventions established through these debates remain in place with the National Organic Program, the past tense is used here both to demonstrate the political construction of the rules and to denote that individual certifier discretion regarding the rules no longer exists.

Processes or Inputs.   Organic agriculture is supposed to be process-oriented in contrast to the input-oriented management of conventional production. Many of organic farming's progenitors, such as Howard's Indore method, Steiner's biodynamic farming, and Balfour's living soil orientation, looked to methods that encourage and enhance mechanisms that recur in nature. In organic farming's formative years, the commonality among organic growers was an emphasis on stewardship of the soil, and the absence of marketable organic inputs reinforced an emphasis on shared practices. Accordingly, the first set of CCOF standards was printed on a single page, and the prevailing attitude toward verification at CCOF was, as a former inspector put it, "we would know it [organic farming] if we saw it."

CCOF first started to disallow certain inputs when it became clear that growers were claiming organic status on the basis of compost use, for instance, even though they did not necessarily forgo other questionable inputs. Urea, found in the urine of animals but also produced synthetically, was the first among many inputs to cause some controversy in this regard. (It is now completely prohibited.) With the growth of an organic input market and organic production itself, growers began to rely more heavily on things that could be bought for soil fertility and pest control. In response, CCOF developed a materials list in the mid-1980s, a constantly evolving list that designates what can or cannot be used in organic production. In a fine example of circular reasoning, the list was first developed by asking existing growers what they were using. Nevertheless, the materials list shifted the focus of regulation even more pointedly to inputs and materials, to the point that it became the crux of organic regulation.

Increasingly cognizant of the ways in which a materials list encourages agronomic simplification, CCOF tried to reinforce a process orientation. Their 1998 handbook claimed that a long-term program of soil management is one of the basic requirements of certification. "It is not acceptable," it said, "to simply eliminate the use of synthetic materials and manage by 'benign neglect.' This approach can lead to exhaustion of soil resources, poor quality crops, and ultimate operation failure" (CCOF 1998b, 26). CCOF also required crop rotations in annual production systems, regular soil fertility tests for all farms, and written justification for use of restricted materials. At the same time, much of their required record keeping continued to focus on inputs (e.g., the Organic Farm Input Report).

Furthermore, both the COFA (the California law) and the OFPA (the federal law) reinforced the input message by defining organic production solely in terms of prohibited materials. The OFPA's only concession to process was the required farm plan, a written statement that is supposed to enumerate intended practices "designed to foster soil fertility, primarily through the management of the organic content of the soil" (Public Law 101–624, sec. 6513). The idea of a farm plan is to encourage growers to attend to processes and to strive to improve measurable elements of these processes (e.g., humus content). Growers set yearly goals on var-

ious criteria, and certifiers are supposed to consider whether improvements have occurred when they recertify. In practice, growers often put
"no change" on their farm plan, and certifiers' assessments of improvement have been "arbitrary and capricious," at least according to Ray
Green, director of California's state organic program (personal communication, 1999). The newly implemented federal rule is ambiguous on
this point. On the one hand, the regulatory text contains several passages
enjoining growers to implement tillage and cultivation practices. On the
other hand, it retains an emphasis on material proscriptions.

Practices or Outcomes.   The debate over whether organic production
was to be defined by the methods used or by the outcomes achieved
reached a temporary resolution early in certification history. This resolution came about as a practical matter, since substances like DDT have
such a lengthy half-life that it would have been ludicrous to make promises of residue-free soils, and even organically grown foods were shown
to have some pesticide residues. California organic farmers came to the
conclusion that while they were "unanimously ready to verify that they
[did] not use toxic pesticides or other harmful chemicals, they [were] re-
luctant to promise consumers that their products [would] be 100 percent
clean of any residues" (Allen 1971, 75). Effectively, the original CCOF
growers defined organic as a production standard for farmers, not a food
safety standard for consumers—thus the use of the terminology organically grown as opposed to organic as an attribute of the product itself.
   This debate reemerged, however, upon the entry of Scientific Certification Systems (SCS) into the certification business in 1986.[5] SCS's NutriClean program began to certify produce as having "no detected pesticide residues" (defined as fewer than 0.05 ppm, or five one-hundredths
part per million).[6] By emphasizing scientifically based residue testing,
SCS sought to replace what was seen as process-oriented certification.
Pavich Family Farms, the largest organic grower in California at the
time, signed on with NutriClean immediately, finding it to be more effective to market grapes certified as having "no detectable pesticide
residues" than as having been "organically grown." In fact, the existing organic market did not support a significant portion of Pavich's production, so most had to be sold in conventional markets, making NutriClean certification an attractive alternative. Strikingly, NutriClean's
use of residue testing as a marketing tool finally led the state of California to be "more apoplectic than the organic industry," as Bob Scowcroft, current director of the Organic Farming Research Foundation and

past director of CCOF, put it.[7] The state of California (and the FDA) had been careful to tone down any implications that conventional foods were unsafe.

For their part, producers wanted to be judged on their actions rather than on conditions beyond their control. For that reason, the CCOF definition of organic agriculture made no guarantees that organically grown produce would be residue free. Eventually, though, CCOF and other certifiers made it a practice to test for residues when there was suspicion of violations. They also adopted a standard that residues must be below 5 percent of EPA tolerance levels, even when caused by unintentional drift.[8] In effect, residue testing came to act as an enforcement mechanism, even if "residue free" never became a widely used organic attribute. The federal rule continues this tradition.

Defining Organic Materials.   The third key debate turned on allowable organic materials. In keeping with a process orientation, at first CCOF growers employed a rather simple criterion. That is, only materials found in nature were to be used in organic production systems, thus proscribing the use of synthetically produced fertilizers, pesticides, herbicides, and other inputs. But such a simple definition raised a number of problems. Some substances found in nature, such as botanical pesticides, were known to be toxic and/or prone to have the same sort of treadmill effects as chemically derived pesticides.[9] Some acceptable materials, such as insect pheromones for mating disruption, were much more expensive than their synthetic analogs. Many necessary inputs, such as seeds and transplants, were not readily available in untreated forms. More profound the use of "natural" or "found in nature" as the basis of acceptability relied on clearly problematic assumptions about the essential goodness of nature and made all decisions subject to endless debate about what constitutes human interference. In practice, materials started to be assessed on a case-by-case basis but always with reference to that more fundamental criterion.

Most certifiers began to use three designations on their materials lists in relation to crop production: "allowed," "regulated," and "prohibited." "Regulated" was the most complex because it allowed questionable materials to be used with certain restrictions. In some cases, use was dependent on the particular source or a "demonstration that the material is free from contamination." For instance, ashes were perfectly acceptable as long as they were not produced from burning plastics or other synthetic materials. Other regulated materials were simply discouraged and acceptable only if there were no alternatives available. Efforts to reduce or eliminate these restricted materials were required in the farm plan (CCOF 1998b, 50). The materials list thus became a primary source of controversy within the industry. Growers liked definitions and restrictions they could easily meet but complained when they felt dependent on particular restricted or prohibited materials. Moreover, they became frustrated by the apparent inconsistencies, gray areas, and fine lines that are indicative of rules that have been made and amended in a constantly evolving climate of availability, need, and politics.

The problems start with the seed. Presumably there should be organic integrity throughout the life cycle of the plant, but growers were compelled to buy conventional seed in the absence of a commercial organic seed market. Immediately striking was the absence of restrictions put on the use of hybrid seed, although hybridization is arguably the basis of industrialized agriculture and certainly the beginnings of the GEO trajectory (Kloppenburg 1988).[10] The more widely voiced problem was the baffling fine lines drawn between seeds and transplants: potato eyes, strawberry crowns, and garlic cloves were considered seeds, which means they could be conventionally grown; transplants, however, including sweet potato slips, had to be organically grown. In effect, growers could buy conventionally grown strawberry starts but not sweet potato starts, although both come from soils that have been treated with methyl bromide.

Perhaps the most controversial material was Chilean, or sodium nitrate, a form of soluble nitrogen. Soluble fertilizers are known to displace and destroy soil microorganisms. Sodium nitrate, although naturally mined, also increases sodium levels and thus is a source of groundwater pollution, leading to eutrophication of freshwater sources (Conway and Pretty 1991). For these reasons, even growers who otherwise supported "reasonable exemptions" such as copper and sulfates felt that sodium nitrate should be banned. Growers who defended sodium nitrate grow winter produce in dry climates and need a quick and easily absorbable nitrogen fix. At one point, three of CCOF's largest growers, Pavich Family Farms, Cal-Organic, and Bornt Family Farms, threatened a walkout if CCOF were to ban the use of sodium nitrate. Because of this controversy, CCOF lagged behind most other certifiers in disallowing it, although its biggest competitor in the certification business, Quality Assurance International (QAI), was even less restrictive. The federal rule adopted CCOF's conciliatory standard: from then on, sodium nitrate use would be restricted to no more than 20 percent of the crop's total nitrogen requirement.

In contrast, copper and sulfur, both of which serve as antifungal agents, were deemed allowable organic inputs in certain forms and engendered much less controversy, even though sulfur is said to cause more worker injuries in California than any other agricultural input (Pease et al. 1993). While copper products, found in Bordeaux mixes, are one of the synthetic exemptions that were "regulated" by CCOF to prevent excessive accumulation in the soil (CCOF 1998b), dusting sulfur, used to control powdery mildew and bunch rot in grapes (see Klonsky, Tourte, and Ingels 1992; Klonsky and Tourte 1997) and is also synthetically produced, was allowed without restriction. Pavich was instrumental in making sulfur dust a permissible input also. Basically, many fruit growers would not be able to produce organically with ease without these tools. The allowance of dusting sulfur in crop production but not sulfites in processing is the reason that huge amounts of wine continue to be produced with organically grown grapes but little of that wine is labeled organic.

In general, the CCOF materials list was the source of a litany of grower complaints, as expressed in interviews. One grower had a problem with organic inputs that are derivatives of processes that are not organic. "Mined dolomite is being phased out, but fish emulsion is allowed, even though you don't know what's in it." "Gibberellic acid, which is synthetically produced [actually produced through a fermentation process], is allowed, but a naturally occurring hormone used to enhance berry size is not, because it is sprayed." Several grape growers mentioned their frustration that cryolite was being phased out as an allowable substance because it is no longer being mined. They were able to use back stock of its natural form (with restrictions), although its synthetic forms are completely prohibited. Black plastic is allowed for solarization or for mulching as long as it is removed from the field after use, yet solarization kills all biological activity in the soil. Chlorine restrictions were softened to "treat" salad mix in the wake of a food safety crackdown, although chlorine was never allowable before. Other comments: "We can use *Bt* but not urea, compost but not fractured [heated] oil. How can you be more natural than crude oil?" "Why is it perfectly acceptable to drive tractors around that not only use diesel fuel but also worsen soil compaction?"[11] "Bone and blood meal, by-products of some of the worst practices in animal husbandry, are completely allowed. . . ."

In 1990, the COFA became the baseline for certifiers' materials lists in

California. Following preexisting definitions of organic, it prohibited "synthetically compounded fertilizers, pesticides and growth regulators," and some toxic materials found in nature (e.g., strychnine) and exempted certain synthetic materials. Complications continued: brand-name products for organic production were quickly coming on the market, synthetic inert ingredients in many compounds were not always readily detected, and the required list was not standardized but instead variously embellished among different certifiers. Also a number of legal challenges to the authenticity of organic inputs occurred. It became clear that a separate "brand names list" was needed in addition to the "generic list."

Upon the initiative of several certifiers, the Organic Materials Research Institute (OMRI) was formed in 1997 to address the complexity of evaluating organic inputs and to provide recommendations for generic materials and brand-name products, as well. According to Lynne Coody, a spokesperson for OMRI and previously a materials reviewer for Oregon Tilth, the criteria for evaluating materials had to move beyond the synthetic/natural divide because there was no "one criterion which could adequately define which materials would be acceptable" (OMRI 1998). At OMRI, materials are evaluated according to toxicity, environmental impact, and synergism, along with the more difficult-to-measure criterion that materials are "in keeping with organic principles."[12]

With the federal rule, all materials have to be approved by the National Organic Standards Board. Therefore, certifiers are supposed to have standardized materials lists. OMRI will nevertheless remain a powerful clearinghouse for input review because of the constant introduction of new materials and the remaining inconsistencies with already used materials.

Becoming Organic.   A fourth series of debates determined how growers, crops, land, and products would become, stay, and be marked as organic. Particularly as more conventional land was brought into organic production and that production began to take place alongside conventional production, temporal qualifications and spatial bounding became important issues. Thus, land is often subject to more scrutiny than what growers do on it. Certification is done on a per parcel basis, although rights of certification are not automatically transferable when the property is transferred.

Land can be designated as organic only when it is relatively clean of prohibited substances. Because rapid entry into organics was not a major concern upon CCOF's inception, CCOF first required a one-year transition period from the application of any prohibited material to the harvest of a certified crop. The transition period was changed to three years in the late 1980s. Not only was that the standard for European markets, but also existing growers felt threatened by the surge of newcomers. As one long-time grower put it, "I've been building up my soil for years. After ten years it's finally what I want it to be in terms of organic content. This new guy comes along, sees the prices I'm getting, and puts up a sign that says he's organic. There's no way his soil could measure up to mine." As for the California law, before 1995 it required a one-year transition period, which was then increased to two then three years. The lack of uniformity between the California law and CCOF standards was also a source of resentment among long-time CCOF growers.

An important question is, Why three years for the transition? Different substances have different half-life periods: DDT remains in the soil for decades; Roundup dissipates fairly quickly. A three-year transition clearly does not rid the soil of all residues, but it does improve on the results of the one-year transition. As evidenced in the preceding quote, some say it actually takes much longer for soils to recover from conventional production and for organic production to take hold thoroughly. So three years is clearly an arbitrary cutoff, yet one that satisfies the needs of the longer-term growers to minimize quick-and-dirty entry without creating an insurmountable barrier to new growers. An alternative approach was to use laboratory tests on soil samples in lieu of a three-year transition. Organic Certifiers (OC), a more recent entrant into the certification business, responded to this arbitrariness by refusing to certify until soil was below a certain threshold of residues. In fact, other certifiers had similar requirements, but soil tests were not necessarily standard procedure. The federal law has since codified a three-year transition.

With the proliferation of mixed growers, more attention to spatial bounds was needed as well. Organic fields next to conventional fields had to be marked by unambiguous permanent physical objects; in addition, buffer zones of twenty-five feet were required between the organic crop and the adjacent area (CCOF 1998b). This, of course, was another arbitrarily defined line, thought to be particularly artificial because pesticide drift cannot be controlled with that sort of exactitude, even less so if applied from planes as opposed to tractor spray rigs.

Finally, it should be noted that crop production practices were just the tip of the iceberg. Only about 1 percent of the materials used in crop production were contentious among certifiers, but evaluating materials became much more difficult in regard to value-added products and livestock. These two areas involved 10 percent of the materials that were unresolved in harmonization efforts as of 1998, according to Coody of OMRI. The bounding issue also became more complicated with value-added products. The standard that was to become federal law stated that processed foods can be designated as fully organic only if 95 percent of their ingredients are grown organically, which allows for the inclusion of spices and microingredients that are difficult to source organically. This, however, has left the door open for routine use of nonorganic additives and processing aids, even though the federal rule applies some restrictions to these (e.g., no additives made with genetically modified organisms can be used). The rule also codifies another, similar convention: a label can state "made with organically grown ingredients" if only 50 percent of the ingredients are organically produced and the related lettering on the package meets certain size requirements. These sorts of standards have caused some in the industry to posit that organic has become most fundamentally a labeling issue, with the ultimate measure involving the accuracy of what is put on a label. Is it possible that such standards also fix product attributes (e.g., organic or not organic) at the expense of attention to the processes that went into their creation?

ORGANIC INSTITUTIONS

Owing to the lack of state support at least initially, the organic movement/industry necessarily developed organic regulations and institutions de novo, which only later became substantially undergirded by state policy. Private certifying institutions became the primary institutional vehicle through which meanings of organic were created, operationalized, and enforced, even though these institutions clearly overlapped with trade organizations. The result was a unique articulation of interests, with regulatory imperatives not altogether clear—at once serving a broad public but at the same time offering self-protection to the existing industry. In that way, the evolution of organic meanings is inseparable from that of the infrastructure that supports them.

By 1997, nine certification agencies were operating in California (table 10), and most of the acreage in organic production was certified, even though over half of organic growers in the state did not certify (see chapter 2, note 10). According to widely held belief, significant differences existed in the standards of these certifiers. Most differences over allowable inputs had been minimized by the mid-1990s, however. First, newer certifiers tended to use already existing standards in developing their own. Second, there were across-the-board industry efforts to harmonize materials lists in the interest of reciprocity (which is critical for processing ingredients) and limiting intra-industry disparagement. OMRI's work was central to these harmonization efforts.

Although it is true that different certifiers took disparate stances regarding materials such as the controversial sodium nitrate, the more marked substantive differences that remained related to guiding principles. On paper, for instance, FVO probably had the "highest" standards, reflecting its close ties to the European market. For example, FVO, along with the Organic Crop Improvement Association (OCIA), discouraged mixed operations by requiring in the farm plan an intent to convert wholly to organic production within a certain number of years. It also banned the use of manure from caged animals and required the farm plan to detail crop rotations, livestock integration, and manufacture of on-farm inputs. Its guiding principles gave a nod to water conservation, labor practices, and small farm size, too (Farm Verified Organic 1999).[13] Less clear is whether these principles were actually operationalized, given the reports of FVO-certified growers.

All told, it appears that the differences among certifiers had less to do with their standards than with their organizational structures and procedures, some of which are itemized in table 10. In other words, uneven verification and enforcement were the deeper political issues. In particular, *third-party* certification assumes a clear separation of interest between the certifier and certified.

The key function of certification is to verify claims of organically grown; it thus presumes preexisting, well-defined rules. To be certified, growers had to fill out elaborate paperwork including a farm plan; agree to initial annual and perhaps spot inspections;[14] fulfill whatever requirements for crop or soil sampling; pay various dues, fees, and assessments; and, of course, agree to abide by the practices and input restrictions designated by that agency and the law.

While certification on its own presented a legal standard that could be enforced by civil law and its less exacting standards of proof than those of criminal codes, most enforcement was extralegal. It usually involved action taken by the certifier: from prohibiting a certain crop to be sold as certified organic (in the case of drift violations), to fines, to decertification. In all of these cases, the burden of proof rested almost entirely on the alleged violator, and varying degrees of due process were involved.

TABLE 10. ORGANIC CERTIFICATIONS IN
CALIFORNIA, BY CERTIFYING AGENCY, 1997–98

Name of Organization	Date Est.	No. of Farms Certi-	No. of CA Farms Cert.[b,c]	% of CA Regis- tered Farms	Base of Operation	Geog. Range of Certification
California Certified Organic Farmers (CCOF)	1973	635	544	24.7	Santa Cruz, CA	Mostly CA, Baja
Quality Assurance International (QAI)[f]	1989	312	83	3.8	San Diego, CA	International
Farm Verified Organic (FVO)[f]	1979	113	13	0.6	North Dakota	International
California Organic Farmers Association (COFA)	1997	11	11	0.5	Atwater, CA	Only CA
Organic Crop Improvement Association (OCIA)	1984	450	8	0.4	Nebraska	International
Scientific Certification Systems (SCS)	1996[g]	9	7	0.3	Oakland, CA	U.S., Mexico
Organic Certifiers (OC)	1996	6	6	0.3	Ventura, CA	Only CA
Oregon Tilth	1974	283	5	0.2	Oregon	Mainly Oregon
Organic Growers and Buyers Association (OGBA)	1977	220	1	0.0	Minnesota	International
No certification	—	—	875	39.7	—	—

[a] Source for number of all farms certified is OFRF 1998; except QAI number from Fetter 1999.

[b] Source for number of CA farms certified is CDFA list 1997, which corresponded with certifier lists received.

[c] When totaled, column exceeds 1,533 growers (the registered grower population at the time of the study) because of dual certification.

[d] Measures of conflict-of-interest policies and organizational transparency are the author's own judgments. Data are based on interviews and review of organizational material, collected and analyzed by both Fetter (1999) and me when made available.

Accordingly, certifying agencies had tremendous power in determining who could participate under the organic aegis and on what terms. Although the more recent involvement of state agencies complicated certification, the basic structure remained intact.

Under the National Organic Program, however, certification is being dramatically reworked. Federal involvement demands third-party dis-

For Profit/	Org. Governance[d]	Fee Structure[d]	Org. Transparency[d]	Conflict of Int.[d]	IFOAM Accredited / Partic. in
NP	Board, committees	Graduated	Good	Good	Yes / yes
FP	Staff	Flat	Poor	Fair	No / no
FP	Staff, cert. committee	Graduated	Fair	Fair	Yes / no
NP	Board, committees	Graduated	Fair	Good	No / no
NP	Staff, chapters	Graduated	Fair	Fair	Pending / yes
FP	Staff	Flat	Good	Good	No / no
FP	Owner	Graduated	Fair	Fair	No / no
NP	Board, committees	Graduated	Good	Good	Yes / yes
NP	Staff	Graduated	—	Good	Yes / no
—	—	—	—	—	—

[e] Indicates accreditation by the International Federation of Organic Agriculture Movements (IFOAM) and participation in the Organic Certifiers Council (OCC) of the Organic Trade Association.

[f] Grower numbers for FVO and QAI are understated because both agencies make it a practice of certifying growers under the umbrella of a packer or other contractor but do not divulge the number of growers they certify in this manner.

[g] SCS was founded in 1989 to do NutriClean certification; 1996 was the first year of organic certification.

tance and due process in certification decisions. In addition, the ongoing advocacy and technical support that many certifiers provided in the past must be curtailed or organizationally segregated.

How, though, did certification shift from a one-pony show to a highly competitive and occasionally back-stabbing business? To answer this, we must look at the organizational structures and practices of the certifiers themselves, how they were represented, and how their activities intersected with state law.

CCOF and the Politicization of Certification

CCOF is not only the oldest and largest of the certification agencies in California, it was, as we have seen, a figurative gathering spot for some of the original back-to-the-land hippies. Some likened it to a club. Even with its original quasi-social-movement bent, its mission gradually turned to the promotion of organic production and trade. It became a key player in developing organic legislation and regulation and, thereby, in creating definitions of organic. Because its organizational structure co-evolved with the development and refinement of standards, it played a de facto role in conventionalizing the practice of certification itself.

That fights were so politicized in CCOF has to do with the nature of the institution's structure and membership. Reflecting its popular origins, CCOF became a nonprofit membership organization, eventually with fifteen active chapters, run by an elected statewide board of directors. Standards and procedures were set by a certification committee, with members from every chapter. On the one hand, its policy of grassroots, committee-based decision making and commitment to organizational transparency created a space for substantive and visible arguments at board and chapter meetings. On the other hand, given that CCOF's voting members were all growers, standards were set according to what growers wanted, not according to a wider public sense. For these reasons the IRS denied charitable organization status to CCOF when it first applied in 1988 and insisted it be organized as a 501(c)(5), basically, a mutual benefit, or trade, organization. Other stakeholders were never brought to the table, although CCOF received substantial support from nonvoting members. For these reasons, CCOF, and others similarly organized, could never offer more than second-party certification, although it continued to call itself a third-party certifier.

In 1988 the CCOF board also decided to levy an assessment in order to ease the transition from club to professional trade association. In addition to an annual membership fee, inspection fees, and other minor fees, growers were thereafter required to pay an assessment of half of 1 percent of all gross sales for crops sold as organic or transitional. Shortly thereafter, CCOF established an assessment cap of $15,000 (equivalent to $3 million in sales) (CCOF 1998b). Pavich, one of CCOF's highest fee payers, took the lead in fighting for an assessment cap. Bob Scowcroft, then executive director of CCOF, supported the assessment cap, so that large growers would not be able to use their assessments as a way of gaining political leverage—a paradoxical stance given how the cap came about. Growers with sales of less than $20,000, however, were not required to pay an assessment. Still, growers complained of the cost structure, not only because CCOF's largest growers paid proportionately less, but also because they felt that membership, certification and inspection fees, assessments, and fees to the state "amounted to quadruple taxation."

CCOF's commitment to transparency was evident from the beginning. It made its policies, procedures, and rules available to the public and provided basic information on grower-members through its publications and, eventually, the Internet. Additional information could be obtained upon written request. Nevertheless, as the organic industry became more competitive, CCOF came under pressure to divulge less information. In particular, it became more careful about disclosing decertifications. CCOF also had specific conflict-of-interest policies forbidding members to make decisions about operations in which they had a material interest, but the group never recognized the sense in which its structure as a trade organization entailed a conflict of interest.

CCOF was often perceived as overly bureaucratic. The certification process came to take several months, for it involved a fairly complicated application, an initial inspection (which may have included soil, water, and crop samples), and a local chapter review of the inspection before any parcel of land was certified. Significant lag time occurred before each next step. In addition, decertifications were issued with some regularity, and the burden of proof lay with the member responding to the judgment and possibly filing an appeal.

Growers complained of the expense and hassle of inspections, the amount of paperwork, the slow response time to many questions, and lengthy committee meetings with endless debates. The peer review system seemed not only tedious but also subject to malfeasance in the context of industry competition. Moreover, with an explosion of the number of new materials available on the market, staff was not able to keep up with materials review, so growers were often told to "use [materials] at your own risk." One grower complained of having a block decertified when he first entered the organic program, because he had used a material that a supplier said was acceptable but apparently was not. These sorts of complaints were behind CCOF's giving substantial support to OMRI.

Among mixed growers, however, the biggest complaint about CCOF was the perceived "puritanism" of the organization. It was seen as run by "hippies, theologians, and philosophers" and, to add insult to injury, "by gardeners, not farmers," who insisted that growers should, for example, compost every year. Since mixed growers were required to do more paperwork, some say there was an explicit bias against mixed farms. As one such grower put it, "The organo-nazis volunteered to be inspectors to catch [those with split operations] in the act." Another major conventional grower who had grown organically for several years left precisely because CCOF was "just too distrusting." For others, there was a strong sense of cultural barriers. Growers felt that CCOF was more lifestyle- than business-oriented, and they joked about inspectors wearing tie-dye and ponytails. Nevertheless, few took these as real barriers to farming organic; some even hired as technical advisers those who fit the image they derided. And, as it happens, CCOF shifted its constitution and hence its political project over time. As more conventional growers entered into organic production and certified with CCOF, they received increased representation on the board.

The other certification agencies with strong "movement" connections either never gained a foothold in California or lost that foothold somewhere along the way. FVO and OCIA in particular came under significant scrutiny. FVO was started by a North Dakota wheat farmer who continued to be an important player in the organic movement. FVO was actually a for-profit corporation that at one point was unique in certifying only licensees that contracted with growers for purchase and subsequent marketing of their product (which is why their grower numbers are understated); only in later years could growers themselves be certified. FVO's problems stemmed from its acting as marketing agent for many of its licensees, although that practice was eventually discontinued. Besides the underlying conflict of interest, growers complained about their lack of control; for instance, FVO would do all the negotiations with buyers and insisted on having its own label on every box.

OCIA, in comparison, was a nonprofit organization that gave significant autonomy to many of its chapters, which created wide disparities in how the different chapters were run. At one point, CCOF was to become a chapter of OCIA, to take advantage of its international recognition, but internal controversies squelched the deal. OCIA went on to establish its own California chapter. But in the 1990s, OCIA received some bad publicity and fell into disfavor. For one, the association used to have growers pay inspectors directly, although this practice was discontinued under industry pressure. Then there were internal controversies, including allegations about improper certification practices and the disbarment of the California chapter, which reemerged as COFA (California Organic Farmers Association)—a name purposely designed to be confusing, given the use of the same acronym for the California Organic Foods Act. Many of these issues came to a head when a 1995 suit named OCIA, along with QAI and the distributor Made in Nature, as having certified fungicide-treated bananas (O'Neill 1995).

Enter the State

Although private certifiers appeared first, they had to comply with state laws, even those of their own making. As of 1990, only about thirty states had passed laws regarding organic production. Some states simply provided a legal definition of organic, under which private associations could certify; other states went on to do their own certification, including Washington and Texas. In states where there was no law for organic production, growers relied on private certification as the only basis of legal recognition. This uneven landscape of regulation was one of the motives behind the creation of the federal OFPA of 1990.

In the absence of a federal rule, the COFA was one of the most stringent laws in the country, which is why products from other states were often labeled "grown and processed in accordance with the California Organic Foods Act of 1990." Even though CCOF was one of the key players behind its creation, its effects turned out to be highly controversial. For one, its standards were less stringent than those of CCOF and other certifiers, because the state stood by the natural/synthetic criterion and did not disallow some controversial botanical pesticides, for example.

Be that as it may, the COFA's underlying purpose was not improved standards but improved enforcement, for certifiers had no power to prosecute fraud and other misdeeds outside their purview. Yet, the COFA did not require regular inspection or verification of practices and was enforced only in cases of confirmed violation (Klonsky and Tourte 1994). Indeed, for a long while it appears that the state did very little in the way of enforcement.

Of the actions taken, most seemed to be nonsubstantive, at least at face value. Three of the largest violations were based on a failure to register properly with the state or have adequate paperwork verifying the origin of products. All of the investigations were complaint driven, although the produce in question was never found to be tainted, and the growers involved continued with the organic program. Another, mostly nonsubstantive complaint eventually caused a grower to leave the organic program, mainly to escape the negative publicity that ensued. In this case, most of the charges were about adequately segregating and identifying the organic produce at direct-marketing venues.

State enforcement was bound to have less of an edge, however. While the degree and kind of state enforcement often reflects political will and funding, particularly among the county agricultural commissioners, burden-of-proof issues also affect the nature of enforcement. State enforcement requires due process, whereas, up until the federal rule, private certifiers could decertify growers at will. It is unlikely that this shift in the legal landscape is one that the organic movement foresaw.

The most controversial effect of the COFA, however, was its creation of a two-tiered system. Basically, it granted growers legal status as organic producers simply by registering with the state, making certification wholly voluntary. When the law was crafted, the alleged purpose was to appease the long-time growers who had rebelled against CCOF's decision to "tax themselves" with assessments. Although certification was a virtual necessity for interstate and international trade and desired by many in-state retailers as well, many of these growers had established clientele—restaurants especially—and did not need certification. Nevertheless, as a direct result of this registration option, grower numbers shot up considerably at the time the law was implemented in 1990, suggesting that growers recognized an easier (and cheaper) entry into the legitimized organic order.

Among certified growers, there was noticeable resentment of the registration option, and many of those who originally supported optional certification found it to be a mistake in retrospect. One certified grower said: "Growers who don't certify compete with certified growers and don't have to spend as much on certification or inputs. A lot of those guys just irrigate and not a whole lot else and call themselves organic. They have no inspection and don't have to use expensive materials like kelp to get a high-quality product." One long-time organic activist was particularly vehement: "The COFA was a big mistake, and CCOF was behind it all they way. The program should be abolished. It doesn't serve farmers, the reporting requirements are unnecessarily difficult, and it provides a cover for those who don't want to certify, which isn't fair and has undermined the organic industry. . . . The money going into [COFA] could be put to better use paying employees' health insurance." So while the proximate issue with the law was the state's lack of enforcement, it was more deeply experienced as requiring an additional tax and allowing unfair competition.

While the COFA remains in effect, the National Organic Program requires all growers with organic sales over five thousand dollars per annum to certify. Insofar as certifiers' fees will increase in regard to *their* need to comply with federal law, that increase could well add another layer of "taxation."

The Marketization of Certification

As the organic industry grew and became more competitive, so did the certification business itself. A few entrants simply saw an easy opportunity to compete directly with CCOF and did so with abandon by borrowing closely related names and using the CCOF Certification Handbook as a basis for their own (Nowacek 1997). These included California Cooperative Organic Growers and California Certified Organic Producers, both of which desisted with threats of litigation. Those that had staying power introduced a much bolder restructuring of certification by offering lower fees and quicker service and by reworking organic definitions and idioms. In effect, regulation became even more politicized around its two key functions of standards setting and enforcement while these agencies traded on various ways to become organic.

Most significant was the entry of Quality Assurance International (QAI), which appeared on the scene after the organic market had its big growth spurt in the mid-1980s. Its founder's prior business was a soil testing laboratory, but QAI's sole focus has been organic certification. Established as an independent for-profit business, QAI measured its growth in annual sales revenues for the company itself (experiencing an 87 percent increase in annual sales in the last half of the 1990s) (*Business Wire* 1999). As a relative newcomer to certification, the company had not been involved in standards development, much less broader advocacy and education. Standards and procedures were set by its staff and owners, who also had final decision-making authority. It had informal provisions to limit conflicts of interest between inspectors and producers but not between decision makers and producers, although, according to Fetter (1999), the principals made a verbal commitment in 1998 to implement a written policy regarding conflict of interest. Annual fees were quoted by staff and were supposedly based on the size and characteristics of the operation (Fetter 1999), but the growers I interviewed consistently stated that they paid a flat fee of twenty-five hundred dollars per year to certify.

The lack of transparency at QAI was widely acknowledged. They systematically refused to answer substantive requests for information and declined to participate in surveys, including the national organic survey conducted by the Organic Farming Research Foundation (OFRF 1999). They refused to participate in this study, even upon written request. Only in late 1999 did they create a Web page where certification standards were posted, albeit without a materials list. Their specific enforcement procedures were not publicly available, other than requirements of an annual inspection, written documentation of production practices, and pesticide residue tests as needed (Klonsky and Tourte 1994). The company's most significant practical difference from CCOF, according to growers, is that QAI asked for less paperwork and had a much quicker turnaround for certification, on the order of two to three weeks.

Dubbed Quick And Instant and a paper certifier, QAI was the target of the most accusations within the industry, for example, for certifying growers whom others had decertified, for failing to decertify growers who had been found using pesticides, for appearing to be too informal and easy, and for lacking grower involvement. Yet, some who dealt with them claim that their record keeping was tighter than CCOF's and that their materials list was stricter than CCOF's, because they disallowed controversial materials and relied solely on the OMRI materials list.

Besides making certification less bureaucratic, the newer certifiers also attempted to trade on notions of scientific legitimacy in lieu of the "muck and mystery" of organic's earlier associations. As we saw, OC and SCS attempted to assess outcomes (e.g., soil and crop pesticide residues) as opposed to processes (or even philosophy) in the interest of "scientific objectivity." Thus, they privileged laboratory testing in their certification process (as presumably QAI did), in some ways addressing the implicit arbitrariness of certifiers who based decisions on "we would know it if we saw it." Nevertheless, all were limited in how far they could rework organic standards because of the state law, and other certifiers were not necessarily opposed to using such tests on an as-needed basis. Equally important, they popularized the idea of certification as a business service. QAI and SCS in particular were wholly separate from the "organic community," in that way offering true *third-party* certification, even though staff and owners operated with ample discretion and were accountable only to themselves.

One of the justifications for the National Organic Program is to offer greater federal oversight in how certification is carried out to eliminate what came to be seen as "arbitrary and capricious" processes in certification decision making (Jones 2000). Certifiers now have to be accredited by the USDA, which means identical standards, complementary procedures, and singular benchmarks of punishable behavior. As many in the movement/industry have been quick to say, "The USDA now owns the organic label." One assured effect is a change in terms by which certifiers compete for clients.

Certifying the Certifiers

Until passage of the COFA, the state had no oversight for certification. Because of some of the problems mentioned above, certifiers were then compelled to register with the state and meet minimum standards of third-party distance. In particular, they were disallowed any financial interests in the sale of the food, the issue that brought FVO trouble (COFA 1998b, sec, II0850). In the absence of a working federal rule, other institutions formed to unify and uphold standards in North America. Most of these were private (nonprofit) efforts themselves. The Organic Trade Association took a leading role in the industry, and one of its working committees, the Organic Certifiers Council (OCC in table 10), actively attempted to work out differences among certifiers. OMRI also played a major role in harmonizing standards, and by 2000, all certifiers in California except for OC subscribed to OMRI, as the California Department of Food and Agriculture did.

Finally, certifier accreditation by IFOAM (International Federation of Organic Agriculture Movements) assumed greater importance in the 1990s. IFOAM was started in 1973 and began to develop standards in 1978. At that time, the standards were written as "ideological documents," and they reflected the concerns of the federation's largely European base with an affinity for biodynamic farming. More current IFOAM standards were developed explicitly to operationalize the principles of agroecology. IFOAM, for example, disallows the use of certain ingredients that are used routinely by organic growers in California, such as sodium nitrate; it also appears to favor small operations that integrate livestock and to discourage mixed operations by asking growers eventually to convert entirely to organic production. It purposely incorporates social considerations, requiring that all operators have a policy on social justice (IFOAM 1998).[15] Finally, IFOAM asks for tight enforcement, such as required spot inspections.

IFOAM's accreditation program, which gives formal recognition to certifiers, was not started until 1992. It began with the purpose of enabling reciprocity among certifiers by giving formal recognition to those that minimally conform to IFOAM standards in their own certification programs. As of 2000, IFOAM had about seven hundred members worldwide, although it had accredited only about twenty certification programs, not least because the process is very time-consuming and expensive, on the order of several thousand dollars for each accreditation.

So, some of the last (pre–federal rule) political contests within CCOF came about because of uneven interest in IFOAM accreditation. On the one hand, IFOAM carries significant weight internationally and is seen as key to European markets. And it would be suspect if the premier California certification agency were not IFOAM-accredited. On the other hand, IFOAM's stance on sodium nitrate and mixed operations was anathema to many of CCOF's biggest dues-paying members, who also abhor standards that go beyond production practices. Consequently, CCOF began to offer two tiers of certification to accommodate growers who did not want to be IFOAM accredited. This dual system was at considerable cost to consumer legibility, which, it should be remembered, was one of the original aims of organic regulation. It remains to be seen how IFOAM accreditation will intersect with USDA accreditation, although there is little question that their differences will be the basis of at least some minor trade skirmishes.

This perverse, if temporary, resolution of the IFOAM debate within CCOF provides a final illustration of how social goals—however vague—were systematically written out of regulated meanings of organic when industry players took the lead in its codification. Yet, standards were not "weakened" as much as they were narrowed. To be sure, almost everyone in the organic community continues to support strong standards, at least in principle, as they understand that integrity of definition is the basis of the organic market.

Therefore, the most defining moment of the history of organic regulation was not the standardization process per se but the facile adoption of an incentive-based approach. When the organic industry made a strategic (if not entirely planned) decision not to ask for direct state support but rather to ask that the state honor and uphold an industry-created definition of organically grown, the implicit goal was to institutionalize a price premium for organic crops. This was to have more far-reaching effects on practices and participation in the sector than any other single aspect of regulation, as chapter 7 illustrates.

CHAPTER 7

Organic Regulation Ramified

Organic producers are currently taking some of the external costs, which would otherwise be borne by society, onto themselves voluntarily. Unless all farmers are required to abandon potentially harmful practices, this process of "internalizing" social and environmental costs can only be sustained in a competitive environment through the market (premium prices) or through agricultural policy support. . . . Financial support policies for organic farming need to achieve a balance between encouraging the expansion of the organic sector and promoting excessive growth leading to market disruption, adverse consequences on existing organic producers, and the possible disillusionment and withdrawal of participants.

   Nicolas Lampkin and S. Padel, *The Economics of Organic Farming*

Organic used to be hard to grow and easy to sell; now it's easy to grow and hard to sell. You have to be able to sit on a price, to turn your crops into soil food, to not take it from buyers . . . especially when growers in Mexico have one-tenth of my labor costs.

   Denesse Willey, T & D Willey Farms, Ecological Farming
   Conference, Asilomar, California, January, 2000

Arguably, the development of organic regulatory institutions and conventions was a haphazard process. The organic sector was simply ingenuous in its beginnings, but its ongoing expansion and change brought unforeseen challenges to making an agreed-upon meaning hold. A seemingly simple definition of organically grown turned out to need constant tinkering; a casual organizational style had to be professionalized and given procedural legitimacy, ultimately creating fairly baroque modes of enforcement. Yet, no matter how new rules and procedures were normatively framed, the underlying concern was self-protection for already-existing producers. Accordingly, standards became stronger yet inconsistent, and practices of enforcement became more surveillant yet arbitrary, effectively giving more slack to those who were already under the organic rubric. From this perspective, more recent state and private-sector intervention in the certification arena was a legitimate effort to break up an "old boy's network," even perhaps to make standards attainable for new entrants. It was not necessarily intentional evisceration.

Anyone directly involved with setting standards has not missed the point that legal definitions of organic do more than affect farming practices; they also substantively influence who can participate in the sector. What have been less obvious—or have, at least, drawn less criticism—are the economic effects of the institutions and conventions developed to operationalize and enforce these definitions, especially insofar as their purpose is to construct financial incentives for organic production. Because of this regulatory framework, no matter how technical and narrow actual definitions of organic are, their import is broad, affecting many aspects of the organization of production beyond farming practices. These include not only farm management, land use, and labor relations but also external economic relationships with suppliers, intermediaries, and consumers, ultimately playing into a larger dynamic of value seeking in the global food economy.

The aim of this chapter is to show how incentive-based regulation has affected the structure and dynamics of the sector and, accordingly, has interfaced with the processes of innovation explored in chapter 4. First, however, the effects of uneven processes of certification, as well as the rules themselves, must be considered in their own terms. This, then, is where the chapter begins—with a more focused look, first, at certifier affiliation, second, at the effects of certification on grower practices, and third, at the effects of certification on entry into the sector. As in chapter 6, some of these findings are now irrelevant; among other things, certifier discretion is being eliminated with the implementation of the federal rule, although I do not expect a radical departure from the trends I describe. Following these discussions, I move on to discuss the effects of organic regulation in terms of structuring the organic sector and interfacing with the wider political economy. For this last purpose, I focus on the organic price premium as a key indicator of shifting power relations within the organic sector.

AFFILIATION

As described in chapter 6, the unique evolution of organic regulatory institutions created a political economy of certification itself, such that certifiers came to trade on competing notions of what *organic* should mean, although their discretion to do so was eventually circumscribed by law and convention, and quite specifically with the implementation of the federal rule in 2002. I have not yet made evident how the strong symbolic content of the certification debates translated into actual affiliations. In practice, patterns of certification were driven more by market considerations than by ideological convictions or were otherwise historically contingent. While many growers undoubtedly have remained with their same certifier since implementation, I have again employed the past tense to illustrate how the uneven regulatory landscape affected affiliations.

It is often assumed, for instance, that not only did certification mark the truly dedicated organic grower but that also CCOF best represented those growers true to the cause. QAI, in juxtaposition to CCOF, was assumed to represent the dilution of organic meanings. Yet, as shown in table 11, mixed growers were more likely to be certified than all-organic growers were, and CCOF had no particular dedication to so-called purists, making it a regular practice to certify mixed growers, as QAI did. The table also makes clear that certification was a virtual certainty for large-scale growers but worked as an option for medium-sized and small growers. In this study, all of the growers with more than $10 million in sales were certified, while only 46.5 percent with sales under $100,000 were certified. This finding is supported by past studies. In 1994–95, certified farms represented fewer than half of all registered farms but accounted for more than 80 percent of the acreage and 90 percent of the value of organic production, a trend that was growing stronger at the time (Klonsky and Tourte 1998b). However, proportional to their total certifications, QAI certified more large growers than CCOF did, which had a significant clientele among small and medium-sized growers.

Up until the implementation of the federal rule, certification decisions were often driven by market considerations. It was usually mandatory for those selling in national and international markets to be certified, a situation that almost always applied to growers with high-volume sales. Since mixed growers were more likely to be involved in organic production at the behest of buyers who sell in national markets, they had to certify to satisfy their marketing contracts. In contrast, growers who did not

TABLE 11. INTERVIEWED GROWERS, BY CERTIFIER, 1998–99

Type	Total N	CCOF		QAI		Dual/Triple		Other		Subtotal		No Certification	
		n	%	n	%	n	%	n	%	n	%	n	%
Mixed	67	39	58.2	9	13.4	8	11.9	4	6.0	60	89.6	7	10.4
All-organic	78	36	46.2	7	9.0	6	7.7	3	3.8	52	66.7	26	33.3
Sales													
<$100,000	43	16	37.2	3	7.0	0	0.0	1	2.3	20	46.5	23	53.5
$100,000–999,999	38	19	50.0	2	5.3	3	7.9	5	13.2	29	76.3	9	23.7
$1,000,000–9,999,999	45	29	64.4	7	15.6	7	15.6	1	2.2	44	97.8	1	2.2
>$10,000,000	19	11	57.9	4	21.1	4	21.1	0	0.0	19	100.0	0	0.0
TOTAL	145	75	51.7	16	11.0	14	9.7	7	4.8	112	77.2	33	22.8

NOTE: Includes only growers who were in the organic program at time of interview. The numbers per certifier differ slightly from table 10 because dual and triple certifications are treated separately here. Again, "no certification" is overstated because of practices of umbrella certification carried out by FVO and QAI. Of the small growers certified by QAI in this table, one was an orange grower who was actually certified under the auspices of a packer.

certify were unaffected by markets that involve certification. Some were too small and sold only at farmers' markets, to local stores, and to restaurants, although there were some farmers' markets (e.g., in Berkeley) in which certification (particularly CCOF certification) gave growers a marketing edge. Some were wine grape growers selling to major wineries, which used organically grown grapes but did not produce organic wines (as we saw previously). Thus, there was little need to certify in that case either.

Contrary to the notion that certification marked the real organic grower, as might have been true before the state law, large-scale and mixed growers gravitated toward certification because it was the only way they *could* establish trust. In interviews, these growers most often framed the advantages of certification in terms of ensuring a level playing field, helping to prevent cheating, and upholding barriers to entry, issues most keenly felt by those at the edges.

Many small all-organic growers, in contrast, worried less that they would be mistaken for something they were not. As such, their dedication led them *not* to be certified. Some felt the costs and hassle of certification to be unequal to the benefits; they did not like the idea of being charged to use the word *organic*, and although many actually followed CCOF guidelines, they objected to supporting a certification bureaucracy for sales that were based on trust. A few characterized certification as a "parasite industry" on growers and claimed they would leave the organic rubric if certification became required under the federal rule. Paradoxically, these quasi-libertarian growers liked high standards but objected to state intervention. A sizable minority claimed they would have preferred government certification that entailed less conflict of interest and manipulation of the rules.

A noticeable geography of certification also existed, paralleling the regional patterns of organic practice discussed in chapter 5 and stylized in table 9. Growers certified with more regularity in the prime agricultural regions, particularly those regions composing the great Central Valley as well as the Central Coast, where crops are grown for major markets. Many of the more marginally situated small-scale growers who sell in local markets declined to certify. Among certified growers, QAI had a much stronger hold in southern California, its base of operations; CCOF's sphere of influence was clearly in the north. Even in the "back-to-the land" regions of northern California (i.e., Cascade-Sierra, the Far North, and the North Coast), where fewer growers certified, those who did almost always chose CCOF.

CCOF's domination of certification continued in the north for three main reasons. The first is historical: they were "the only game in town" for a long time. Other, older certifiers captured growers in certain crops or certain regions on the basis of particular marketing networks, but their overall influence in California was limited. Growers usually had little incentive to change agencies once certified. Such was the case for the typical Central Coast grower described in chapter 5. The second reason for CCOF's dominance is that the organization continued to have social movement connotations, so even growers who increasingly questioned the need to certify at all stayed with CCOF as an act of loyalty to a cause. This was the justification for the typical Solano-Yolo grower. The third reason is that CCOF had the reputation, well-founded or not, of being the most stringent, which even skeptical growers saw as a marketing advantage. The basis of its reputation was rigorous practices. Attention to procedural detail, having a membership base, and organizational transparency were all seen as credibility enhancing. The disciplining effects of enforcement actions were most crucial in this regard. Many growers and CCOF staff spoke of other growers who were decertified by CCOF and then certified by QAI a week later. In fact, new growers were attracted to the CCOF label precisely because it gave them instant credibility.

Nonetheless, QAI's numbers also grew significantly in the 1990s because it catered to a different niche from that of CCOF. Its southern California base provided distance from the northern California counterculture imagery. Its flatter fee structure, discouraging to small growers, encouraged large growers, whose assessment would have been higher with CCOF. The fee structure also involved less hassle for mixed growers, who, with CCOF, had to track their organic sales separately in order to derive assessments. Another reason that growers were attracted to QAI is that they were "treated as customers rather than members," because QAI was ostensibly much more service-oriented and moved more quickly. Finally, they appreciated that QAI took a more hands-off approach to financial and other proprietary information (enabled in part by the flat fee). The West Valley grower of chapter 5 is typical of growers who chose QAI. To hedge their bets, however, many new large growers certified with both QAI and CCOF. They chose QAI to get up and running but simultaneously started the process with CCOF, whose certification they believed ultimately held more meaning in the marketplace.

In some cases, certification status simply reflected commodity-specific business networks. FVO once served as a marketing organization for its growers, with most of its crops destined for the European market. Thus,

FVO, the common certifier of East Valley growers, was involved only in certain crops in California: mainly raisins, prunes, and almonds, that is, nonperishable produce that could be shipped to Europe. Strangely, FVO's farming principles regarding rotational systems were largely inapplicable to the very crops in which FVO involved itself. As for FVO's growers, many were concerned about the pressure from FVO's European market not to allow mixed operations and to require "social" standards in accordance with IFOAM. OCIA, one of the largest certifiers internationally, also had a limited presence in California, mainly connected to the rice-growing region of the Sacramento Valley. This, too, was historical, related to the early entrant Lundberg Family Farms and the network of rice growers with whom they contracted. Its debarred chapter, COFA, was active primarily on the east side of the Central Valley. Like FVO, those growers who maintained OCIA certification in California almost always did so in addition to another certification.

Finally, some growers less connected to the old symbols of organic farming chose to affiliate with certifiers that offered different interpretations of organic production (to the extent that the law allowed). Those that were drawn to the other, newer agencies, SCS and OC, were particularly motivated by food-safety issues—indeed, seeing them as the essence of organic—as well as the more "scientific" approach to certification.[1] As one grower put it, "NutriClean certifies authenticity of process; FVO certifies lifestyle." So even though growers' affiliation with certain certifiers was largely a marketing decision, it was also where they contested and negotiated organic meanings.

PRACTICES

The variegated landscape of certifier affiliation raises the question of the effectiveness of these institutions in enforcing the rules. Did they encourage growers to incorporate agroecological principles and ensure integrity? Did it matter with whom growers certified or if they certified at all? Again, although it is likely that past certifier affiliation affects practices into the present, I employ the past tense to emphasize that the entire regulatory structure has shifted with implementation of the federal rule.

The materials list, although "not a recipe for organic farming" (CCOF 1998b, 49), nevertheless provided minimum standards for organic crop production. Despite all the controversy surrounding it, many growers admitted in interviews that the list provided a definitive guideline for what they did in their production system. True to its intent, the materials list set a floor of allowable practices. Inspectors—referred to by one grower as the "input police"—seemed to do the job of keeping growers in line, too. For even the disciplining effects of inspections tended to enforce cultural norms. Moreover, many uncertified growers went by CCOF's list, extending its impact far beyond CCOF member growers, arguably a positive free-rider effect.

The more unexpected consequence of this sort of regulation was that it also created ceilings. No doubt the more all-encompassing agroecological ideal is hard to meet, especially with certain cropping systems, but the materials list made it that much easier to do the minimum, as we saw in chapter 3. Newly converted growers found allowable substitutes for materials normally used in conventional production. Even committed organic growers looked to the handbook in a pinch and used a material they may not otherwise have considered. More profound, the handbook/materials list served as the norm for organic. Enhancement is easier said than done, especially when there is no external imperative for it.

Table 12 makes the existence of ceilings and floors clearer. It distributes the agroecological coding described in chapter 3 according to certification status. As seen in the table, pre–federal rule certification kept people from cheating (or at least from admitting to it) in that there were no 0 ratings among certified growers. By the same token, the only growers who received a 5 were either not certified at all or were certified by the Demeter Association, a biodynamic certifier that is not recognized as organic. Many growers with 4 ratings were also not certified. Among certified growers, practices remained input-oriented, meaning that process- and design-oriented controls were incorporated to only a modest extent. It is also worth noting that the proportions of growers within each rating group showed remarkable parallelism between certification through CCOF and through QAI, contrary to prevailing mythology. Those who obtained dual or triple certification tended to receive 2 ratings, which suggests that additional certification was never evidence of trying harder. Certification, in short, tended to have a middling effect.

Why is this so? First of all, a process orientation to farming was never codified, precisely because it is difficult to set standards for processes. For example, cover cropping and composting, the two keys to organic soil management and fertility, were highly recommended but not strictly enforced. There were no particular incentives for making one's own compost, and many growers relied on external sources of fertility. Similarly, CCOF claimed to require rotations for annual crops; however, the organization's loose definition of this allowed for the growth of native

TABLE 12. INTERVIEWED GROWERS, BY CERTIFIER AND AGROECOLOGICAL ASSESSMENT, 1998–99

| | Certification | | | | | | | | | | |
| | CCOF | | QAI | | Dual | | Other | | Any | | None | |
Rating	n	%	n	%	n	%	n	%	n	%	n	%
0	0	0.0	0	0.0	0	0.0	0	0.0	0	0.0	1	3.0
1	8	10.7	2	12.5	0	0.0	0	0.0	10	9.0	1	3.0
2	28	37.3	7	43.8	10	76.9	4	57.1	49	44.1	11	33.3
3	25	33.3	4	25.0	2	15.4	2	28.6	33	29.7	10	30.3
4	14	18.7	3	18.8	1	7.7	0	0.0	18	16.2	7	21.2
5	0	0.0	0	0.0	0	0.0	1	14.3	1	0.9	3	9.1
TOTAL GROWERS OBSERVED	75	100.0	16	100.0	13	100.0	7	100.0	111	100.0	33	100.0

species during fallow periods or simply a shift of crops for the next growing season, a practice followed by most conventional growers too. In
terms of insect pest management, the use of soaps, oils, garlic, and *Bt* was
perfectly acceptable, even though their use arguably signals a system out
of balance. Since these are narrow-spectrum controls, the main effect of
their approbation was a wait-and-see, as opposed to a prophylactic, approach to pest management.

The farm plan required by all certifiers served as a proxy for judging
process, but certifiers relied fundamentally on inspectors' judgments of
growers' intent. At best, mixed growers complained of inspectors has-
sling them about the absence of certain practices, but no one was decertified for failing to plant a cover crop. In fact, most agencies admittedly
certified farms with some deficiencies in their practices, holding to an
ideal of *improvement* as the crux of organic agriculture (Fetter 1999).
Most decertifications were only for intentional use of prohibited substances or inadequate segregation of organic crops and materials from
nonorganic ones. Even then, if the situation was handled astutely, a
grower could simply withdraw the affected parcel from the program for
three years.

Second, certification tended to have a middling effect because the idea
of restricted (or "regulated") materials sent an ambiguous message, and
certifiers had the option of granting exceptions when unrestricted materials were not commercially available. For their part, growers who used
restricted materials were from across the ideological spectrum. For instance, one of the most popular mulches among all sorts of growers was
black plastic. Many growers used botanical pesticides as well, although,
in some cases, the cost of these pesticides was so prohibitive that they
were most favored by small-scale farms selling high-value products. Generally, growers (and their certifiers) justified the use of restricted substances by arguing that a given substance was absolutely necessary for a
particular crop, or in a particular region, or for a particular period.
Those who defended sodium nitrate, for instance, tended to grow winter crops or apply it during the three-year transition period, which they
likened to purgatory. Many defended restricted materials for cosmetic
results, without which crops would not be accepted in certain markets.

Third, certifiers for the most part accepted arguments that dependence
on particular inputs resulted from so-called technology barriers. Some
crops are simply hard to grow organically, especially when allowable inputs have yet to be found for seemingly intractable pests. Weed control,
for instance, is considered one of the biggest obstacles to conversion to

organic production, especially with field crops, which are otherwise mechanically managed and harvested. Many growers who would otherwise convert do not want to forgo their use of Roundup. Of course, this attitude about the necessity of certain materials is a common defense against all sorts of regulation and has allowed the continuation of many so-called hard pesticides past their regulatory due, methyl bromide being the best example. The basic problem here is that farmers come to depend on usable "tools," and they are differentially available for various crops. Specialty crops get less attention from agricultural research, and the lack of funds for organic research is even more glaring (Lipson 1997). Yet (as explained in reference to herbicidal soaps), "just because weeds are a tough problem for many growers, it doesn't mean that we should allow a material which offers an easy way out of the problem when practices for weed management can provide adequate control if used properly and conscientiously" (OMRI 1998, 15). In other words, not all quarters hold that difficulty is an adequate excuse for failure to meet agroecological goals; indeed, many think that organic regulation should presumably be "technology-forcing."

Nevertheless, in actuality tools were evaluated according to the basic organic criteria in uneven and politicized ways. This was illustrated in the previous chapter by the fight over sodium nitrate. There are many other examples: Without synthetic pheromone disruption for the coddling moth, pome fruits and walnuts would have been very difficult to grow organically and, at the very least, could not meet fresh-market cosmetic standards.[2] Copper-based Bordeaux mixes likewise have facilitated organic stone fruit production, and sulfur has made grapes by far the highest-volume organic crop in California. In contrast, the absence of usable controls for, say, the plume moth in artichokes meant that there were few organic artichokes until a seeded variety was introduced in the late 1990s. Likewise, strawberries were seen as impossible to produce organically until growers started experimenting with various plastic mulches and crop rotations (and farming away from the main strawberry regions). Meanwhile, avocados, which are evergreens that need formidable nutrition in the dead of winter, were often sold as "pesticide free" by growers who did not want to forgo commercial fertilizers.

A fourth reason certification tended to be less than wholly effective in radically altering farming practices is that the practices not explicitly addressed in the regulations were simply not addressed on the farm. As the clearest example, water conservation was never considered part of organic farming, so growers rarely implemented water conservation measures unless they had other economic or philosophical reasons to do so. The exceptions were growers who installed drip irrigation because it happens to work well for weed control. Likewise, the absence of regulations regarding local marketing meant that even the most committed growers sold produce to large handlers when a good price came around, albeit often with sheepish regret.

Finally, and most unfortunate, rule-based standards elicited practices deliberately designed to circumvent the regulations. I was told of two examples of such circumvention that had been contemplated but presumably not tried. One was to use a prohibited insect-attracting substance outside of the boundary of the organic field; the other was to rotate crops in and out of organic production to maximize market opportunity and optimal growing conditions. Although these sorts of practices were considered "not in the spirit of organic," they were not grounds for decertification per se. In fact, the application of methyl bromide to clean out fields before beginning the three-year transition to organic production is a practice not in the spirit of organic, yet Pavich Family Farms (among others) were known to have engaged in this practice without reproof. But a neophyte grower had his entire operation decertified for using a disallowed substance in one field, although he claimed no intention of selling that particular crop as organic. This last example suggests that enforcement of standards was indeed dependent on the clout or longevity of the grower in question, exactly why certification was increasingly viewed by state and federal regulators as arbitrary and capricious.

ENTRY

At the same time that organic rules were regularizing the practices of organic agriculture, albeit in highly politicized ways, they were also limiting who could participate and on what terms. The disallowance of efficacious inputs acted as a powerful disincentive to organic production, as did processes intrinsic to certification (and state registration), including fees and compliance costs, bureaucratic hassles, and unusual levels of surveillance. Growers of all sorts were keenly aware of these barriers, and many supplements and additions to the regulations were inventions of those already in the fray, including the phasing out of several materials.

As a barrier to entry, the most important amendment to organic regulation was the establishment of a required transition period to organic production and then its extension to three years, both of which were devised by already existing CCOF organic growers. Crops were prohibited from being harvested and sold as organic unless one year, and then three years, had passed since the last disallowed substance was applied to the land on which they were grown. During these three years, many growers operate on a lower margin or even a loss; yields generally decline because the fields "go into shock," as some put it, at the same time that crops had to be sold at conventional prices.[3] The stated purpose of extending the transition was to minimize toxic residues in the soil, it was widely understood that it also prevented rapid entry into the organic market by those who sought "to make a fast killing." In that way, it was also intended to reduce fraud, for many violations of the rules were made by growers who quickly entered and exited without ever fully learning what organic means.

The progressive lengthening of the transition period clearly worked to the advantage of longer-term participants. Many of the original organic growers started their farms on what was once pasture and never had to undergo a transition. More recent entrants had to convert already existing operations. When CCOF standards for transition were more lax, growers were able to finesse an organic designation after one crop cycle. Another subset of this last group initiated their organic program at the inception of the state program, when only a one-year transition was required for registration with the state, in anticipation that they would be certified after three years. So it is primarily growers who started to farm organically after 1996, when the state began to require a three-year transition to match the practice of certifiers, who were most stymied by the transition period.

Still, like the other rules, the transition period was subject to a good deal of manipulation, so that few actually suffered the costs of a three-year investment. Perennial crop growers, for example, saw no incremental costs if their trees and vines were young or planted anew; they would not come into production until the three-year period was long past. For this reason, many growers timed their entry into organic production to when they were removing old rootstock, changing varietals, or shifting from annuals to perennials. The decision of row-crop growers to produce organically, especially large-scale conventional growers, was often predicated on finding an available piece of land. Many chose previously fallow or abandoned land for their organic operation as a way to avoid the three-year transition. Some were able to start on federal Conservation Reserve land when restrictions on that land were first removed in 1996.[4] Of the growers interviewed in this study, mixed growers took advantage of that option far more often than all-organic growers.[5] In short, the most salient effect of the three-year requirement was aberrant entry into the sector.

Fortified barriers to entry contributed to more than rule bending; a far more troubling concern was the mixed signals they sent regarding growth in the organic sector. This is best illustrated by a latter-day battle within CCOF over certifying land in Mexico. Until the late 1990s, CCOF positioned itself as a membership organization that served only California growers and processors (CCOF 1994b; cf. CCOF 1998a). Given CCOF's early preeminence on the national stage, this effectively acted as a barrier to entry in its own right. When several of the organization's most prominent growers expanded their operations into Mexico and demanded that CCOF certify land there, other growers were justifiably fearful of the competition this would bring and wanted to bar such activities. Yet, they based their argument on the rather hollow claim that such certification would be inconsistent with other rules, since CCOF required that growers be registered with the state of California and no Mexican grower could be. In rebuttal, growers in favor noted that such expansion would not create more competition among growers in California, because Mexico supplies off-season produce. Plus, they argued, having more organic food in the marketplace year round would be good for everyone, because it would effectively heighten awareness and demand.

In other words, those defending barriers framed the issue as ensuring organic integrity; those who sided for lower entry barriers framed it as expanding the organic market. Underlying this ideological tussle, then, was the recognition that upholding an organic price premium and expanding market share are not always compatible goals. This fundamental tension between holding organic principles dear and "feeding the world" became explosive by the late 1990s, a product of the regulatory battles and the changing economic dynamics of the organic sector.

FARMING STRUCTURE

Virtually all aspects of organic regulation have had some implications for the structure of the sector, although not all have been intended to. Some of the clearest impacts arose from the nonsubstantive procedures and policies of certification before implementation of the federal rule. For instance, the costs of registration and certification in general favored large-scale growers, especially after CCOF imposed its assessment cap. Since growers were assessed at ½ of 1 percent of sales, and the maximum assessment was $15,000 annually, growers earning over $3 million were exempt from further assessments. While most of the very largest operators handled other growers' products, it was not unusual for them to have $10–20 million of their own sales, so the assessment cap gave them a huge break on their costs. Although CCOF had an exemption from assessment for growers earning less than $20,000 in organic sales, this effectively favored only part-time growers and the many growers dabbling in organic. QAI favored large growers even more with its flat-fee assessments. Fees for state registration were also prorated by sales and ranged from $25 to $2,000, where they were capped for growers making over $5 million. Consequently, midsized growers, the very ones who were attempting to make a livelihood from organic production, paid disproportionately more for certification and registration. This fee structure may have contributed to the bifurcation that characterizes the sector. Although the federal rule makes no stipulation regarding certification fees, as certification practices become harmonized it is likely that fees will too.

Conversely, many growers felt that the implicit purpose of CCOF certification was to discourage larger-scale farmers. There is some truth to this. If organic regulation was as process-oriented as it was intended to be—that is, if it were able to enforce on-farm compost production, diverse cropping patterns, and so forth—the management requirements could be prohibitive to large-scale operations. Growers who had left the program felt they had been pressured to conform to this ideal. And, as we have seen, there are ways in which the idioms of organic, as expressed, for example, through inspectors' attire and attitudes, acted as cultural barriers. But, in practice, an input orientation (and good humor) erased many of those barriers.

Though politically contested, the allowability of mixed operations also has affected the structure of the sector. It bears repeating that IFOAM discouraged mixed operations. OCIA claimed to require whole-farm conversion within five years of beginning the program, and QAI, FVO, and Organic Growers and Buyers Association (COGBA) claimed to encourage it, but CCOF made no stipulations in this regard.[6] Ideological concerns aside, in the interest of maintaining the integrity of an organic product, skepticism toward mixed operations is well founded. It stands to reason that those with mixed operations are asked to pay careful attention to buffer zones and boundaries, clean out equipment after use of prohibited substances, and maintain separate storage facilities for their inputs. Most certifiers also required extra paperwork, and CCOF disallowed an inactive status for mixed growers when they were not growing an organic crop. A couple of major mixed growers left the organic program and reverted to all conventional because of the difficulties of being a mixed operation.

Mixed operations were finally allowed on the supposition that it would be economic suicide to transition an entire (large) operation all at once, and it would be unconscionable to discourage people from trying a little at a time. Yet, as a rule, mixed growers have not converted piece by piece. In fact, many mixed operations continue to straddle the organic-conventional divide on the basis of market demand and crop specificities. In regard to the latter, many growers are mixed on the basis of what they *can* grow organically. The organic production of crops such as onions and garlic, processing tomatoes, and salad mix components is scarcely different from their conventional production (which is to say that interviewed growers who had eliminated a disallowed control did not see significant losses). Thus, it is common for the largest of vegetable growers to start with these and more cautiously move into head lettuces and carrots but steer clear of celery, for instance. Equally common are growers who produce fresh-market crops conventionally and sell their organic crops to the processing market. One grower went so far as to say that growers, not the land itself, should be certified, so that a mixed operation like his could rotate conventional cotton with organic melon!

Another structural aspect of organic regulation that clearly continues with the federal rule is its near presumption of landownership. Requirements such as the transition period, land history documentation, and the need to control the land to prevent application of prohibited substances favor landownership or secure long-term tenure. The idea that organic production is most successful when there is long-term investment in the soil certainly adds to the sense in which land ownership creates an advantage.

Yet, in areas with encroaching real estate development, land with long-term assurances is simply lacking. Many interviewed tenant farmers felt all too susceptible to landlords' whims, fearing that landlords would not renew leases, raise the rent, or take over if production went well, all of which have occurred in the relatively short-lived organic sector. In fact, for many of these growers, farming on leased land was one of the main obstacles to starting or expanding their organic program, suggesting that the rules of organic have been, in one important sense, incompatible with the existing structure of land tenure in California. The tentativeness and perversity of some of the situations where marginal land has been brought into leasing arrangements drive home the point.

Given the geography of land tenure in California, the ownership presumption has also strongly favored certain classes of growers. For one, it favors those who have bought land in the interstitial spaces that were previously not in production; many of these are gentleman farmers. Longer-term growers situated in agricultural zones where leasing is predominant, which include some of the best agricultural land in California, have been at a distinct disadvantage. Given some fairly intransigent racial barriers to landownership, the presumption has also worked as a racialized exclusion from organic production, one of the reasons that many small farmers of non-European origin sell their produce as "pesticide free," not organic. Still, the insecurity of tenancy has been more a problem for small tenants; large growers tend to have a combination of leased and owned land, and many of them have chosen to do organic production on the land they own.

Finally, by informing what crops and cropping patterns are more amenable to organic production, the input emphasis of organic regulation has had the strongest influence on the structure (and scope) of the sector. That there is far more grape acreage than any other organic crop in California is an uncontested consequence of the permissibility of sulfur dust. The less acknowledged point is that input substitution has allowed growers to bring with them the structural conditions and social competencies of preexisting commodity networks when they have converted to organic production. Many grape growers are long-time owners of their land, which tends to be held in midsized parcels. Because of the short harvest season (and the political construction of farm labor relations), they also tend to use labor contractors. As a result, these growers have brought the presumption of secure tenure coupled with vulnerable labor to the politics of organic production.

The effects of allowing the controversial fertilizer sodium nitrate provide a separate example. Arguably, sodium nitrate has been instrumental in the consolidation of the organic salad mix market. Although salad mix was once a premier product of smaller growers, effectively they have been competed (and regulated) out of this business. Consolidators such as Earthbound Farms/Natural Selection increasingly contracted with conventional growers who have off-season operations in the desert valleys and have relied on sodium nitrate to jump-start their organic operations. Having arrangements with southern California contractors gave the consolidators a significant marketing edge, enabling them to be in the market year round.

Their edge was furthered by an incident in Hollister, where sixty-one out-of-state illnesses were linked to bagged organic lettuce tainted with *E. coli* O157.H7 (*Food Chemical News* 1998). This, along with other food safety concerns, brought increased surveillance by county agricultural commissioners and health inspectors. In response, CCOF eased restrictions on chlorine use. In addition, growers were forced to upgrade the light processing involved (e.g., mixing, washing, spin drying, bagging), bestowing the industry leaders with scale advantages. Thereafter, several small producers pulled out of the salad mix market, leaving this most lucrative of organic commodities to the largest operators—a consequence of regulation in several senses.

THE PRICE PREMIUM

While organic regulation has had important effects on the organic sector qua regulation by circumscribing how producers behave, its most dramatic ramification is its particular intersection with processes of valorization in the wider political economy. That is, if organic growers were to realize market prices that cover only the direct costs of certification, registration, and the amortization of the three-year transition, there would be no short-term *economic* reason to enter into organic production. But, as we have seen, the underlying purpose of defining organic in the way it has been is to provide a *financial incentive* for it, or, put another way, to create and uphold a price premium. The question, then, is how that price premium has fared with such rapid growth and change in the organic sector. Before we begin that discussion, though, it is important to analyze the different elements of the price premium.

Costs

Some advocates of organic farming argue that the price premium simply reimburses the incremental costs of farming in accordance with organic standards. Organic food necessarily costs more to grow because organic regulations have the effect of internalizing the costs that have been progressively externalized with modern farming (Lampkin and Padel 1994; Jackson 1990). Or, to put it in the analytic terms of environmental economics, the low costs for conventionally grown food are an example of the market failure that occurs when firms take into account only the market price of a resource (or a material input) when deciding how much to use (Turner, Pearce, and Bateman 1993). If all externalities were imputed into the costs of conventional agriculture (e.g., failed salmon runs, toxic cleanup, public health effects), so the theory goes, organic food would seem a relative bargain. If nothing else, this approach points to the massive subsidy that conventional agriculture receives from nature, mediated by the state.

Grimmway Enterprises' experience with organic production illustrates that it may indeed entail internalization of costs. Managers at Grimmway, which specializes in carrots, were stymied about how to rotate their organic land. Their conventional land was leased out during the years they were not growing carrots, but they could not risk the inherent loss of control with their certified organic land. In the context of their usual mode of operation, a single-crop system, organic appeared not to be profitable after all, since they had to factor in the cost of idle land or a rotation of barley every three years, compared with the revenue of a lease out.[7] One of the reasons they contracted out twenty thousand of their forty thousand acres of total production—or, as they called it, "grew on a cooperative basis"—was to avoid such costs to capital.

Sweet potato production in Merced County, where most California sweet potatoes are grown, provides an even better example. Rather than integrate a rotation crop, conventional growers typically lease ground for two or three seasons, fumigate it with methyl bromide between plantings, and move on to another parcel when the land is used up. Growers in this area who were experimenting with organic production did not wholly alter this pattern. They found land to lease that was previously fallow, had it certified immediately, squeezed out two or three seasons of sweet potato production, then let it go when problems of overuse and disease inevitably arose. Although one has to question how this fallow land is so routinely available in this particular area—it is unclear who is leasing in the rotation period and what they are growing—the irony of this single-crop production system is that growers were financially better off leasing land and letting it go than managing it back to health. Only one interviewed grower in that area had given the problem any careful consideration. Having been in the organic program the longest, he had been fallowing land regularly between sweet potato crops, even leased land. When land prices became too costly (capitalized on the high value of sweet potatoes), he tried to keep going without fallowing, using, for example, biological controls, solarization, and humus treatments to cleanse the soil of nematodes. His costs rose accordingly, but he remained with a one-crop rotation.

For many crops, however, organic production is not necessarily more costly, at least with current practices.[8] With an input substitution strategy, the cost differential between organic and conventional production boils down to the cost of the inputs themselves. In some cases, organic inputs are more expensive. For example, some of the new designer inputs (e.g., microbiological products) are priced to recoup the costs of research and development. The cost of purchasing and hauling custom-made compost can be very high compared with applications of commercial fertilizers, thus is particularly a problem with evergreen orchards, which need fertilizer in the heart of winter. If rain is scarce, the cost of a cover crop seems equally exorbitant, because growers pay for water on top of the cost of purchasing seeds and managing what is effectively another crop. Even postharvest handling can create additional costs. Many conventionally grown crops destined for storage are fumigated with methyl bromide after harvest (including sweet potatoes, dates, raisins) to kill insects and their larvae; organic packers must freeze these crops instead, which contributes to much higher energy costs. All that said, most growers find that they save money on pest control inputs, either because the requisite organic inputs are cheaper or because they find they can make do with less intervention than they previously imagined.

In the absence of efficacious purchased inputs, labor substitutes for materials, driving up costs in another way (despite what other social benefits labor-intensive production might entail). For example, in almost all cases where weeds present a problem, organic production is more costly because of the labor involved in hand and mechanical weeding. For a few crops, alternative pest controls can be expensive to purchase *and* labor intensive. Pheromone traps and ties for apples and walnuts must be fastened to trees and visually inspected. Likewise, organic fungicides (e.g., sulfur, copper) used on deciduous fruits require multiple trips through a field and individual applications. With organic dates, growers tie sacks around date bunches to keep insects out. In the most extreme case, some growers remove problem insects by hand, a solution possible only on a very small scale. Biointensive cropping strategies (i.e., polycultures) are almost always labor intensive, although some of the costs are hidden by the farmer's self-exploitation.[9]

With fewer material inputs allowable, organic production can also involve slower and/or more uneven biological production. In crop production, this is often measured as yield, a catch-all term for the number of units harvested, size per unit, and tonnage. Newer growers, especially, complain of decreased volume yields with organic production. Some of that is related to the shock of input withdrawal, especially because many cultivars are developed specifically to be used with certain inputs, and growers sometimes stay with these same cultivars after switching to organic production (Shennan et al. 1991). Yet, most of those who stay the course notice that yields eventually return to an acceptable level or even surpass what they once were in conventional production. One mixed grower who was hardly an advocate of organic farming said that his organic carrot yields surpassed those of conventional production from the beginning, because of the fertility program alone. Of significant note, those interviewed growers who complained most of diminished (volume) yields started their organic programs on marginal land, to avoid the costs of transition. One almond grower began with an orchard that was already past its productive prime so that he would face less risk of diminishing yields—a catch-22 if there ever was one! Most commonly, new growers said that yields become more volatile with organic production, no doubt because it forces them to relinquish some mastery of nature.

Besides leaving growers with less of a crop to sell, uneven or reduced yields can impose other costs (despite systematic overproduction). For instance, a mixed grower of fresh tomatoes found that harvest costs were much higher with organic production. Because fresh varietals do not ripen at the same time, picking crews had to go through a field five or six times, whereas a conventional field could be picked in one or two sweeps, because green tomatoes could later be "ripened" with ethylene gas. Likewise, a strawberry grower had to pay pickers twice as much per box because there was less fruit in the fields and it took twice as long to fill a box. Conversely, one grower claimed that it was the philosophy of delivering quality fruits that motivated him to spend more on picking and packing than "any conventional guy would tolerate," making his per unit costs 30–40 percent higher.

Cull rates, then, which are clearly socially prescribed, seem to be the most critical factor affecting yields. For instance, growers needing to meet marketing order standards either for size and/or blemishes have much higher cull rates and thus lower yields. In this vein, one grower purposely kept his organic fields to just under twenty acres so that a marketing order would not apply. As a result, his cull rates were higher in conventional farming, where he did have to meet marketing order standards. Cull rates otherwise depend on marketing venue, with wholesale having the most stringent standards and farmers' markets and on-farm sales offering a much more lax sales environment, in which growers can "educate" buyers about the constraints of organic production. Farmers who were organic by neglect had the poorest yields, often because they had very high cull rates.

In sum, for some commodities, organic production necessitates a less intensive use of land, slower and/or more uneven biological production (particularly in the case of livestock), and the substitute of labor for inputs. When the price premium makes up for these higher costs and lower yields, that premium is plainly due compensation. For other, "easy" commodities, it seems like a nice bonus, although the so-called laws of supply and demand seem to be leveling this particular playing field. Still, to be a consistent incentive for organic production, the price premium must do more than compensate costs.

Rent

As alluded to in chapter 4, the portion of the price premium that does not go to costs is by definition an economic rent, an additional return above and beyond costs and a "normal" rate of return. This rent is a function of both market availability related to difficulty in growing (scarcity rents) and consumer meanings (so-called consumer surplus). Both aspects crucially depend on maintaining quasi-monopoly conditions through the vehicle of regulation, to restrict supply and to keep prices up. Barriers to entry are in that way a necessity for incentive-based regulation. It follows that organic regulatory institutions were designed in part to erect these barriers to entry. Let me be perfectly clear on this point: While there might have been good agronomic reasons for amending organic regulations, there was always an element of self-protection among existing growers in making it tougher to be a new organic grower.

To create scarcity, regulations not only erect barriers to entry; they also constrain substitutes. To that end, many states' organic regulations and the first proposed federal ones restricted the use of terms such as *naturally grown, ecologically grown,* and *biologically grown.* Owing to much opposition in the face of a potentially weak standard (an irony, given that the organic industry originally wanted to limit substitutes), these prohibitions were removed in the final version. As stated in the rule, "These phrases may be used as additional eco-labels, provided they are truthful labeling statements." Nevertheless, "they are not permitted as replacements for the term 'organic' " (United States Department of Agriculture 2001).

To generate consumer surplus, regulations must do the discursive work of convincing buyers that the product they receive is valuable. In other words, they must impart symbolic use value beyond the material use value of organic food as sustenance. Organic farming's entry barriers are clearly somewhat permeable; the true success of organic regulation has been in valorizing the organic commodity. Not only does the organic designation inform consumers that organic food may be safer and/or environmentally protective—characterizations that arguably have an empirical basis—it also inscribes significance in areas where organic falls short: from saving the family farm, to providing a better working environment, to provisioning whole and/or more nutritious food. In this case, having a social movement behind the development of regulation bestows much more meaning and durability to the term *organically grown* than a brand name might. The baroqueness of the regulations themselves only lends further credibility, making consumer trust the basis of rent.

In this and many other respects, the existence of rent presents a major normative quandary vis-à-vis the underlying goals of organic production. On the one hand, it can provide some economic space to remunerate the "real" social and ecological costs of growing food. At the very least, this rent has allowed small-scale producers to prosper in otherwise inhospitable markets. On the other hand, it is based on legally constructed barriers to entry and socially constructed preciousness, hardly a recipe for the spread of sustainable agriculture.

While there is much to criticize about cultural expectations of cheap food, the rent portion of the price premium first and foremost depends on the construction of organic food as a niche market. It is broadly recognized that organic food is disproportionately chosen by affluent consumers, although the web of causality is hard to untangle precisely because of the economic rents involved. In other words, is the "choice" of organic food limited to affluent buyers because it is more expensive, or is it more expensive because affluent buyers will choose it? Even a cursory observation of the history of a commodity such as salad mix points to the latter. Even when retail prices dropped substantially, salad mix retained the gentrified status it had acquired through the restaurant trade (although in the process lost its identity as a necessarily *organic* commodity) (see Guthman 2003). As wholesale prices for other organic commodities have dropped or were never high to begin with, retail prices remain high, suggesting that retailers are able to play on this same presumption. Either way, the result is that good food and meaningful food choices are available only to the well off (DeLind 1993, 7).

That said, positioning organic food as "an option for the rich and neurotic" (Clunies-Ross 1990b, 262) was not entirely the responsibility of the food industry or even the "yuppie" restaurants that featured organic vegetables on menus. It must be recognized that this positioning was an inevitable result of an incentive approach to regulation and ultimately was the basis of federal support, however begrudging, for an organic standard. This latter point was made all too clear in 1997, when former secretary of agriculture Dan Glickman announced the release of the proposed rules, couching them in terms of giving consumers "freedom of choice" and providing a niche market for financially strapped farmers. This stance allows organic food to be grown and sold alongside conventional food without disparaging the rest of the food supply that the federal government must stand behind (Clunies-Ross and Cox 1994).

Unfortunately, the problems with rent do not stop there. Since rents are the more ephemeral portion of profits, they are inherently dynamic, potentially shifted to other actors in systems of provision or eliminated altogether in periods of intense competition. They can also be capitalized into land values. As a consequence, not only are rents a dubious basis of small-farm viability; they also instantiate the mechanisms by which all growers are pushed to intensify land and labor productivity.

WHITHER THE PRICE PREMIUM

As we saw in chapter 2, much of the growth in organic production has been driven by producers seeking more value relative to the land they farm. In other words, promises of premium prices are the major draw for many new growers. Yet, aside from those that circumvent the investment of transition, most interviewed growers said that as time marches on, organic prices cover differentials in costs and yields at best—a tendency that is in accordance with microeconomic theory.

In some areas and crops, growers claimed that organic production was not profitable at all but meant the difference between a total loss and a marginal economic return. Since much of the cost is intrinsic to picking and packing, the "return to field" improves with just a small price increase. In San Diego County, for example, citrus growing was generally a money loser (unless the rest of the state experiences a freeze, as happened in the winter of 1999). The only way to make any money, growers said, was to find cheaper access to water (i.e., illegal appropriations of runoff), do one's own marketing, and/or own the land free and clear—hardly a replicable small-farm survival strategy. Growers who sold through the packers did little, if anything, to farm organically that they would not do otherwise and probably would not have marketed their fruit if not for these packers; so the pennies they received for any given orange were still a positive return on almost no investment.

More often, growers expressed the economic problem as one of greater price volatility. One walnut grower said that premiums fluctuated between 8 and 50 percent, although in this case the high end of the premiums had most to do with the below-cost prices of conventional walnuts. A sweet potato grower saw no premium one year and thus sold his organic on the conventional market but the following year saw a 40 percent premium. A mixed grower of vegetables summed it best, "With organic, you can hit a home run on one crop and have a disaster on another," but he also admitted that his profit margins on conventional productions averaged about half of those of organic (before amortizing the three-year transition). In these instances, the apparent problem is that the organic market is much more vulnerable to short-term flooding than the conventional one because of its much smaller absolute size. If growers increase production, they can ruin their own market, many say, and when larger growers with larger volumes come in, they "blow the bottom out of the market." Many organic crops end up being sold as conventional for this reason (thus avoiding certification assessments), which some said is "trashing the market." It is this sort of activity that caused some mixed growers to either give up on organic production or do it only on a fixed-price contract.

By most accounts, it is the superprofits—the economic rents—that have gradually eroded. One of the foremost pioneers in the salad mix market speculated that the widely circulated rumors about returns of $35 per pound or $100,000 per acre for mesclun, which drew so many into organic salad mix production, never existed in the first place. "Countercultural economics," as he called it, "was based on heavily extrapolated data and ultimately did a huge disservice to the sector." But what is more frightening, he said, is that organic prices merged with conventional ones, without any reductions in cost. As he put it, "Salad mix has become a commodity." So where margins used to be 25–30 percent, growers were losing money, except in the distribution end. Again, many of the early salad mix innovators exited that market in the wake of the big Salinas growers' entry into it and the rapid expansion of Earthbound Farms/Natural Selection.[10] Well-entrenched medium-sized organic growers in other crops were similarly faced with serious price competition.

From the perspective of the large organic grower-shippers, this trend was inevitable, representing the maturation of the industry, which now seeks market share rather than premiums. According to one representative, "The one- to five-acre farms throughout the state will soon be a thing of the past" as organic prices near conventional ones. The only way these small farms will survive, he said, "is to develop alliances with sales companies and live up to what they say." Although this company representative was prone to hyperbole, the industry is clearly consolidating, although it is doubtful whether these microfarms (other than the orchards) to which he made reference will ever be substantially subsumed by large buyers. But it is true that with increased price competition, what were once the most successful organic farms, particularly those specializing in salad mix, have had to develop new strategies to stay afloat, as rent has been displaced elsewhere in the chain of provision or whittled away completely.

How were the smaller growers I interviewed responding to this changing climate? Some were, in fact, starting to sell to larger grower-shippers in the spot market, because the latter occasionally face supply shortfalls of certain commodities, especially when their newly converted suppliers find that they do not have the requisite technical knowledge. Among themselves, many such growers have done what they call co-opetition: they share equipment and ideas and even trade commodities, though they continue to sell independently. Some smaller growers were reconsidering cooperative marketing, although the direct marketing laws (upon which they vitally depend) discourage growers from selling one another's produce. Mostly, growers were seeking new ways to fortify economic rents by growing food that is hard to grow industrially (and constructing desire around them) and by looking to go "beyond organic."

In and of itself, organic agriculture is hardly a formulaic solution. It works well only when consumer meanings are well coupled with scarcity. Thus, at the time of the interviews, the highest-value organic products (in the sense that they generate rent) were the ones that posed the most significant challenges. These included stone fruits, artichokes, strawberries, avocados, fresh apples, and sweet corn. Most organic stone fruits, for instance, were grown by small to medium-sized operators who could give considerable field attention to problems such as brown rot, which can be alleviated with painstaking minimal applications of copper. At the time, growers who were successfully growing such crops often saw price premiums well over 100 percent of the conventional price, much higher than for other organic commodities. In contrast, there was no effective organic treatment for the corn borer found in sweet corn. Organic growers who were producing this highly desirable summer crop had high cull rates or were otherwise put in the position of having to train their customers to accept noticeable insect damage. Thus, most of the organic sweet corn found in direct-market venues has been dependent on close relationships between buyer and seller.

Growers who have been willing to give the intense care required to grow these crops organically have been able to forge a livelihood on as little as five acres of land, but these small to midsized growers have depended on economic rents for their survival. To stay ahead of the game, they often have diversified into yet-to-be commercialized crops, occasionally introduced by high-end restaurants. Salad mix was once such a crop, but it is no longer. At the time of my study, strawberries, which face formidable overproduction in conventional agriculture, were still realizing premiums when produced organically, but such premiums were dropping. In a particularly unusual case, a group of growers in the Far North region farmed organic botanical herbs, which they marketed cooperatively.[11] Whereas hay, the usual crop grown there, grossed a hundred dollars per ton, echinacea grossed up to twenty-three dollars per pound at the time. In the short run, this seemed a fine strategy, but as growers told it, there is little in growing botanical herbs to prevent appropriation by larger-scale growers once markets are forged.

For these sorts of reasons, many small and medium-sized growers began to stake their livelihoods on crops with characteristics (and skills needed to grow them) that put them out of reach of the large grower-shippers. Heirloom tomatoes are one such crop. While some growers expressed apprehension of increased competition even here, the very nature of an heirloom varietal is one that is not amenable to an industrial way of farming. They are low yield, hard to handle, highly perishable, and otherwise delicious. In other words, by their very nature they are the opposite of what money-making crops are supposed to be, and this, paradoxically, gave these growers an edge.

Back to the Land Values

A final ramification of the rent-generating capability of organic regulation is the effect on the value of agricultural land. As far back as 1996, some experts predicted that the demand for chemical-free land would

drive up the price of immediately certifiable land, including that being released through the USDA's Conservation Reserve Program. On this
count, the empirical evidence is shaky. In a few cases, organic land has
changed hands and reverted to conventional farmland, completely sink-
ing the original investment. In one such transaction, the seller did not
want the buyer to know it was organic land, in order to keep the organic
market small. In other words, he felt he would do better keeping his
prices up through excluding others from organic production than by realizing the possible short-term gain of selling the land as organic.

In other cases, organic land has stayed organic but has not necessarily brought a premium. In these cases, however, turnover in land has
been directly predicated on failure. Missionero's rapid involvement in organics was in no small part a result of once-dominant TKO's bankruptcy
and the ability to get already converted land quickly. Natural Selection
took over organic leases throughout the state, especially in the Imperial
Valley and the Westlands district, where less-than-committed growers
had given up on organic production quickly. Finally, too many entries
have occurred on marginal land as a direct result of efforts to skirt the
barrier of a transition period. As these possibilities dry up or receive
more regulatory oversight, land supplies should tighten.

Even with these instabilities in the organic land market, many growers have shown reluctance to grow organically on leased land precisely
for fear that landowners will raise their rents when they note higher crop
values. This prediction is fully in keeping with the classic theory of rent
(see, e.g., Fine 1979; Harvey 1982). For land values reflect more than just
short-term fluctuations in land markets created by a disarticulation of
supply and demand. In addition, because land, particularly good land, is
necessarily a scarce and monopolizable resource, landowners are fundamentally guided by the logic of highest and best use, in this case a high-
value production scheme. Therefore, surplus profits, even those that are
short lived, are almost immediately capitalized into land values.

In this crucial way, organic farming regulatory conventions contribute to the historical rise in land values that has characterized California agriculture. Particularly because the process of certifying land creates a quasi-monopoly in land appropriate for organic production, once
the market in certifiable land tightens, land values could rise considerably. Taken to an extreme, organic regulation has the potential to create
conditions on par with wine appellations, where fortified barriers to
entry are directly imputed into land costs. In terms of structuring the sector, rising land values favor highly capitalized tenant farmers and mini-

mally leveraged land owners (i.e., agribusiness growers and gentleman farmers). Yet, because high land values drive further innovation, ultimately, the social and ecological ramifications are much deeper than that. I will return to this paradox in the concluding chapter.

BEYOND ORGANIC

Organic rules and regulations have been an important site of interface between the organic movement and the organic industry, forcing them to operate on the same terrain. By legitimizing organic in the market, movement actors have been caught up on the proverbial treadmill of needing to shore up profits and make payments to land. For their part, industrial actors have to operate within the confines of rules that were nominally developed in opposition to their own practices. Although ideological tensions always existed, as evident in the politicized nature of standard setting, they were made particularly manifest around the proposed federal rule, which was both a symbolic and a material turning point in the evolution of organic agriculture. Factions within the organic community have since come to articulate different moral visions that are inseparable from the political economies that are implicated (see McCarthy 1999 on this point).

One vision is to expand the sector. From this perspective, the idea is to "get people into the fold, and the philosophy can come later," to make it easier for growers to convert and thereby proliferate ecologically sounder practices, even "to feed the world."[12] Promoters of this vision do not frown upon mixed operations but instead assume they will eventually be converted, and they are skeptical of ideas that everything should be locally scaled. It is a defensible position. Moving in this direction will bring prices down and make organic less of an elite project. Organic food will be available in outlets where it is now absent. More acreage will be farmed with fewer toxic substances. Of significance, this vision is not being promoted by conventional growers who know they are merely dabbling in the sector. It is the vision of the industry leaders, who are well poised to benefit from the expansion of the organic market. In the words of a major organic broker I spoke with, "They [the small farmers] are not going to feed the masses. If good, nutritious food is going to get out to people—not just yuppie food—you need to have economies of scale. Large farmers are the future of organic. This is not to minimize what others do: the direct marketers, the CSA's—what they do for the soul is priceless."

Juxtaposed to this is the so-called movement perspective.[13] This vision is one of deepening the sector, to have organic mean more than a particular set of production inputs, be it a scale of production, a way of tightly linking city and country, or a way of life. Adherents of this vision see their philosophical and agronomic ideals compromised by growers moving into organic "just to make a buck." Moreover, they are frightened by the competition as their profits are being eroded. So they look for other ways to revitalize the meanings in organic and at the same time uphold their premiums through fortifying barriers that in various ways go "beyond organic"—efforts, in DeLind's words, "to commodify intangibles such as 'trust' and 'rurality' " (1993, 9). Growers involved in such initiatives express varying degrees of disgust with CCOF's "being in bed with the big boys," the overinvolvement of the state, and the loss of organic's social agenda.[14] Now that the USDA "owns the organic label," many are exiting the formal organic sector altogether and finding other ways to differentiate themselves.

For example, several growers throughout the state have affiliated with the Demeter Association for the purpose of going beyond organic agronomically. Demeter is an international organization that promotes biodynamic farming, with exacting standards that far exceed the expectations of most organic certifiers and the finalized federal rule. Although biodynamic farming is ridiculed for being overly mystical with its attention to "teas" and "brews," from my observations, growers working with Demeter farmed the most closely to the agroecological ideal.

Others have joined up with California Clean, which formed in direct response to some of the institutional problems with organic. In an effort to give encouragement to small family farmers who are "burnt out on organic/conventional divides," its founder purposely limited the number of standards. The primary criterion for participation is that farm size be one hundred acres or less for fruit and vegetable production and five hundred acres or less for forage crops. Inspections include an evaluation of working conditions; growers are expected to have a direct relationship with their workers, not use labor contractors, and actually participate in picking and packing. In terms of inputs, California Clean evaluates them on the basis of safety, not according to a mythologized standard of naturalness. To that end, growers are prohibited from using chemicals that the EPA has identified as known, probable, or possible carcinogens, although they are allowed to use Roundup, for instance, for spot treatment of noxious weeds. Growers are equally entreated to concern themselves with how much, in what manner, and at what time they use inputs, and inspectors look for butterflies, birds, and worms as evidence of biological pest control. The clincher is that California Clean does not actively seek a price premium, in recognition that the premium creates self-destructive competition and ultimately undermines the ethical basis of ecological farming.

Several emerging initiatives are a cross between more standard eco-labels and *terroir*-type labeling. Organic growers in Marin County have developed a marketing program that draws upon Marin's idyllic setting and goes further than organic ecologically.[15] To participate, growers have to include cover cropping in their soil development program and address water and habitat issues. Growers in Yolo County's Capay Valley have also considered a separate appellation, which would play on the valley's isolation from what one grower calls the "killing fields" of the main Sacramento Valley as well as on the Capay Valley's emergence as a center for more radical organic growers. Meanwhile, growers in the South Coast region have discussed a community certification program based on "honor and trust." Thus, it would include direct marketers only, and rather than having inspections, farmers would sign off on a charter.

It is striking that after all the efforts to define and defend organic, some in the movement have already abandoned or are about to abandon the name "organic" for its failure on both social and agroecological fronts. These are among the state's most radical growers, both socially and ecologically, and they see these initiatives as overt attempts to recover some of the organic movement from the organic industry. It is an important contradiction that this seemingly more radical position is also self-serving—and wholly depends on consumers to pay the difference. In other words, it depends on a vital politics of consumption, which does not include cheap food.

CHAPTER 8

The Agrarian Answer?

This isn't what we meant. When we said organic, we meant
local. We meant healthful. We meant being true to the ecolo-
gies of regions. We meant mutually respectful growers and
eaters. We meant social justice and equality.

> Joan Dye Gussow, nutrition activist, author, and farmer

The 2002 implementation of the new federal rule for organic production
has generated a palpable sense of loss within the organic farming movement. Undoubtedly, many of organic farming's most solid devotees
share Gussow's view, whose editorial appeared in *Organic Gardening*
during the period in which the new federal rule was being implemented.
As evidenced in the written comments to the first proposed federal rule
in 1997, die-hard organic consumers had the most demanding expectations of what organic should mean vis-à-vis industrial farming (Vos
2000). But did the rule itself undermine the promise of organic agriculture, or, as I would argue, is the rule a culmination of a more protracted
process of evisceration, which was in some sense overdetermined?

The success with which organic farming was adapted to a California
model of agricultural industrialization suggests a path dependency that
few acknowledge. Against a background of urban wealth and cultural
support for social experimentation, both of which bolstered demand, organic production was otherwise layered onto an already existing landscape of agricultural industrialization. Given disparate regional histories
within California, the degree and kind of industrialization was geographically uneven and crop specific. Sometimes it took the form of intensification, resembling McWilliams's ([1935] 1971) factories in the
field; other times it involved appropriation of smaller farmers' surplus,
as Kautsky ([1899] 1988) might predict. In either case, particular tenure
patterns, cropping patterns, modes of extension, marketing outlets,

labor arrangements, and so forth were already in place, presenting substantial obstacles to those who wished to alter these conditions. This is not to say that organic producers uniformly attempted to break those patterns; certain growers were perfectly content to have organic farming operate as agribusiness-as-usual. But even those with the best intentions were circumscribed by the economic constraints they faced.

Nevertheless, this unlikely marriage also rests on the particular vehicle of regulation that the organic farming movement chose to promote its goals. The organic movement saw itself as not just offering critique but also providing positive alternatives. For that reason, it set out to codify an alternative way of farming and win its recognition in the market. In effect, organic regulations made the organic commodity the centerpiece of the movement, creating a fundamental tension between social regulation and business goals and laying the groundwork for old-fashioned interest politics to play a large role in defining organic. In turn, many of the rules that define organic production, though highly contested, were ultimately made to limit the scope of what organic agriculture addressed. At the heart of this regulated definition, moreover, has been a technical focus on production practices, where out of practical necessity, the avoidance of certain inputs and the allowance of others became a proxy for prescribing these practices. One result of this technical focus is that the ability to produce organically has become less dependent on how a grower manages production than on what crops he or she grows. Finally, the conventions erected to enforce these definitions, while designed as barriers to entry, have had the paradoxical effect of attracting entry into the sector by playing into a logic of valorization but, in turn, undermining the self-protection many growers originally sought.

While deeply disappointing, this unexpected complementarity between organic regulation and industrial agriculture has effectively reinvigorated the movement. Particularly as producers who identify with the movement have seen their own livelihoods affected by growth and change in the organic sector, they have started to fight back. Since I have begun this project, I have witnessed growing interest in making social justice a vital component of organic agriculture, another way in which to go "beyond organic." For some, this means an additional or alternative label, since the USDA now controls the organic label. Although this is a step in the right direction, I argue that this potentially powerful rhetorical move is somewhat misguided. In brief, organic growers are looking to the wrong imaginary to reanimate their politics, as well as to the wrong instrument.

THE AGRARIAN IMAGINARY REDUX

At the 2001 Ecological Farming Conference in Asilomar, California, a plenary speaker gave a scathing critique of the new federal rules, claiming they have brought industrialization to the organic sector. His speech was extremely well received throughout, but he drew thunderous applause when he called for a renewal of small-scale independent farming (Ikerd 2001). This speech, then, was a typical example of the agrarian populist rhetoric that increasingly pervades the organic movement. It was anticorporate, to be sure, but centered on a defense of individual farmers' rights; collective action to redress growing economic power was never entertained, nor were the needs of other constituencies. And at the heart of it was the idea that scale is a proper measure of industrialization, deeming the "small-scale family farm" a proxy for social justice. That the smallness of scale of organic farming operations both reflects and contributes to the social good that organic production instantiates seems undisputed, at least among those close to or within the organic movement (see, e.g., Vos 2000).

Yet, there are some significant problems with the small-scale family farm ideal. First of all, although it is highly critical of mainstream agriculture, the agrarian imaginary is equally bound up with a sort of cultural conservatism and even with Christian fundamentalism. As Brass (1997) argues, agrarian populism, with roots in conservative notions of an organic society, consistently links small-scale property with family values and tradition.[1] Moreover, by failing to question the race and gender relations that enabled the family farm, as noted by Allen and Sachs (1993), it inherently glorifies them. Not only do these often romanticized notions of the family farm take as perfectly unproblematic patriarchal exploitation of women's and children's labor (Allen and Sachs 1993; Sachs 1996), they also ultimately uphold white privilege by ignoring the racial history of U.S. land policy (Romm 2001).[2]

Second, this ideal is strikingly anachronistic and misplaced. It draws on, say, early twentieth-century South Dakota, when the tractor made it possible to make a market-based livelihood growing wheat on 160 acres, using only family labor (Friedmann 1978). And while the struggle between large growers and small growers has continued to be a salient dynamic for the Midwest, in the Far West the central struggle has always been between industrial producers and wage labor (Gilbert and O'Connor 1996).[3] Let me repeat: *California never had an agrarian tradition.* But by adopting an agrarianist rhetoric, the organic movement's stance amounts to a stunning erasure. Not only does it further naturalize the organic landscape, as if no work goes into its making except for the hard labor of the yeoman farmer and "nature's work" itself (Mitchell 1996); more cynically, it implicitly favors a redistribution of surplus to the glorified figure of the organic family farmer at the expense of farm labor. Indeed, once hired labor is admitted into the analysis, there is no evidence to suggest that working conditions and remuneration on small "family" farms are better than on large "corporate" ones.[4] And considered more closely, the notion of "more eyes on the crop" turns on the organization of production, not necessarily on its scale. Simply put, there are no apparent structural reasons that the exacting and labor-intensive precepts of agroecology cannot take place on larger farms once the dual issues of labor remuneration and enfranchisement are adequately addressed (admittedly, formidable hurdles themselves) (see Allen et al. 1991; and Lasley, Hoiberg, and Bultena 1993 on related points).

Third, besides being steeped in nostalgia, the small-scale ideal does not hold up empirically to the realities of the California organic sector. We have seen that some operations in organic production are large-scale by any standards. These include fresh vegetable operations with several thousands of acres spread out across several different regions. We have also seen that conventional growers with annual sales well over $10 million are finding comfortable niches within organic production without having to thoroughly change the ways in which they operate. Nevertheless, Claire Cummings, who speaks in this book's opening epigraph, is correct to point out that most organic farms are small, on average much smaller than conventional farms. Lower-than-average farm size is attributable to the disproportionate amount of acreage in fruit, vegetable, and nut production, which usually takes place on a smaller scale than grains, in large part because there is more value per acre to be extracted from produce crops. It also signifies that a disproportionate number of part-time and hobby farms are farmed organically. These one- to five-acre ranchettes could hardly be the agrarian ideal that is the rhetorical focus of this debate.[5] If anything, their existence points to an industry structure that is increasingly dominated by a few.

If any farms come close to the agrarian ideal, it is the "disappearing middle," those farms that enjoy neither the economies of scale afforded by large farms nor the subsidies from other income sources bestowed on small ones (Buttel and LaRamee 1992). While not the bulk of the sector in either grower numbers or acreage, viable midsized organic farms exist, owned by families or partnerships of unrelated individuals. Their growers are able to carve out livelihoods on anywhere from ten to two hundred acres, depending on the crop mix, and so far have thrived on the premiums that organic production offers. Even then, they are not family farms on which family members provide most, if not all, of the labor. In California, they rely heavily on the wage labor of those of Mexican descent. Moreover, as industry players increase their market share and, consequently, are better able to define the terms of trade, even the most successful of the middle-sized farms are occasionally pulled into unfavorable relationships with buyers. More often, they face increased price competition as the major operators bring in new growers, making the price premiums on which the independent growers depend all the more tenuous.

In this light, the glorification of the organic price premium as a means of small—or, in this case, medium—farm survival is troubling. A label that augments existing definitions of organic may fare no better. Not only do purposely constructed premiums pose some thorny issues regarding equitable access to safer and healthier food; they also are regarded as if they were immune to the forces that are cause for the inequitable distribution of risk, work, and wealth in agrofood systems. This, then, is the most damning problem with the small-scale ideal: it loses sight of the *processes* of industrialization for its *forms*.

THE AGRARIAN PARADOX

Although unintended, the agrarian populist imaginary has powerfully articulated with the politics of organic regulation and the place of California. The site of this articulation is the land. Organic philosophy began as a philosophy of the soil, and soil quality was the first test of organic affiliation. Subsequently, processes of certification looked to the parcel of land as an object of delineation, inspection, and sanction. Currently, the improvements that land must undergo to be certified as organic are the key barrier to entry and, thus, the legal basis of any economic rents received in the market. Reciprocally, these market rents can be capitalized into higher land values when landowners of a scarce resource exert their power to take their cut of the premium prices. This approximates the mechanism that classical political economists refer to as monopoly rent.

Land values have also been the router for California's agricultural development writ large. As new waves of innovation and reorganization introduced newer, higher-value crops (valorization) and sped up production of those that were more commonplace (intensification), regional land values were capitalized on the basis of these innovations. At the same time, specialty crop production coevolved with, indeed, profoundly depended on, the overexploitation of both labor and nature. The profits gained from a highly subsidized labor force (in the sense that state policy was instrumental in keeping agricultural wages low), as well as growers' below-cost access to resources and virtually unrestrained license to pollute, were also capitalized into land values. As a consequence, these subsidies came to be taken for granted in certain ways, reinforcing the mutuality between the ecological dimensions of intensive production and the social dimensions of cheap labor.[6] Growers came to expect (and demand) a constant supply of low-cost labor, just as they came to dismiss any sense of limitation in water use, as the green fields of the Imperial Valley desert attest.

That said, growers did not necessarily retain those profits. The appropriation of surplus profits by agro-industry compelled growers to accept lower rates of profit or even no return at all, if holding on to their land was a matter of personal urgency to them (Ball 1980). Some adopted higher-yielding proprietary varietals, thereby tightening their relationships with seed companies despite whatever hesitancy they had. Some became unwillingly dependent on buyers, perhaps entering into contracts as a way of minimizing the risk of selling their crops at next to nothing.

In other words, the necessity of land as the primary medium of agricultural production has almost always ensured that the squeeze is manifest elsewhere, although land is occasionally devalued in times of severe agricultural crisis. In short, mechanisms of land valuation reflect and inscribe the social and social-natural relations that constitute California's industrial agriculture, including excessive input dependence, the dominance of high-value specialty crops, the exploitation of marginalized groups for labor, and an industry structure where risk is diffuse but economic power is oligopsonistic.

Ultimately, the agrarian imaginary is about land as well. It draws in part from the physiocratic notion that land and its products are the only true sources of wealth; it takes as axiomatic the idea that independent and egalitarian ownership of land is critical to democracy and stewardship. So when the primarily urban counterculture went "back to the land," many within it became smallholders or aspiring smallholders and began to see themselves as part of this yeoman tradition. Mindful of how corporate activity reconfigures food and farming in ways that both interrupt self-balancing systems and marginalize rural producers, they were particularly drawn to populist ideas, suggesting that the problems lie with big business, political injustice, and greed (Brass 1997, 155). But embracing an agrarian populist ideology also helped efface their discomfiture as capitalist producers, allowing them to take an anticorporate stance and at the same time take existing property relations as sacrosanct. So, while the link between organic philosophy and a structural critique of agriculture might have been tenuous, the result of this embrace was an implicit refusal to look at the ways that private property in land itself was implicated in the denaturing of agriculture.

Herein lies the paradox of organic farming in California. Like all growers, organic growers must make payments to land. Since past rounds of intensification and innovation have been capitalized into land values, current land values reflect the social and ecological exploitation that produced profitability in each of those rounds. Indeed, since much land in California has been capitalized on the basis of intensive horticultural production, it has been made too costly for alternative sorts of production systems. Unless growers find some other subsidy to land, they must replicate such exploitation to remain financially viable.

At the same time, organic regulations undermine the ability to subvert industrial processes, because they, too, contribute to land values through rent-creating conventions. Indeed in a state where past agrarian transformations have forced high agricultural land values, growers are moving to even higher-value production schemes, such as organic production, in order to survive. In other words, organic production is not only bound by, but may also be contributing to, the trends in intensification and valorization that have characterized late twentieth-century California agriculture. The most striking irony is that the imperative of agricultural intensification undermines the practical basis of an ecological farming strategy on even narrower technical terms! Such a strategy depends on rotations of marginal-value crops for fertility and on noncommodity crops for pest control, yet many growers simply cannot afford to take land out of crop production to allow these agroecological processes to take hold. So while it may be the case that the larger organic movement never meant to alter the entire food system systematically, the existing structural conditions of agriculture have limited its reach in surprising and profound ways.

WHAT CAN BE DONE?

Could organic agriculture have done more and can it yet? Is it possible to forge a radically different way of producing food within the confines of existing social structures? Despite my strong criticisms, I am not willing to write off the transformative potential of organic—or, better said, alternative—agriculture, for I believe that the way organic has been codified into a legally enforceable meaning is the basis of the problem, for several reasons. First, organic agriculture as it is currently defined is a technical fix, and a fairly limited one at that, focusing primarily on a set of materials that can or cannot be used. Second, the capacity to uphold this definition turns on entry barriers, which, by definition, are highly antithetical to widespread transformation in agrofood systems. Third, the unfortunate confluence of regulation-driven rents with existing mechanisms of intensification contributes to some of the ecological problems that organic farming is supposed to alleviate.

These failures of organic regulation on its very own terms raise the question of whether labeling, and certification to verify those labels, is the best vehicle to accomplish agroecological goals. So-called market mechanisms are favored in a neoliberal political climate precisely because they do not interfere with business as usual. To the contrary, they help create new markets. Juxtaposed to these private means are state-led reforms, hopelessly out of style these days. Yet, because of its redistributive capabilities, only the state has the capacity to unlock some of the mechanisms of agricultural intensification. The following is not intended to be a comprehensive policy discussion, only suggestions of other means to a more ecologically sound agriculture. They all involve enrolling the state in a substantive way.

More Technical Support

Research and extension funding for sustainable agriculture has been dismal compared with that for conventional chemical agriculture. Along with its unflagging support for an organic standard in the interest of trade, the organic industry has been strongly critical of the lack of research support for organic agriculture (Lipson 1997). This was certainly one of the earlier rallying cries of the Rodales and raison d'être for their experimental farm in Emmaus, Pennsylvania. The Organic Farming Research Foundation (OFRF), an offshoot of California Certified Organic Farmers, was established in the early 1990s. Its primary purpose is to fund national-level research related to organic production and to disseminate the results to those interested in organic agriculture. Its public policy goal is to encourage the USDA and the land grant colleges to reconsider their research priorities.

The organic industry is less supportive of technical initiatives outside the organic rubric. Yet, those initiatives that exist have had a palpable influence on production techniques. Within California, among these is the BIOS program (for Biologically Integrated Orchard Systems), a program of Community Alliance with Family Farmers. The BIOS program is a voluntary pesticide reduction program that provides direct, crop-specific technical support to farmers. One study found that orchards in the BIOS program are reported to have a significantly lower proportion of fields treated with registered pesticides as compared with a matched group of cohort fields (Villarejo and Moore 1998). Several growers interviewed for this study started with BIOS and either converted to organic from there or found that the program offered a lower-risk way to experiment with sustainable farming methods. Although these farmers forgo a premium, many are happy to avoid the bureaucratic complications.

Similarly UC-SAREP, authorized by the California 1986 Sustainable Agriculture Act, supports research and experimentation with alternative methods. Criticized for its lack of radicalism, it nonetheless brings in growers who would otherwise not be organic. Several large-scale conventional growers have come into organic by starting with SAREP programs. They were convinced by the techniques, although clearly preferring a more gradual approach to conversion. Like growers involved in BIOS, those involved in SAREP seem to take seriously the environmental externalities of what they do (including the effects on workers) and are less concerned with the food safety concerns of consumers. This non-premium-oriented approach does not transform the social relations of agriculture in California, but neither does it contribute to the problem. Large increases in this sort of support, in addition to existing research and extension networks divorcing from the chemical and seed companies, could have a tremendous influence on agricultural practices.

Stronger Regulation

The organic movement has conspicuously shied away from the area of so-called command and control pesticide regulation, wanting to present a positive solution. At the same time, many organic producers complain of the injustice of having to prove what they do not use, although there are no required labels for conventional agriculture. Accordingly, some organic growers advocate imposing a labeling burden on conventional agriculture. This, however, is effectively another market-based solution that puts regulatory decisions into the hands of individual consumers.

Past pesticide regulation has been woefully deficient, in large part because of the opposition of the agrochemical industry. But, growers, as we have seen, are very watchful of the changing regulatory climate around agriculture. For instance, many began to try more sustainable methods well in advance of action taken by the EPA as part of the Food Quality Protection Act of 1996.

In other words, much more could be done to make pesticide regulation technology-forcing, including, but not limited to, banning all known and probable carcinogens. It seems so obvious.

Subsidies

The provision of high-quality cheap food presents a major quandary. If organic food were truly produced by reinternalizing the costs that have been externalized with industrial agriculture, as Lampkin and Padel (1994) suggest, then it would likely cost even more. Ultimately, these costs are borne by those whose labor is most involved in growing, processing, and distributing food, including farmworkers, household food providers, and farm "families." In order not to be wholly dependent on the ethical capitalist once the organic premium is diminished, isn't it time we thought about some new ways to subsidize the processes of food provisioning?

Direct subsidies to growers who transition to organic production are a policy mechanism being implemented with much success in Europe, but these subsidies have barely reached the table in the United States. Although the 2002 farm bill included the new Conservation Security Program, which is supposed to provide payments to farmers who address site-specific environmental challenges, as of this writing the financial future of the program is uncertain (Lohr 2002), and it would be highly limited in any case. Such subsidies are a far cry from the commodity supports that encourage the intensive monocropping of chemical-dependent crops, which constitute the bulk of farm bill supports.[7] Still, in order not to capitalize these new subsidies into land values, as commodity supports have been, we must design them with the specific purpose of breaking the vicious relation of cheap labor, intensive production, and high land values.

WHITHER SOCIAL JUSTICE?

Even with more state intervention, organic agriculture can curtail some amount of agricultural pollution and perhaps save some lives from cancer, but it can go no further—even ecologically—without addressing the social foundations on which agriculture rests. A true transformation starts with the defetishization of food, that is, with an increased knowledge of the social and ecological conditions under which food is produced (Allen and Kovach 2000; Hartwick 2000). Bell and Valentine (1997) reflect on how the new politics of consumption, manifested as eating green, eating locally, and fair trade, are exemplary in this regard, for they help to "thicken" connections between producers and consumers and create such knowledge (also Cook and Crang 1996). Yet, it is too easy to fetishize the alternatives, to take them as unquestioned positives. A truly contrarian strategy must go much further and open up to scrutiny the practices that come under such headings as "green" and "socially responsible." In the case of organic agriculture, we must cease, at the very least, to mystify what it does and does not do. A viable politics of consumption can realistically do no less.

Yet, transformation requires not only scrutiny—as with a "right to know"—but also a willingness to transform the institutions and structures that underlie the fetishism of commodities. While the so-called food system is a highly complex web involving international relations, government regulations, corporate actors, health professionals, advertisers, farmers, and so forth, there are three areas, vis-à-vis the argument I have been forwarding, that must be brought to prominence in any vision of sustainable agriculture. One of the key areas is labor. Just as there has been a certain mutuality between the intensification and pollution of both labor and nature, there is a potential mutuality between ecological well-being and economic equity, or, to put it another way, between environmental justice and a just working environment. For example, it is becoming increasingly clear not only that industrial agriculture exposes people of color and poor people disproportionately to environmental risk but also that more sustainable forms of resource use may provide them with well-needed job security (Pulido 1996).

The organic movement has given little intellectual space to consider the role of laborers as both agents and beneficiaries of environmental care. Yet, every technique used in organic agriculture requires some sort of labor practice, whether it be monitoring, applying, cultivating, spraying, harvesting, or packing, many of which are often performed in painstaking ways. In setting the research agenda and evaluating the appropriateness of new organic technologies, these work processes must be considered, along with the efficacy and environmental safety of any given control. Organic farmers have contented themselves with the idea that they expose workers to fewer toxic substances—that is, until one considers that sulfur dust is a widely used fungicide in organic farming—while they continue, with a few important exceptions, to replicate the labor conditions found in conventional agriculture.

That said, grower initiative in addressing labor issues has its limits, for it veers toward patronage. For growers to make labeling claims that their labor practices are better without substantially involving workers in the process of evaluating and monitoring such practices would be nothing short of hypocritical. The parallel case is sweatshop monitoring, in which manufacturers hire independent monitors to certify the legality of working conditions. As Esbenshade (2001) convincingly argues, this has ushered in a new sort of social contract between producers and consumers, with laborers left out of the negotiations. Arguably, only collective action by and for agricultural workers can break the cheap labor link in the chain. Why haven't farmworkers been brought to the table in setting research agendas or formulating organic rules?

While the reasons people eat what they do are far more complicated than what can be addressed here, a fair and equitable agrarian order must incorporate the equity issues around food consumption. The construction of organic food as a niche market, albeit not what the movement had intended, has bestowed organic food with the image of preciousness. Retailer-set price premiums, along with high-end restaurants that provision with rarefied organic food, encourage some consumers to purchase relative freedom from risk while most eat the worst of mass-produced food (Beck 1992).

The issue, however, is not organic prices relative to conventional food prices; indeed, we have to find ways to pay the cost of producing food in ecologically rational, humane, and socially just ways. The issue, rather, is inequitable access to safe, nutritious, and tasty food. As Eric Schlosser drives home in *Fast Food Nation* (2001), the production of cheap food makes food workers particularly vulnerable to workplace risk and all of us vulnerable to food safety and environmental risk. Yet, as real wages have dropped, poor people have come to depend on the cheapness such production systems allow. Following the logic of Henry Ford, who knew that to sell cars one had to adequately pay those who make them, it is imperative to pay living wages to those people who produce, process, and prepare our food and find other ways of subsidizing those who still cannot afford good food. Where have advocates for the food insecure and the poor been in the construction of organic rules?

Farmers need and deserve an adequate livelihood. Besides farmworkers, farmers are most affected by the problems of cheap food, increasingly so as large institutional buyers set the terms of trade. In addition, farming, as it is widely recognized, is one of the most high-risk vocations, in large part because farmers themselves, not the seed companies, tractor manufacturers, canneries, or retailers, are most vulnerable to the vagaries of nature. Public policy toward farming has been a disaster; price supports, for example, have exacerbated tendencies of intensification and appropriation, so that undercapitalized farms truly are at more risk. Given the dynamics of the food system, it seems logical for farmers to take more collective action as opposed to insisting on their independence and smallness. Collective power is an underutilized instrument for ensuring a fair return and spreading risk. Yet, only very recently have organic farmers begun to reconsider cooperative marketing. OFARM (Organic Farmers for Relationship Marketing) was recently formed under the old Capper-Volstead Act, which allows communication and joint action among farmers in setting prices. Thus far, only midwestern grain and oilseed producers have joined OFARM (Brussel 2002). And again, California's direct-marketing laws preclude cooperation at farmers' markets.

Still, if the worse aspects of the industrialization of agriculture are in part driven by land values, as I have argued, in the final analysis the problem is rooted in the way that land itself has been appropriated and commodified. The issue is not only inequitable access to land, important though that is, but also its high cost; as an investable and transferable commodity, it can never support a kinder and gentler form of food production without substantial policy interventions that maintain or reduce the cost.[8] In other words, any transformative politics of sustainable agriculture must squarely face the dynamics that arise from private property in land itself. Yet, the agrarian tradition is implicated in this undying support for private property rights.

One possible starting point to a fairer and more equitable food order—a utopia of process, as Harvey (2000) might say—are new institutional forms like Community Supported Agriculture. In the ideal they represent a substantial decommodification of food, with eaters investing in the equity of the farm and sharing both its risks and its fruits.[9] The more common and less radical version of Community Supported Agriculture, the subscription farm, does not erase all of the vestiges of industrial agriculture; for example, substantial agronomic intensification, along with specialty-crop production, is what makes them viable. Moreover, they tend to attract high-income consumers, although some have a few low-income shares (Hinrichs 2000).[10]

Nevertheless, subscription farms do exemplify an interesting reworking of both social and ecological relations. Because they depend on direct marketing, whether through subscriptions or farmers' markets, they must ensure a constant supply of a variety of food. Accordingly, these farms tend to have the most innovative cropping systems, with complicated rotations, integrated livestock, and tremendous diversity. At the same time, they depend on knowledgeable and committed labor to deal with extraordinary variation in crops, the management of cropping cycles, and the need to get food to market on a regular basis. As such, these farms tend to employ fewer workers but on a year-round basis. As we have seen, some of these farms also offer significantly higher pay and real benefits, such as health care and vacation.

Their improved labor conditions are made economically viable by three factors. One, these farms retain more value because they market directly. Two, they are worked very intensively; viewed from a revenue perspective, few are small scale. Three, and perhaps most crucial, several of these farms have received some subsidy to land, either through inheritance, or landowner largess, or foundation and state support to buy the land.[11] What is striking, then, about these farms, is how the transformative agronomic methods, the *reworking of nature* that occurs on such farms, are clearly driven by the decommodification of food *and* land, which opens up an economic space where social divisions can be eroded rather than accentuated. This is an alternative agriculture of substance, because it provides an alternative not only to production inputs and method but to the entire system of industrial farming.

Appendix

This appendix is designed for those readers who desire more specifics about how research was carried out.

ON RESEARCH DESIGN AND DATA ANALYSIS

The research aims laid out in the opening chapter called for a multi-method study. Essentially, research activities were completed in three phases, as follows:

Phase 1

The first phase of research was dedicated to obtaining and organizing heretofore uncorrelated survey and archival data into a multirelational set of Paradox databases, with which I could perform systematic data analysis. I was able to obtain a 1997 listing of all "registered" organic farms from the California Department of Food and Agriculture (CDFA) in Sacramento, which, as publicly available information, included only the names and addresses of growers and the commodities sold. Since the public information sheets from which this database was built were supposed to include whether and what third party agencies certify the growers, I was able to obtain separate listings from the CDFA from seven of the nine certifiers who do business in California. This "population" database was supplemented with the detailed database of California Certified

Organic Farmers (CCOF), which at the time certified about 25 percent of all organic growers in California and most of the large growers. CCOF also provided data on acres in organic production, years certified, and acres in conventional production.

My database was further supplemented by the now-dated database of the California Institute for Rural Studies, which included all California growers who had filed the required pesticide use permits with county agricultural commissioners in 1994 and 1995. Organic growers therefore showed up in this database when they have mixed conventional and organic operations or when they use allowable organic pesticides (e.g., sulfur). The CIRS database showed acreage by section-township-range for most farms listed and enabled me to estimate total acres in production. My main database was also supplemented with information on corporate status as obtained from filings with the state's attorney general, other business databases, other organic directories, and news stories. Eventually I was able to identify most of the large growers (whether all-organic or mixed) in organic production. For historical perspectives, I obtained previous statistical surveys (Klonsky and Tourte 1995) and directories of certified organic growers from the CCOF archives.

Having established the "population" database, I proceeded to cross-tabulate the database along a number of dimensions: certification status, type of crops grown, whether growers were all-organic or mixed, geographic region, and acreage. Although there remained many growers about whom I knew nothing except for their name, address, and commodities sold, eventually I was able to make educated guesses regarding their attributes. For instance, hundreds of uncertified apple and citrus growers were situated in two particular areas. Through interviews, I soon discovered they all "farmed" one- to two-acre parcels and sold to one of a handful of regional processors/packers.

Finally, I compared much of this data regarding the structure of the sector with data from the agricultural census (e.g., farm size, type of ownership, demographic attributes) to note taxonomic difference between organic production and all agricultural production. I did a similar comparison with a recent national survey of organic production, to note ways in which California organic production is exceptional. I also compared my data with past surveys taken of organic production in California to examine the nature of growth and change within the sector.

Phase 2

The second phase of research involved semistructured interviews with over 150 growers, which elicited both quantitative and quasi-ethnographic data. I designed the research sample so as to enable an intensive examination of how practices and motivations vary among different categories of growers. To generate the research sample, I stratified the population database, primarily by estimated acreage in production and whether growers were all-organic or mixed. I then created four provisional scale categories for each type of grower. I used this stratification as the primary method of selecting growers for interviews and interviewed approximately equal numbers of growers in each category. When selecting growers to interview, I also attempted to mix the sample according to geographic region, crop mix, and certification, even though a certain amount of covariation occurred among these categories. The 150 in the sample represented approximately 10 percent of the research population at the time. Given the nature of my stratification, the research sample represented a much higher percentage of actual acreage in organic production.

Having created a starting sample of growers, I sought interviews through introductory letters and phone calls. When reached, close to 70 percent of growers agreed to an interview. When an interview was refused or the grower was unreachable, I sought another grower of similar attributes. Interviews took place in several settings: walking (or driving) around the farm, in growers' houses or offices, and, in a very few cases, on the telephone. Our conversations focused on the following areas: (1) structure and ownership of holdings, including land history and land tenure, acreage, and enterprise age; (2) agronomic practices (e.g., cropping patterns, pest management, input sourcing), which were often the lengthiest part of the interview; (3) issues related to marketing, vertical integration, economic viability, and industry structure; (4) labor practices; (5) the timing and nature of entry into organic production and motivations for doing so; and (6) the basis of certification decisions, opinions on organic regulations, regulators, and the industry as a whole. At times, I was able to use on-site observation to confirm the types of farming practices and postharvest practices employed.

I manipulated some of the data collected in the structured parts of interviews into variables, both categorical and continuous, grouped so as to be used in cross-tabulations. These included region of operation, grower type, gross sales, types of crops grown, years organic, proportion of organic to total acreage, proportion of leased versus owned land, and certification status. In addition, I coded growers' extended responses in order to develop scalar measures of the degree of employment of agro-ecological method and grower commitment to organic production. In all cases, I verified these correlations with chi-square statistics.

Other qualitative data from the structured portion of the interviews were not subject to statistical analysis per se. At one level, I did not want to create too many variables in a limited sample size, nor did I want to reduce complicated answers to binary or overly simplified variables needlessly. At a more fundamental level, I was wary of mistaking correlation for cause, and heavy reliance on statistical method was not in keeping with my ontological assumptions. By using Paradox as a database program, I was able to include textual material within the database. Occasionally, I used this qualitative data statistically when more generalized patterns existed (e.g., X percent of growers expressed concern with increasing pesticide regulation as one of their reasons for converting to organic production). More often, I have incorporated this qualitative data into the text as ethnographic examples.[1] I was also able to develop a matrix of six typical (but not actual) growers as a way of consolidating qualitative data into an ideal type format.

Phase 3

The third phase examined the origins of organic regulations, chronicled their shifting politics, and assessed the impacts they have had and may continue to have on the sector. I accomplished this through analysis of certifier handbooks and other documents and in-depth interviews of representatives from several of the certifying agencies that operate within California. I also conducted interviews with other public officials, advocates, and technical experts, attended four industry conferences, at each of which several panels focused on regulatory issues, and followed Internet discussions. Subsequently, I was able to compile the legislative history of state and federal organic regulation, analyze past and present certification requirements from the nine certifying agencies that do business in California, and keep abreast of various debates over regulation. Aside from chapter 6, which describes the evolution of organic rules and institutions, these findings were integrated with field data to analyze how regulation has shaped both organic practices and the overall structure of the sector.

ON COMPILING GROWER STATISTICS
AND CONSTRUCTING THE SAMPLE

All scientists work with frustrating data, and this was no less true in this study. Yet it is also part of the organic story that such poor data exist, for statistics often do not exist until there are reasons and mechanisms to do the counting. Data collected by certifiers and other organizations that serve the organic community represent only self-selected growers. In California, state-level statistics were not generated until the 1990 COFA mandated them, and then they were not adequately collected and analyzed until 1992–93 (Klonsky and Tourte 1995). As of this writing, the last years to be analyzed are 1997–98 (Klonsky et al. 2001). Even then, the 1997 figure of 1,533 registered growers is surely understated. Several growers who were certified with CCOF and not registered claimed to be certified but were not on certifier lists, or they were listed in the CAFF national organic directory but were neither certified nor registered. From time to time I have heard of organic growers who were not listed in any of these places, including those who sell to some of the finest restaurants and speak at industry conferences. This inconsistency is indicative of a much deeper politics about who is called organic.

To stratify my sample, I needed acreage figures on both the organic and the conventional portions of operations.[2] Without the state's confidential data, certifier data were the next avenue to pursue, but certification data were remarkably opaque. Only one agency (CCOF) gave public access to growers' acreage figures. Since it required its member growers to report the amount of acreage in conventional production, this additional information was available upon request. With non-CCOF growers, I reconstructed some of these data from news clippings, the CAFF directory (which as paid advertisement can be inconsistent), and the all-important CIRS database of pesticide use permits.

As befitting the source, the CIRS database tracked acreage treated with pesticides, so it was most useful for determining mixed growers and the acres they had in production. I may not have found all organic growers who reside in this database, however. With more than eighty thousand growers in California, some names were too common to find an assured match. There were also cases in which the person who filed the pesticide permit was different from the contact name in the organic database, making for difficult matches. Additionally, the CIRS data were from 1994, the last year that was consistently available, although

I occasionally used data from other years if 1994 was not available and noted so in my own database. Accordingly, some of the data are clearly outdated, especially among lessees who constantly change their holdings.

In calculating acres in production, I excluded CIRS' categories of fallow, range, leased-out, and otherwise unused. Then, I added the acres in production for every parcel, careful not to repeat parcels that had multiple crop rotations in a year. Even then, different reporting practices for different counties posed some problems. Some counties provided detailed information of each parcel on the permit; at the other extreme, some just listed crops grown and estimated acreage. In some cases, the CIRS staff had placed a "sum of veggies" figure to signify when growers did not know how much of each crop they would plant but there was a set amount of physical acreage. Yet, in Monterey County, the reports were extremely difficult to decipher, in part because the land from the Spanish and Mexican land grants was never surveyed. On the basis of calculations for small farms or those I had knowledge of, I was able to see that the county used "undeclared commodity" as a placeholder for actual acreage. From that, I was able to do rough, case-by-case calculations for acreage in production in that county.

After matching all available data, I still had no acreage figures at all for about two-thirds of the list. Although it had been suggested that I sample only CCOF growers because of this problem, I felt that would narrow my study considerably; in particular, it would leave out the dynamics of certification as a topic of inquiry. So when constructing the sample across regions, I made sure to include a consistent proportion of those for whom I had virtually no information. As it turned out, most were small (less than five acres), giving me a modicum of confidence that the CIRS data had captured most of the "mixed" and large growers in the sector.

One possible caveat regarding my research is that, by stratifying my research sample, I skewed it so as to underplay the "movement" forces that continue to exist within the sector. This assessment is correct, in that any statistical data derived only from interviewed growers weigh heavily toward mixed and large growers. Nevertheless, I am confident that I interviewed a sufficient number of growers, including several leaders, who identify with the social movement aspects of organic farming to represent their views and practices adequately. Moreover, because my sample is representative of the vast majority of *acres* under organic produc-

TABLE 13. INTERVIEWED GROWERS, BY TYPE
AND BY GROSS SALES, 1998–99

Sales	Organic	Mixed	Ex[a]	Total n	Total %	1997–98 Data[b] n	1997–98 Data[b] %
>$10,000,000—agribusiness	4	15	2	21	14	—	0
$1,000,000–9,999,999—large	15	30	2	47	31	27	1
$100,000–999,999—supporting	21	17	1	39	26	183	8
<$100,000—hobby/part-time	38	5	0	43	29	1,323	91
TOTAL GROWERS INTERVIEWED	78	67	5	150	100	1,533	100

[a] Category includes growers who were no longer with the organic program at the time of the interviews.
[b] SOURCE: Klonsky and Tourte 2001.

tion, if not *growers,* I believe I have provided a substantially accurate picture of where organic agriculture is headed in California.

ON CONSTRUCTING SCALE CATEGORIES

Although I was forced to rely on limited and inconsistent acreage data to construct my sample, I thought it unsatisfactory for analyzing and reporting my findings. During interviews, most growers were willing to provide sales figures. With others, I was eventually able to hazard educated guesses given their crop mix, marketing strategy, and available cost studies. Certainly these guesses were good enough, considering that I coded responses into broad taxonomic categories. Even then, I had to decide where to make the cutoff to limit the analysis to a manageable number of scale categories. I ended up with four. Coming as a matter of experience, these categories seemed to best differentiate farms that could be described in the vernacular as hobby/part-time farms, self/family-supporting farms, large-scale /profit-making farms, and agribusiness, although almost all hired wage labor.

Table 13 shows the stratification of the research sample as compared with 1997–98 data excerpted from Klonsky et al. 2001. Unfortunately, the categories I used are not comparable with Klonsky and Tourte's because my figures(1) are based on combined conventional and organic sales; and(2) combine both farming and handling sales, to capture the increased complexity of a vertically integrated operation. Table 14 shows the number of growers interviewed from every region, segregated according to whether they are all-organic or mixed.

TABLE 14. INTERVIEWED GROWERS, BY REGION, 1998–99

Region	All Organic	Mixed	Ex[a]	Total Interviewed n	Total Interviewed %
Cascade-Sierra	0	0	0	0	0
Far North	10	0	0	10	7
North Valley	8	3	0	11	7
North Coast	11	1	0	12	8
Solano-Yolo	8	2	1	11	7
Central Coast	10	13	0	23	15
West Valley	1	12	0	13	9
East Valley	7	20	1	28	19
South Coast	8	5	1	14	9
South West	10	4	0	14	9
Desert Valleys	5	7	2	14	9
TOTAL	78	67	5	150	100

[a] Category includes growers who were no longer with the organic program at the time of the interviews.

ON CODING INTERVIEW RESPONSES

Reasons for Conversion

Growers were asked open-ended questions regarding their motivations to convert to organic production or attempt to do so. One important caveat is that I did not necessarily interview the owner of each operation: managers and owners are not always of the same mind where organic production is concerned, and, for that matter, business partners may disagree. First their responses were coded into themes; then the themes were grouped into three broad categories for analytical coherency in chapter 2. Many growers offered more than one response, so they are not mutually exclusive. Table 15 lists the most common responses as they were thematically coded.

Agronomic Practices

As part of the interviews, I assessed growers on the degree of adoption of agroecological practices (on organic fields only), supplementing where possible with the visual cues of on-site observations.[3] One of the many challenges was to use criteria that would not covary with respect to scale or certification, because part of my task was to see if, indeed, certain cat-

TABLE 15. REASONS GIVEN FOR CONVERSION
TO ORGANIC PRODUCTION

N	Response
44	To get more money; get more value per acre
35	Do not like or would like to avoid pesticides or other chemicals
29	Like to innovate, experiment; like the challenge
26	Possibly better way to farm; more practical, less costly
19	Buyers or other customers requested it
16	Seems like the right/ethical thing to do
14	Noted soil improvements
13	Risk-free opportunity presented itself
10	Ease of commodity involved; ease of environment for bio-control; seemed like a "natural"
9	Need to get more tools for when pesticides are regulated away
7	Condition of lease; inherited operation
6	Demand is out there
6	Direct-market customers asked
3	To get a better-quality product

egories of producers were more or less agroecological than others in their practices. I also had to choose criteria that could be reasonably discernable within a California context, for many precepts are simply not incorporated at all into California cropping systems. And significant problems occurred in comparing orchard systems, grain rotations, diverse vegetable operations with one another. The criteria for these assessments were selected in consultation with Sean Swezey, then with the UC Santa Cruz Center for Agroecology and Sustainable Food Systems and current director of UC-SAREP. Miguel Altieri's *Agroecology: The Science of Sustainable Agriculture* (1995) was used as an additional reference, as were course notes from a class he held at UC Berkeley. The criteria by which growers were assessed included:

- degree and extent of on-farm fertility management through composting and cover cropping;

- degree of on-farm biological pest management;

- employment of innovative weed control practices such as mulching;

- employment of biodiverse cropping patterns, including systematic crop rotation, intercropping, integrated livestock; varietal diversity for perennial crops;

- avoidance of legally restricted or controversial materials;

- evidence of planning, testing, and intensive management (as opposed to "organic by neglect").

Growers were given one point for each criterion substantially met, except for the first two, which were given double weight, allowing growers to earn a middle rating for these two criteria, since there is a much wider spectrum of practices in these areas. For example, a grower who cover-crops a portion of the farm every year and purchases compost from a supplier would receive one point, one less than a grower who provides all the farm's fertility needs through on-farm recycling and cover crops, but one more than a grower who purchases all fertility inputs. Points were added and then calibrated to a 1 through 5 aggregate rating, 1 being assigned to growers who took none of these affirmative steps and 5 going to those who took all steps. In addition, a rating of 0 was assigned to growers if they were in obvious violation of organic codes and practices. When rounding was required, additional factors were considered, such as attention to water conservation or on-farm seed and transplant development, although neither is considered in the construction of organic rules.

Labor Practices

In this portion of the interviews, growers were asked some basic questions regarding the size of their workforce, recruitment strategies, and pay and benefits, and they were given opportunities to expand on any of these. The proxy measures used in chapter 3 were coded as follows: Regarding the use of labor contractors, responses were coded as "routine" if a major segment of the operation was contracted every year; they were coded as "occasional" if contractors were used on a more ad hoc basis. Year-round employment was calculated as a proportion of permanent or near permanent (e.g., ten months per year) full-time employees to total number of laborers used, contracted or not. Thus, growers who provided part-time employment year round or permanent full-time employment for six months of the year were not coded high in this category. Growers who used only unpaid family labor were coded as such, but if the workforce included family labor plus a contracted workforce, the percentage of permanent employment was coded as 0. Growers that were more vertically integrated (i.e., with packing houses) tended to have higher year-round employment. Regarding pay and benefits, responses were coded as a composite of starting wages, health and welfare benefits, bonuses, and living expenses. Generally, all wages $.50 above the minimum wage of $5.75 were considered in the second category; above $7.50, in the highest ("unusual") category. Yet, if a grower offered exceptional benefits (e.g., good on-site living, paid health care, paid vacations, or real bonuses), this jumped them into a higher category. Piece rates were generally coded as minimum on the basis of the assumption that people work fewer hours as a whole with piece rates. If, however, growers guaranteed a certain minimum per pay period, piece rate work was counted in higher categories. Wages paid through contractors were not counted in this measure.

Notes

CHAPTER I

Epigraphs: Claire Cummings, "Some questions about the organic standards," on KPFA radio, February 6, 1998; Patricia Untermann, "Faith healing," *San Francisco Examiner*, April 19, 1998; Colin Duncan, *The centrality of agriculture: Between humankind and the rest of nature* (Montreal: McGill-Queen's University Press, 1996), 15; Wendell Berry, "Whose head is the farmer using? Whose head is using the farmer?" in *Meeting the expectations of the land*, ed. W. Jackson, W. Berry, and B. Colman (San Francisco: North Point Press, 1984), 24; Wendell Berry, *The unsettling of America: Culture and agriculture*, 2d ed. (San Francisco: Sierra Club Books, 1986), 219–20.

1. Even among those fully versed in the structural dynamics of the world food system, there is a tendency to frame organic agriculture as a binary opposite to industrial agriculture, and organic food to fast food, as if organic agriculture were immune to these broader dynamics (Friedmann 1992; Goodman 1999; Heffernan and Constance 1994; Whatmore 1995; cf. Friedland 1994a).

2. *Industrial agriculture* is not a straightforward term and is often conflated with *corporate agriculture*, for example. Chapter 4 will give more sustained attention to some of the various definitions and spell out the one favored in this book.

3. See James 1993 on the multiple meanings brought to organic food.

4. See Peters 1979 for an early social history that focuses on the first three of these threads.

5. The critique of industrial farming is not necessarily what motivates growth in the organic sector—at least in the United States. It appears that most organic food purchases are guided by vague health and environmental concerns and amorphous notions of quality, as a few studies (Hartman Group 1997; *The Packer* 1996) and a great deal of anecdotal evidence suggest. My own anecdotal

evidence includes shoppers' and diners' comments I overhear, as well as those I receive when I tell people about my work. A typical comment would be, "I don't care who produces it, just that it's grown without pesticides." Many others within the industry or movement corroborate these perceptions with similar anecdotes. Nevertheless, consumer perceptions and practices in regard to organic food remain strikingly under-studied, and it would be premature to interpret such surface understandings of organic agriculture among consumers as the product of either false consciousness or deep reflexivity (see DuPuis and Goodman 2002).

6. Beeman (1995), Clunies-Ross (1990a), Harwood (1990), and Mergentime (1994) have all written histories of the organic or sustainable agriculture movements that focus on the production aspect of the critique.

7. In 1942, Rodale started a magazine called *Organic Farming,* later renamed *Organic Gardening and Farming.* The deliberate use of the term *organic* makes him the undisputed father of the U.S. organic farming movement.

8. Although the first efforts to ban or limit chemicals were administered under the 1906 Pure Food Act, support for nonchemical agriculture was not integral to the pure food movement or its progeny. On the contrary, many agroecological ideals fly in the face of pure food notions. For instance, using natural enemies to fight pests or developing a "living soil" that stimulates microbial action are both anathema to efforts to sanitize food. Thus, even though notions of food safety undergird the movement for organic agriculture, this coupling remains uneasy, and controversy over it continues to manifest in regulatory battles.

9. See Blaikie 1985 and Watts 1983 for seminal academic contributions to these ideas.

10. The provincialism inherent to bioregionalism has not gone unnoticed. More damningly, organic farming has appealed to the worst of nationalist movements, precisely for its bioregionalist meanings. The appeal of organic farming to the British Nationalists in the 1930s was that it would be part of a program of national self-sufficiency (Reed 2001); for the Nazis, it was a recognition that it was dangerous to depend on imported agricultural inputs during wartime (Bramwell 1989).

11. The sustainable agriculture movement more generally has come to give inordinate attention to scientific research, scientific research institutions, and agricultural research policy, an emphasis that reinforces the privileged role of science and "the shorthand postulate that technology shapes social structure, rather than vice versa" (Buttel 1994, 31). Thus, "sustainability has come to be defined in terms of bolstering productivity (through reduction of use of purchased inputs) within a larger capitalistically or instrumentally rational framework" (33).

12. There is ample criticism of the notion of sustainability itself, which can be construed to mean sustainable economic growth for capitalist actors (Lele 1991; Sachs 1992). For this reason, Allen and colleagues (1991) justify the continued effort to define sustainable agriculture just so its successes are not defined solely by farm level resource conservation and profitability.

13. In marked contrast, Colin Duncan (1996) argues that the key to effective stewardship in England's period of high agrarian capitalism was a separation of

management and land control. Landowners' long-term interests in the fertility of the land compelled them to require extensive rotations in lease contracts, while owner-operators were solely led by market conditions, and thus tended to over-intensify production. Thus, the larger questions of whether landownership elicits sustainability or, reciprocally, whether sustainability demands ownership are both complicated and can only be answered historically and empirically.

14. "The modern failure of marriage that has so estranged the sexes from each other seems analogous to the 'social mobility' that has estranged us from our land, and the two are historically parallel. It may even be argued that these two estrangements are very close to being one, both of them having been caused by the disintegration of the household, which was the formal bond between marriage and the earth, between human sexuality and its sources of sexuality in the Creator" (Berry 1986, 124).

15. There is some evidence for this presumed reciprocity between the scale of the operation (i.e., sufficiency to support one household without the use of hired labor) and the ability to implement certain sustainable technologies. In the midwest corn belt, for instance, full-time family farms (as opposed to part-time family or quasi-capitalist farms) have been most likely to adopt a low chemical input tilling system, which involves a sequentially complex set of field operations (Lighthall and Roberts 1995, 325).

16. David Vaught's (1999) recent intervention, for example, which refutes the industrial character of specialty-crop agriculture by claiming that early horticultural growers had special moral commitments, does not undermine the essential class character of specialized fruit production in an analytical sense.

17. Through this inspiration, she also altered the meaning of "organic" in ways that, quite unintentionally, were clearly implicated in the trend that shifted organic from a movement to an industry.

18. A technical counterpart in southern California never really existed. The Division of Biological Control, once based in Riverside, was one of the University of California's flagship programs for its early success with controlling cottony-cushion scale, a disease that affects the cosmetics of oranges. Although the division later came up with technologies that helped organic farmers, such as *Bt* (an insecticide composed of the bacterium *Bacillus thuringiensis*), most of the staff never took a radical position. The problem was that biological control lacked commercial potential, and much of the work done through the division merely served to supplement chemical-based farming (Sawyer 1996).

19. Buyers sign up in advance to receive a weekly box of produce. In other types of CSAs, as they are called, consumers become equity investors so that they more fundamentally share the risk of farming.

20. The California Organic Foods Act of 1990 (COFA) requires all growers who sell crops they claim to be organically grown to register with the California Department of Food and Agriculture (CDFA), whether or not they choose to certify. Although the basis of Klonsky and Tourte's reports, these figures are widely believed to be understated. First, growers were not counted when registration fees were not paid up. Second, I counted at least fifty growers who were certified but not registered (which is technically illegal) and, thus, not counted. These

were primarily wine grape growers who were not selling the finished product as organic but who accounted for a significant amount of acreage. For this reason, the USDA's Economic Research Service reported a much higher amount of certified acreage (102,819) for that same year, although little could be done to control for multiple certifications (Cathy Greene, personal communication). Third, as noted by the authors, there were additional reporting incentives and procedural problems that encouraged understatement of scale. Finally, there are always growers who follow organic standards but refuse to participate in these regulatory schemes and, consequently, are never counted at all. Many in the organic industry hope that such discrepancies in data collection will eventually be rectified by the federal rule that went into effect in fall 2002.

21. In 1985, several growers were found to have used the highly toxic Aldicarb, usually used for cotton, in their watermelon fields. Then, in 1988, stories started leaking out regarding the Natural Resources Defense Council's 1989 report condemning the use of Alar as a growth regulator–ripening agent for apples on the basis that it was found to be highly carcinogenic.

22. Here it must be said that during the time that I was researching and writing this book, a federal rule for organic production was being negotiated, finalized, and implemented. As you will learn, aspects of this new regulatory scheme could substantially alter the dynamics of the organic industry. For this reason, I have chosen to end my analysis with the implementation of the federal rule. Because much of the basic regulatory framework remains intact, I do not expect the federal rule to alter the direction in which organic agriculture is headed. If anything, the federal rule is likely to exacerbate existing tendencies within the California organic sector.

CHAPTER 2

Epigraph: Leslie Aileen Duram, "A pragmatic study of conventional and alternative farmers in Colorado," *Professional Geographer* 49, no. 2 (1997): 202–13.

1. One must also consider those growers who have adopted most, but not all, of the practices now codified as organic. Some of these "near-organic" growers readily joined the fray when they realized it would require only one last step (usually eliminating herbicides), not a sea change in the way they were farming. Others chose to limit or even shun their involvement with organic production per se, seeing no market advantage or simply preferring to retain their "last resort" tools. Still others felt there were other, perhaps deeper, ways to promote sustainable agriculture than the organic label with all of its inconsistencies and biases. Some of these last growers are appreciably more zealous about alternative agriculture than many organic growers.

2. Friedmann (1992, 1993b) and others (Le Heron 1993; McMichael 1994) have posited these shifts as indicative of the nascence of a "third food regime:" a whole nexus of state, capital, and civil society relations around the delivery of food. From this analytical vantage point, the post–World War II surplus regime (1947–72) was characterized by national regulation, subsidized grain production, chronic food surpluses, and a commodity focus on mass-produced durable foods; the incipient "third" regime looks to be characterized by international

production-consumption links, international free trade regulation, the demise of farm-based price supports, and a shift to nontraditional exports and "niche" commodities, especially fresh fruits and vegetables. Whether this phase has assumed anywhere near the coherence to be called a regime is highly debatable (see, e.g., Campbell and Coombes 1999; Goodman and Watts 1994; Le Heron 1993). Consider, for instance, that fresh fruits and vegetables have been a cornerstone of the California economy for at least a century, and many of California's standard commodities (e.g., lettuce) were once considered specialty goods. Yet, there is no question that, as tendencies, these developments have created openings for different modalities in food production and consumption.

3. In the United States, changing national support for agriculture followed on the heels of the 1980s farm crisis when it became all too apparent that fifty years of price supports and production controls for certain "strategic" commodities had created chronic conditions of oversupply. Production controls as a way to boost prices were equally incompatible with efforts to expand exports through maintaining competitive pricing and gave other countries the incentive to protect their own domestic farm programs through trade restrictions and/or price supports (Friedmann 1993b; Le Heron 1993; Orden, Paarlberg, and Roe 1999). The United States' zealous promotion of agricultural free trade in the Uruguay Round of GATT was a final effort to address problems of chronic oversupply (Friedmann 1993b). While the Uruguay Round of GATT, which concluded in 1994, did not eliminate state support for national agricultures in the way free traders envisioned (nor did NAFTA, for that matter), it did establish a timetable for phasing out tariffs (Goodman and Watts 1997; Orden, Paarlberg, and Roe 1999). More recently, the 1996 Federal Agriculture Improvement and Reform (FAIR) Act, previously dubbed the Freedom-to-Farm Act, gave farmers in the United States increased planting flexibility by turning cash subsidies into fixed payments, "decoupled," so that cash supports of farmers would no longer be directly related to market prices or acreage planted (Orden, Paarlberg, and Roe 1999, 5). However, the 2002 farm bill, dubbed the Farm Security and Rural Investment Act, is considered a step backward in that it returns to massive subsidies for certain "strategic" commodities.

4. These two aspects of productivism are intrinsically related, because the diminishing importance of national food security in industrialized countries has brought more scrutiny of the side effects of agricultural productivity, including both (1) the environmental externalities of agricultural production, such as soil erosion, nutritive depletion, fouled water, and unconscionable effects on animal health, and (2) the impacts on food itself vis-à-vis its safety, nutritional content, and aesthetic qualities (Buttel 1994; Lowe, Marsden, and Whatmore 1994; Marsden 1992).

5. Social resistance to the by-products and practices of agricultural industrialization, whether in the form of increased demands for regulation or changes in consumption habits, can be seen as a modern example of Polanyi's (1944) double movement: an organic reaction to an unbridled market logic that leads to deterioration of the conditions on which production depends (see also Barham 1997; O'Connor 1989). O'Connor calls this the second contradiction of capitalism, "the process whereby capital is its own barrier or limit because of its self-

destructive forms of proletarianization of human nature and appropriation of labor and capitalization of external nature" (1989, 13).

6. As a consequence, demand for high-value foods almost necessarily comes from "relatively privileged, higher income, higher educated, well-traveled professionals increasingly concerned with food quality, safety, and variety," and "a relatively unprivileged strata less concerned and sophisticated about food variability, less educated, and only fitfully concerned about food safety" continues to eat mass-produced food (Friedland 1994b, 219). Echoes Friedmann: "While privileged consumers eat free-range chickens prepared through handicraft methods in food shops, restaurants or by domestic servants, mass consumers eat reconstituted chicken foods from supermarket freezers or fast food restaurants and dispossessed peasants eat none at all" (1992, 86).

7. This broad canvas of political and economic restructuring admittedly begs the question of individual change. After all, new or expanded organic operations do not simply appear out of thin air, nor are conventional growers converting to organic en masse. Incentives and disincentives to organic production are differentially constituted in space and time. Spatially, access to appropriate inputs, technical assistance, and markets all matter, and so does the health of the surrounding regional economy. Timing counts as well, especially when the goal is to "make a killing" in a new market. There are myriad other factors that affect grower decisions, including the availability of technologies to deal with particular crops, access to suitable land, individual risk profiles, and even grower attitudes and ethical dispositions. Many newly converted growers are simply early innovators. Thus, the purpose here is not to wholly disregard the ways in which personal beliefs count but to encourage a finer tuning, so that ideological convictions and individual choices are understood as being in reciprocal and evolving relationship with the political and economic contexts in which farmers are located.

8. Unfortunately, statistical data of growth in the organic sector are limited. Organic farming grew out of a culture that defied state intervention, and, for the state's part, organic lacked the legitimacy and importance to justify record keeping. Until it was required, many self-professed organic farmers did not join certification programs, and many others adopted organic practices without naming them so. In California, all of this changed with the passage of the COFA, which among other things required all growers to register with the CDFA and report basic farm level data. Enabling legislation, however, was not implemented until 1992, so 1992–93 is the first fiscal year in which data were collected. Prior to that, the only data kept were those by private certifiers and perhaps sales records of individual retailers, the latter of which were never sufficiently aggregated. Although record keeping among certifiers varies greatly in terms of accuracy and availability, it is fortuitous, for these purposes, that up until about 1990, California Certified Organic Farmers dealt with most California growers who chose to certify. As such, CCOF constituted the "formal" organic sector for most intents and purposes, making its records the best basis for describing growth in the organic sector up until 1992.

9. While some acreage figures were listed, I deemed them unreliable, because one key grower was listed as having substantially more acreage in 1972 than he has even today.

10. The registration requirement is a process separate from certification, the latter of which has been voluntary in California—all of which changed with the implementation of the federal rule in 2002. Between the enactment of the COFA and up until 2002, there were always more registered growers than certified growers.

11. In 1996 Muir Glen was bought out by Small Planet Foods, a Disney-related corporation, which also owns Fantastic Foods and previously owned Cascadian Farms, a major organic processor. A couple years later, General Mills purchased Muir Glen and Cascadian from Small Planet.

12. Since then, the operations manager has sat on the CCOF Board of Directors, representing the processing chapter.

13. This buyer-led, as opposed to producer-led, system in some respects resembles the globalized commodity chains that Gereffi and Korzeniewicz (1994) see as emblematic of flexible production networks. Gereffi and Korzeniewicz, however, are making claims about new systems of manufacturing, whereas mass food production has always been coordinated by marketers.

14. Apples are difficult to grow organically even with well-managed operations. These operations, which are "organic by neglect," often produce fruit that can be used only for low-grade purposes.

15. The federal Reclamation Act of 1902 imposed acreage restrictions on landholdings with water irrigation developed by the federal government. The original restriction was 160 acres per family; by the 1980s, the limit was raised to 960 acres. Compliance has never been whole-hearted. See, e.g., Hundley 1992; and Worster 1985.

16. These crops are eligible to be labeled "certified transitional," so they may reap higher prices than conventional crops do, but the transitional market has not really been established in California.

17. See Wargo 1998 for a detailed look at this regulatory history and Whorton 1974 for the previous history.

18. Methyl bromide is supposed to be completely phased out by 2005 in industrialized countries, according to the 1987 Montreal Protocol for abolishing ozone-depleting substances (Boulton 1997).

19. As urban dwellers have moved out to rural areas, conflict has heightened over pesticide use, odors, dust, noise, and other "nuisances" of farms. Many social conflicts at the rural-urban interface have been resolved with "softer" production schemes (Daniels and Bowers 1997; Handel 1998).

20. Sandra Steingraber's *Living Downstream* (1997), purposely modeled after *Silent Spring*, brings together heretofore uncorrelated EPA toxic-release inventories with cancer registry data. In my opinion, she makes a convincing argument that environmental contamination from the postwar petrochemical industry is the predominant cause of the contemporary increase in cancer rates.

CHAPTER 3

Epigraph: Michael Pollan, "Fried, mashed, or zapped with DNA?" *New York Times Magazine*, October 25, 1998.

1. Acreage is a highly inexact measure of scale because it is a poor indicator

of the complexity and intensity of any given operation. For one thing, in relation to the level of mechanization, there are obvious economies of scale in the production of field crops, and even certain produce crops, that simply do not exist for crops that require more delicate handling and/or intense management. Lower-value crops are characterized so in part because they require less labor. Second, some of the largest growers in purely acreage terms are contract growers, which also simplifies aspects of their operation. In other words, a grower farming wheat that is mechanically harvested on a contract basis may have several hundred acres of crops but has a much less complicated operation than a vertically integrated stone fruit grower on fifty acres who hires pickers and does his or her own sales. Third, using acres as a measure of scale minimizes the significance of the many operators who handle and market other growers' crops.

Still, there are also significant caveats for the use of sales as a measure of scale: (1) gross sales are "skewed" by higher crop values in which some elements may reflect economic and ground rents in addition to higher production costs (strawberries being the best example); (2), better managed (or more intensively cropped) farms appear to be of larger scale than farms of similar size but less well managed (or less intensively cropped) (Strange 1988); and (3) sales figures exhibit substantial variability from year to year, even when the same amount of acreage is farmed.

2. Clearly, there is more to tenure than land title. In the U.S. context particularly, the degree that land is mortgaged has important implications for farming practices. Farmers who are heavily mortgaged or who used their farm as a bank for working capital are more constrained in their abilities to experiment with alternative practices.

3. This misrepresentation is not a reflection on the integrity of their methods, only a reflection of the data they had to work with.

4. Besides the CIRS database and CCOF membership directory, sources for these statistics include the *Los Angeles Times* 1986; *PR Newswire* 1987; Carnal 1996; Stevenson 1987; and Groves 1991.

5. Still, conventional agribusiness involvement in organics, in terms of on-farm production, remains experimental, tentative, and protracted, and there is a significant amount of exit as well. For example, Sun World International, the second largest citrus marketer in California behind Sunkist and now owned by the Cadiz Land Company, attempted organic production on a limited amount of acreage but found no marketing outlet. (The main thrust of Cadiz's business has been buying up Mojave Desert land with water reserves in the hope of eventually marketing the water (Carnal 1996)). Harris Farms, which had 20,000 acres in crop production and ran an 80,000-head feedlot (Groves 1991), combined their 550 acres of certified organic acreage with two other Westlands growers in 1998, under the banner of Greenway Farms. The idea behind Greenway was to economize on scale because each farm had difficulty meeting its marketing obligations separately. Double D Farms of Coalinga, another large grower, experimented with organic production but leased out their 300 acres of certified land to Natural Selection when they experienced difficulties in growing crops. And Harlan and Dumars of Woodland, Jack Brothers and McBurney of Brawley, and La Brucherie Ranch of El Centro exited altogether, feeling that or-

ganic prices never seemed to accommodate the additional costs of growing organic and the regulatory hassle it entails. All the same, there are new entrants all the time, wanting to take a stab at the fastest growing sector in agriculture.

6. Small farms in California are larger than those placed in this category nationally, reflecting relatively high sales of high-value crops.

7. Actually, several of the large all-organic producers deal in some conventional product, either as a way not to flood the organic market (i.e., selling organic as conventional) or ostensibly to sign on more growers to ecological methods by giving them technical support in near-organic methods. In effect, this allows large operators to avoid organic regulations in markets where they get little benefit.

8. In any case, the axis of corporate versus family farms is a more salient category for the Midwest, where it more reliably signifies a distinction between capitalist farms and petty commodity producers (i.e., farms that do not depend on hired labor) (Gilbert and O'Connor 1996). In California, this crucial structural difference was eradicated a long time ago and never had much analytical purchase to begin with. In general, growers tend to choose ownership forms on the basis of tax and liability considerations. Moreover, there is increasing debate as to how much the corporate form in and of itself matters in terms of the social issues at stake (see, e.g., Welsh 1998).

9. Coincidentally, one is Cadiz International, which bought out Sun World International and its small organic operation. In processing, handling, and distribution, the story is quite different, of course, and Horizon Organic dairy, for example, is now publicly traded.

10. For tax reasons, many family-held farming corporations own no land and lease it from individual principals who are the owners of land. Since this is a case where ownership has not been substantially separated from control, these farms are counted as "owned" land, as is land that growers lease from other family members.

11. The principles behind organic are quite parallel to those of agroecology, as demonstrated in the CCOF handbook (CCOF 1998b). It is the rule making that makes organic narrower, as will be explained in chapter 6.

12. Indeed, it is only in prime areas that contiguous activity is sufficient for the contractors themselves to survive economically.

13. The potential liability of a worker using a disallowed substance surely contributes to this concern.

14. There is, however, a social division of labor on these farms between whites and Latinos. White employees work at the farmers' markets more often, for which they are almost always paid in cash; "Mexicans" are preferred for their skills as fieldworkers.

15. Some growers are actively reconstructing consumer tastes toward food that is local and seasonal and that fits well with an ecological farming strategy. In an extraordinary feat of producer control, aided by the dissemination of recipes and exhortations to buy seasonally, they have introduced their customers to the likes of kohlrabi, green garlic, and kale.

16. Because of extralocal availability of seasonal produce, the net of the region has been flung wider. Aside from the organic produce that it obviously "im-

ports," be it Washington State apples, Caribbean bananas, or Chilean raspberries, the northern California region has been quietly extended to include the Imperial Valley, Arizona, and Baja California, where many large organic firms now operate to provide such desirables as cherry tomatoes and baby lettuces in the dead of winter. While some may argue that this greatly expands product availability—often considered a good thing—others say such a broadening goes against the grain of a foodshed.

17. The 1999 OFRF national survey stated that 21 percent of growers know that their product reached foreign markets.

18. Of course, not all wholesale arrangements relinquish control. There may be scale economies in postharvest processing, for instance, which can be met through cooperation among growers. Some packing relationships are informal "sweetheart" deals, where one grower with the appropriate postharvest capacity packs or sells for other growers in the region. They tend to be run like marketing cooperatives, where participating growers simply pay their share of expenses and receive their share of revenue. Yet, only one true marketing cooperative exists for organic: an herb cooperative in Trinity County, which was partly funded by community development grants. At one point, growers in Yolo County had formed a marketing cooperative called Yo-Cal. It was short-lived and apparently failed because of poor management. Growers who lived through this experience express a clear preference for separate marketing, even though it involves competing with their friends and colleagues.

19. It is not only competition that causes dissonance among these movement growers; they also increasingly face compliance issues in areas such as labor, food safety, or environmental impacts, causing them to resent state regulation in these areas. It bears mentioning that many organic growers have strong libertarian tendencies anyway, stemming from the USDA's historical disregard for alternative agriculture and more recent frustration over organic rule making at both the state and federal levels.

CHAPTER 4

Epigraphs: Carey McWilliams, *Factories in the field* (Santa Barbara, Calif.: Peregrine Smith, 1935; reprint, Berkeley: University of California Press, 2000), 48; Karl Kautsky, *The agrarian question* (1899; reprint, London: Zwan Press, 1988), 284.

1. I must clarify here that Pollan drew some of his conclusions from my earlier article on the same topic (Buck, Getz, and Guthman 1997). Pollan also interviewed me in the course of preparing his piece.

2. In terms of on-farm production, concern with "the disappearing middle" (Buttel and LaRamee 1992) maps onto the agrarian populist imaginary, suggesting that the scale of production is an appropriate measure of agricultural industrialization.

3. Economic returns of mechanization in agriculture are minimal compared with returns of intensification (Scott 1998), so, at least with some crops, insufficiently capitalized growers can compete with scaled-up operations by working the land harder (cf. Cochrane 1993; Johnson and Ruttan 1994). In fact, low fixed

costs and flexible family labor may be a scale *advantage* in what are risky enterprises (Friedmann 1978; Goodman and Redclift 1991; Watts 1993).

4. In truth, Goodman, Sorj, and Wilkinson (1987) break this notion of appropriation into two processes. They use *appropriation* to refer to the process by which products and processes once integral to on-farm production are refashioned as inputs, making way for more factory-like production on the farm. They use *substitution* to refer to processes by which postproduction value added becomes such a high proportion of the total value of the commodity to the point that industrial processes may wholly substitute for rural products. For simplicity, I am using the term *appropriation* to capture the transfer of value from farmers to others in the commodity system.

5. Kautsky posited that direct on-farm production is of little interest to industrial capitals, which would leave it to producers who have either less power or other reasons to self-exploit.

6. The classical political economy theory of rent goes like this: All else being equal, access to better land translates into surplus profits for farmers on that land. Without having to apply more labor, they can get better yields simply from the land's unusual fertility. The source of these surplus profits is thus a "gift of nature," not derived from human effort. Yet, because land is both scarce and privately held, landowners have monopoly power over it. So, if better land fetches higher profits, landowners intervene to appropriate those extra profits, having the power to expel the farmer from that land. This ability of landowners to exercise such market control over even the worst land is the basis of what Marx termed absolute rent, the price that every farmer must pay to have access to land (Ball 1980; Harvey 1982; Walker 1974). Even when a farmer is also the landowner, it does not necessarily eradicate the rent relation. The selling price of land is rent capitalized, so some farmers pay rent through land purchase (Ball 1980, 304). More often, owner-occupancy conceals a mortgage or credit relation, where rent takes the form of interest (Harvey 1982, 365). In the case of freehold land that is handed down from generation to generation, "the income forgone by virtue of the fictitious capital locked up in the 'value' of the land cannot be cavalierly thrust aside" (Harvey 1982, 365).

The ability of landowners and creditors to appropriate rent effectively equalizes rates of profit among agricultural producers no matter what their resources. Those who can produce better yields pay higher rents—what are called differential rents. As a result, farmers must compete on the basis of new methods or lower wages; that is, they try either to increase productivity or to lower costs (Harvey 1982; see Ball 1980 on how rents reflect depressed agricultural wages). Only in fully developed land markets, where land is treated as a pure financial asset, will landowners not draw off all productivity gains. Recognizing that cooperation with capitalist producers will enhance ground rents, so the theory goes, landowners come to encourage technological innovation (Harvey 1982).

7. State subsidies as well are capitalized into land values. These include technical and research support provided by the land grant universities, price supports for certain commodities, cheap credit, and infrastructure development, all of which benefit producers unequally.

8. Land valuation (i.e., rent) for land with monopoly characteristics operates

differently. Monopoly rent derives from the scarcity of land with exceptional properties in terms of quality or location. In this case, it is the *producer* of the agricultural commodity who has a monopoly, because the product can be sold at a monopoly price (Ball 1980; Harvey 1982). Napa Valley vineyards, for instance, exact monopoly versus differential rents, because it is the Napa location (i.e., the label), not its higher productivity, that drives the market in land. The rent is based on a return that the producer gets in the market for a specially valued wine grape, which in the first instance is independent of the relationship with the landowner (Ball 1980). That relationship comes into play when the producer must pay the asking price for renting the land to continue growing the valued crop. Harvey (1982) plays down monopoly rent as being "of peripheral concern to any study of general commodity production" because it is based on "prestige and status" (350); however, monopoly rent assumes greater importance where high-value crops become central to the agricultural economy because it can thrust land values above an established equilibrium.

9. For other periodizations see, for example, Jelinek 1979; Leibman 1983; and Worster 1985.

10. These immigrant specialty croppers included, among others, Japanese truck farmers, Italian and Armenian viticulturists, and Chinese fruit growers, all of whom came with substantial expertise in different aspects of specialty crop production. The Alien Land Laws, designed to stave off competition from Japanese growers, and anti-Asian sentiment in general forced persistent tenancy on some of these groups, but others starting off as tenants were able to buy back land and become small freehold farmers (e.g., European immigrants).

11. In 1910, DiGiorgio bought Earl Fruit Company, a distributor, and between 1915 and 1939 acquired 15,855 "parched" San Joaquin acres, which were later transformed by irrigation. By the 1930s, it was the largest fruit distributor and second largest wine maker. Cal Pak, in comparison, started from a 1916 merger of several packing companies. It owned and leased several thousand of its own acres and also contracted with thousands of growers, which was possible only with the guarantee of irrigation. In 1937, for instance, it bought crops from 6,611 growers (Jelinek 1979).

12. This is in reference to a long-standing debate, rooted in Kautsky [1899] 1988 but mainly taken up in rural sociology, about the class relations of farmers (see, for instance, Friedmann 1980; Goodman and Redclift 1985; Mann 1989; Mooney 1983).

13. Paris green, an arsenical compound, was toxic enough and had to be certified by the University of California (Stoll 1995), but it was supplanted by the more deadly lead arsenic, which remained the most popular insecticide until DDT (Whorton 1974).

14. Biological control refers to the use of predators, parasites, and pathogens to control insect pests.

15. At the same time, the Salinas Valley experienced a reinvigoration of moderately sized farms: many erstwhile sugar beet contractors were able to break away and grow lettuce and other fresh vegetables as well as barley and dry beans, marketed through growers' cooperatives and specialty shipping firms (FitzSimmons 1986).

16. Crop price support payments were an additional subsidy that affected California agriculture more than is often recognized. In 1969, 71 of the largest 178 federal payments went to California (Jelinek 1979). Jelinek also notes that because these payments had no maximum ceilings until 1970, large-scale farmers received the lion's share of payments; J. G. Boswell, the largest cotton grower in California, received over $7 million in support one year.

17. According to Gilbert and Akor (1988), intensive drylot dairying owes its existence to the urbanization of southern California. As the population grew, dairy farmers were able to sell their land at extraordinarily high prices, which gave them the capitalization for industrial production in the valleys farther east. Dairy's consistency (table 6) thus speaks directly to the interplay between escalating land values and intensive production. As further proof, dairy land in southern California was valued at $135,000 per acre in 2000, reflecting comparative residential land values and high demand from the Los Angeles market (Burnham 2000) but also, no doubt, the ability to produce more on less land.

18. Although this model was developed primarily to the specifications of the vegetable industry, it set a broader standard, so that by the year 2000, 45 percent of the value of all fruits and vegetables produced was earned through marketing contracts (Economic Research Service 2000a).

19. In the 1930s, agriculture employed a substantially white labor force for the first and only time, when dust bowl refugees migrated westward. As befitting the times sociopolitically, this was also the era of the bloodiest labor struggles (see Daniel 1981; Mitchell 1996).

20. Wells (1996) argues that the labor-intensive nature of specialty crops is precisely the factor that buffers them from crises, because it lessens the cost-price squeeze of high capital investments in machinery and land. As evidence, she notes that in the 1980s some growers discontinued mechanical procedures and readopted manual techniques, also because the labor force had been made more malleable by the swell of undocumented immigration. Thus, she suggests, the move to high-value crops was as least as much motivated by the availability of cheap and plentiful variable capital relative to the high costs of fixed capital as by the certainty of higher per acre income.

21. The decline in field crop production was precipitated by two factors: price declines made them less attractive, and the government commodity program required growers to set aside acreage in those years to establish program eligibility (Villarejo 1989, 2).

22. Labor contractors proliferated on the heels of the UFW successes and were employed, in part, to break the union (Martin 1987). More recently, they have been used for growers to evade INS-wrought liability and other "paperwork" involved in being an employer, such as worker's compensation. Also, as a virulent reaction to escalation of the border control, almost all California growers these days claim that labor shortages exist; therefore, labor contractors are felt to help with recruitment. Paradoxically, they help reproduce the labor surplus that contributes to the ongoing "casualization" of the California agricultural labor market (Martin 1987).

23. The term *self-exploitation* derives from the work of Chayanov ([1924] 1986) and Kautsky ([1899] 1988), both of whom address the capacity of peas-

ants to work harder in order to keep their own land in times of farm differentiation.

24. As Patricia Allen (1999) argues, the construction of desire around notions of health, freshness, and guiltless taste indulgence is highly ironic, given
that strawberries are grown in the most toxic and unjust of circumstances. Strawberries receive an average of three hundred pounds per acre of pesticide active
ingredients per year, over twice that of the next most heavily applied crop. Basically, there are four very toxic chemicals used in most conventional strawberry
production: two sterilize the soil (including the nerve gas methyl bromide), and
two are fungicides listed by the EPA as probable human carcinogens (captan and
iprodione) (Liebman 1997).

25. At the same time, many individual farming communities have been dis-
rupted or even dislocated. Major swaths of coastal southern California farmland
were taken out of production some time ago, as were the once-thriving dairies of
the "inland empire" (Riverside and San Bernardino counties), which have since relocated to Kern County—greatly improving prospects for alfalfa farmers in that
region. Some of the farmers who fled to the inland valleys are now coming under
pressure again, for there has been substantial real estate development around
major towns and cities of the Central Valley (e.g., Sacramento, Stockton, Fresno)
within commuting distance of the San Francisco Bay Area. Particularly in the
coastal areas of Oxnard, Santa Maria, Salinas, and Hollister—still known for high-
quality farming land—agricultural land values have continued to escalate, less because of "scarcity" than because expectations of residential and commercial real
estate are imputed in the cost of land (Sanders 1998). According to a study of the
Oxnard-Ventura area in the South Coast region, even land in designated greenbelt
zones has become subject to speculation. When rents become too low relative to
debt payments, landowners are forced to rezone the land (Moore 1998).

26. The amount of land going into vineyard production has become highly
controversial in Sonoma County. Some say vineyard production provides a good
way to protect land from housing development; others worry that it will permanently drive up land prices (Podger 1999). Recent controversy over prophylactic spraying of the glassy-wing sharpshooter has tightened the alliance between
advocates of open space and organic farmers, who also object to the erosion
promoted by planting on steep slopes.

27. For this reason, growers interviewed in San Diego County were vehemently opposed to development restrictions, because most of them had purchased their land in expectation of subdividing it to pay for retirement. Few
growers are willing to foreclose the opportunity for themselves or their heirs to
sell their land to developers (Sanders 1998).

28. Conservation easements are the difference in value between what a property can fetch on the open market and what it would be worth with a restriction
on it for certain purposes. Easements are supposed to encapsulate the differential value between pure agricultural land and "highest and best use." Landowners who create an easement on their property and donate it in perpetuity can use
it as a charitable deduction for income tax purposes. Conservation easements
may also reduce property taxes and lower the value of the property for estate tax
purposes (Daniels and Bowers 1997).

29. Furthermore, factors that might have made organic production different have been overridden by the political construction of the farm labor market in California. The created availability of cheap harvest labor has historically made labor-intensive specialty crop production viable where otherwise the costs of such fruits would seem prohibitive, perhaps leaving such production to home gardens or rendering it a sideline to a more integrated calorie-intensive production system. The manufactured vulnerability of farm labor has allowed growers to specialize unreflectively in one or two crops, whereas laborers move from crop to crop on a tenuous basis. Their vulnerability also accomplishes the need for their care and commitment (Wells 1996), although not always perfectly.

CHAPTER 5

Epigraph: Philip Fradkin, *The seven states of California: A natural and human history* (Berkeley: University of California Press, 1997).

1. In the 1970s the alluvial benches above the Salinas Valley were put into wine grapes (Eysberg 1990); more recently, in a series of valleys just inland from the coast, involving Monterey, San Luis Obispo, and Santa Barbara counties, huge swaths of oak woodland have been tilled and planted to wine grapes, owned by several large wine consortia, such as Beringer, Mondavi, and Kendall-Jackson. Such plantings have turned out to be highly controversial in several respects: they have involved what may be unnecessary destruction of oak woodland in the face of an imminent crisis of overproduction (many vineyards are not even bearing yet) (Boxall 1999); and premium production on a mass scale threatens to wipe out many of the small boutique producers who started the very wave that corporate wineries are riding.

2. To some extent, those interested in pursuing organic production had little choice but to farm in the margins; prime vegetable land in California is generally leased, and initially few landlords were interested in taking on organic tenants.

3. See Almaguer 1994, for example, on how newly arriving whites were able to pry land from the once thriving *ranchero* elite. Commercial debt, competition, and intermarriage all played a part.

4. In California, real estate speculation played a major part in the development of agricultural land (Davis 1992; Henderson 1999). Much of this land was originally obtained from the federal government in the form of railroad grants, statehood grants, and aberrations of the Homestead Act of 1862, which limited grants to individuals to 160 acres.

5. On average, wages are lower in the prime agricultural regions, where, paradoxically, labor markets are fully developed. The key exceptions are the coastal regions, where the social coordination required in highly mechanized vegetable harvests has given a modicum of power to workers, although some of the gains from unionization have been eroded (Bardacke 1999; Thomas 1985).

6. So salient are these differences that crop-specific regional land values started to be reported separately in California by the National Agricultural Statistical Services starting in the 1950s.

7. The web site of the California Chapter of American Society of Farm Man-

agers and Rural Appraisers provides a range for land values in different areas. These statistics reflect the approximate middle of the range.

8. Although there is substantial overlap, I did not use the same regions as Klonsky and Tourte's study (1998b), which is purposely overaggregated to protect grower confidentiality. Their particular divisions missed what I felt was some critical ethnographic differentiation within California. Nor did I use CCOF chapters as regions, for they are more the reflection of their institutional particularities than the sector as a whole. While I sacrificed some basis of comparison, I was able to use Klonsky and Tourte's earlier study (1995), based on the state's fiscal year 1992–93 data, which are broken down by counties.

9. Although generally treated as one region, I treat the eastern and western parts of the San Joaquin as distinct.

10. Since many dairies relocated to this area to escape the real estate pressures in Riverside County, alfalfa hay does economically well in this region.

11. Many grapes are grown organically mainly because the allowance of sulphur dust makes it easy to do so, but little wine is produced organically because the disallowance of sulfites makes it difficult to do so. Even though wine with sulfites can be labeled as "made with organic grapes," winemakers do not want the extra burden of segregating their organic grapes and monitoring their growers. Fetzer has its own organic line, "Bonterra," made with grapes from its own estate.

CHAPTER 6

Epigraphs from published sources: John Mackey, cited in Ronnie Cummins, *U.S. organic standards: The battle continues,* Food Bytes e-mail publication no. 8, Pure Food Campaign/SOS (Save Organic Standards), April 21, 1998; CCOF, *Certification Handbook* (Santa Cruz: California Certified Organic Farmers, 1998), 49.

1. As Nowacek (1997) points out, reference to food now as just "organic," as opposed to "organically grown," is more convenient parlance but at the same time elides the process orientation that organic agriculture is supposed to instantiate.

2. That said, the distinction between movement and industry involves more an analytical divide than a clean mapping of players. Most organic producers sell their products and, thus, are subject to some market logic; however, those who are involved in organics primarily for pecuniary reasons still maintain an interest in upholding organic meanings. Accordingly, most organic growers are inclined to mix movement and industry perspectives in any given discourse. Still, as the organic movement has become more business-oriented, the language by which participants refer to themselves has evolved from "organic movement" to "organic community" to "organic industry." "Organic community" seems the preferred parlance, because it downplays some of the underlying tensions that still exist.

3. The USDA did not repeal this rule until 1999, only after its first proposed federal rule for organic production caused such a furor.

4. Still, even without a formal standard, scale constraints are imputed into agroecological ideals in certain ways, and many larger-scale growers feel there is an implicit bias against them. As one grower put it, "CCOF had it in for anyone with more than ten acres."

5. What follows is taken from Nowacek 1997.

6. It should be noted that the detected presence of pesticide residues on food is determined by the inherent environmental persistence of any given pesticide but has little to do with its relative health or environmental safety. Thus, for instance, captan will consistently show up in residue tests on strawberries, but methyl bromide will not.

7. This quote is from Nowacek's interview of Scowcroft (Nowacek 1997).

8. In cases of unintentional drift, generally the crop is decertified as opposed to the land. The purpose here is to protect the grower from false allegations and to support the grower should he or she seek restitution (CCOF 1998b).

9. Apparently, Sir Albert Howard found that protecting crops with any sprays and powders was unscientific and unsound, but Rodale, the pragmatist, came to accept botanical and microbial pesticides such as pyrethrum, rotenone, ryania, and *Bt* (!) as necessary evils (Quarles 1995, 10).

10. Hybridization overcame two important obstacles to private investment in plant breeding and hence development of genetically engineered varieties: (1) Since hybrid seed does not breed true after one generation, it forced farmers to buy new seed every year; that is, it allowed commodification of the seed itself. (2) Since seed became a matter of invention, it enabled patent protection for breeders; that is, it furthered protection of intellectual property rights in seed development (Kloppenburg 1988).

11. For these reasons, a few radical growers have moved toward "live power"—for example, the use of livestock for tilling.

12. These are tricky issues with brand-name products, especially because *public right to know* is creeping into the organic lexicon. In many brand-name products, the active ingredient is natural but the inert ingredients, such as adjuvants, may be synthetic or otherwise unacceptable. Such materials remain undisclosed as a matter of trade secret under the Federal Insecticide, Fungicide, and Rodenticide Act, purportedly to encourage innovation. Some input suppliers, moreover, refuse to submit their product to extensive review, seeing it as a regulatory burden.

13. In terms of labor provisions, FVO required nothing beyond following laws that already exist within the United States.

14. Inspectors were expected to report facts and not make certification decisions. A separate association, the Independent Organic Inspectors Association, trained and accredited inspectors. Inspectors were either employed or contracted by certifying organizations, and many inspectors worked for more than one certifier.

15. Specifically, IFOAM asks that "social security needs should be met including benefits such as maternity, sickness and retirement benefit" and "all employees should have equal wages when doing the same job," but there are no particular standards recognizing rights to collective bargaining, for example.

CHAPTER 7

Epigraph: Nicolas Lampkin and S. Padel, "Organic farming and agricultural policy in western Europe: An overview," in *The economics of organic farming,* ed. Lampkin and Padel (Wallingford, England: CAB International, 1994), 439, 454.

1. SCS's NutriClean program is much larger than its organic clientele.

2. In conventional production, coddling moth in fresh-market apples is often controlled by Guthion (azinphosmethyl), a material that has been on the regulatory chopping block. Although pheromone-disruption technology has had some successes in organic systems, it is very expensive and still not as efficacious as commercial sprays. Consequently, cull rates are significantly higher in organic than in conventional production.

3. The real time involved to build the soils back up after their withdrawal from chemical treatments to a point where yields return to or even surpass conventional standards is thought to be up to ten years.

4. The Conservation Reserve Program, a statute of the 1985 farm bill, paid growers to remove what was considered highly erodible crop land from production on a voluntary basis for ten years. It follows that when prices were high, fewer would be enrolled. Accordingly, much of the land that was freed up after the first ten years of the program was brought back into production in the late 1990s.

5. The strategy of leasing abandoned and/or marginal land for organic production is not without its costs. Fallow land is not that easy to come by, and where it exists, it is often erosive, noncontiguous to agricultural services, or hilly. As many growers say, unfarmed acreage is so for a reason. By starting their organic programs on land that is evidently marginal, growers not only lessen the likelihood of success; they also undermine some of the land conservation goals that one presumes go hand-in-hand with organic agriculture. It is hardly surprising that those who pursue this strategy are disappointed with the results. Some even revert to converting conventional acreage, despite the three years it takes to get it certified.

6. Other certifiers operating outside California required nonorganic fields to be treated with least-toxic methods, but none of the California certifiers asked this. The federal rule disallows any specific requirements such as these, but it is unclear how the rule will affect what certifiers can claim as organic principles in their written guidelines.

7. See also Campbell 1996 for parallels in New Zealand organic vegetable production.

8. Clearly, there are tremendous crop specificities (made all the more complicated with polycultural cropping systems) and variations in management technique and technologies applied. Yet, the most widely published studies of the economics of organic production are based on grain-legume rotations, not the horticultural crops that dominate California agriculture.

9. While all farmers self-exploit to various degrees, the labor substituted for chemicals on a tightly held organic farm often falls to the farmer.

10. In this light, it is interesting that some of these growers are trying to de-

velop a mechanical harvester to minimize the labor component of production, because this would offer even more advantages to well-capitalized operators.

11. This project was initiated as part of a Trinity County community development program that seeks to encourage high-value agricultural production.

12. The "feed the world" refrain often heard among conventional growers emanates from a broader discourse within the agrofood industry that justifies the pursuit of high-yielding technologies to counter world food shortage. The idea that underproduction is the source of hunger is, of course, widely contested.

13. Of course plenty of growers do not identify with either one of the visions. They want to uphold existing barriers to retain superprofits and market share and have little engagement with the moral politics at all. One such grower felt that "taking organic mainstream" would destroy his livelihood. "Those guys that want [the sector] to grow are those running on a percentage."

14. Some who promoted a federal rule recognize that, in its finality, it serves as a floor, and thus, efforts should be made to address social and ecological issues outside that final definition.

15. To comply with the new federal rule, the label for this program is distinct from the USDA organic label.

CHAPTER 8

Epigraph: Joan Dye Gussow, cited in Kim Severson, "Agribusiness goes organic: New law and growing appetite for wholesome foods bring mega-growers to the table," *San Francisco Chronicle*, October 13, 2002.

1. This points to one of the ways in which the meaning of *organic* can be deeply conservative. In addition to the definition of *organic* as nonsynthetic (a latter-day meaning), the etymology of *organic* suggests holism, a necessary interrelationship of parts. This sense of *organic* conjures up "natural" forms of social-ecological organization, suggesting a return to a not-so-just premodern past.

2. As noted by Romm (2001), at the same time that the federal government was giving land away to whites in the American West, postslavery land reform was failing in the South.

3. That said, Walter Goldschmidt's (1947) famous study showing how large farms deteriorate the quality of life in rural communities was based on two California communities (see Guither 1983 as an example of a more recent take on that argument; Buttel 1983 for a critique). While Goldschmidt's theory still holds some validity, to me it suggests that the underlying problem may be one of xenophobia. In California, that is, where a large farm is not the equivalent of a reduced workforce, the issue may rest on who is counted as part of the community (and who has income sufficient to have multiplier effects). Also, unlike in the Midwest, in California mechanization was not the key factor that contributed to a reduction of the farm population and the concomitant decline in rural living (cf. Buttel 1983). Indeed, mechanization was always epiphenomenal in specialty crop production, often contingent on the state of labor relations (Friedland 1984; Wells 1996).

4. Don Villarejo, past executive director of the California Institute for Rural

Studies, has, in fact, observed the opposite, although the definitive study is yet to be done.

5. The United States as a whole has seen an increase in small-farm acreage and numbers, which is largely attributed to the growth in part-time farming and hobby farming. Like these organic farms, many such farms are subsidized by other sources of income or by their ability to sell high-value specialty products (Buttel and LaRamee 1992).

6. There are trenchant similarities between these mechanisms and those driving land degradation in the Third World, as theorized in earlier works of political ecology. Watts (1987), for instance, argued that peasant producers squeezed by declining terms of trade will either consume less or produce more, in either case creating superexploitation of land and labor (see also Blaikie and Brookfield 1987; and Blaikie 1985).

7. In this light, it is unfortunate that the U.S. position in the World Trade Organization is to discourage the European Union from deeply subsidizing its agricultural production.

8. Conservation easements are one such policy instrument, although their current structure benefits already wealthy landowners. See chapter 4, note 28.

9. I use the awkward term *eaters* here to differentiate from consumers and the associated discourses of market choice.

10. In addition, many subscription farms end up buying and/or trading food from other farms to ensure that consumers are happy with the box they get and are constantly having to deal with buyers who expect off-season produce. For their part, consumers feel a lack of choice in what they get and pressure to work on the farm. In other words, some of the experiments with subscription farming have been frustrating for both parties, given the way people are used to thinking about food (DeLind 1998).

11. In this vein, it is important to note that the only interviewed organic grower with a union contract farmed on leased land. Being undercapitalized, he claimed, allowed him to pay a union wage and still make a profit.

APPENDIX

1. In most cases, I did not cite growers by name or other identifying information, unless information was otherwise publicly available (e.g., in newspaper articles). The purpose was either to protect confidentiality, as requested by the grower, or to suggest that such comments were typical.

2. Klonsky and Tourte's studies do not include conventional acreage, so farms that might be very large show up as small ones in these studies when they have only twenty acres or so in organic production (Klonsky and Tourte 1998a, b; Klonsky et al. 2001).

3. I had to take what growers said at face value. I am not an organic inspector (though more than one grower suspected that I was), and I am in no position to say whether growers followed practices as they stated, unless I witnessed specific examples or abuses.

Glossary

AGROECOLOGY the science of sustainable agriculture

ALTERNATIVE AGRICULTURE an umbrella term for agronomic practices that are opposed to conventional agriculture, including sustainable, organic, low-input, biodynamic, and regenerative practices. Alternative agriculture also refers to alternative crops, new uses for traditional crops, and crops grown for industrial production.

BIODYNAMIC AGRICULTURE a nonchemical method of agriculture that is both spiritual and proactive in its farming prescriptions. It is based on a series of lectures given by Austrian philosopher Rudolf Steiner in 1924.

COMMUNITY SUPPORTED AGRICULTURE a direct financial relationship between particular farms and groups of consumers through, for instance, advance purchases of food or equity investments

CONVENTIONAL AGRICULTURE high-input, chemical-intensive agriculture; also known as mainstream agriculture; used as a term opposite *organic agriculture* and *alternative agriculture*.

INTEGRATED PEST MANAGEMENT (IPM) an approach to crop protection that combines biological, cultural, physical, and least toxic chemical tools and uses more toxic chemical tools only as a last resort.

NATURAL FOODS foods processed and packaged without certain chemical additives. The use of the term *natural* in labeling is regulated by the FDA in the United States.

ORGANIC AGRICULTURE a farming system that largely avoids the use of synthetically produced inputs by incorporating practices that restore, maintain, and enhance natural means of crop protection and fertility management. Un like other terms in alternative agriculture, the use of the term *organic* is regulated, giving it significant power in the marketplace.

PERMANENT AGRICULTURE a precursor to today's sustainable agriculture and a movement that arose directly out of the dust bowl tragedy. While the focus of permanent agriculture was on soil conservation, its concept incorporated ideas of interdependence and organicism.

SUBSCRIPTION FARM a form of community supported agriculture in which consumers make an advance commitment to purchase food from a farm in exchange for which they receive a weekly box of food chosen by the farm management.

SUSTAINABLE AGRICULTURE another broad term for nonconventional agriculture. As applied in the United States, sustainable agriculture usually refers to a system of agricultural production and distribution that integrates environmental health with economic profitability. When applied to Third World settings, goals of social and economic equity receive more emphasis.

References

Ableman, Michael. 1993. *From the good earth: A celebration of growing food around the world*. New York: Harry N. Abrams.

Agricultural Research Service. 1958. *Current developments in the farm real estate market: November 1957 to March 1958*. Washington, D.C.: U.S. Department of Agriculture.

Allen, F. 1971. Postscript to the California Growers Meeting. *Organic Gardening and Farming*, June.

Allen, John C., and Kevin Bernhardt. 1995. Farming practices and adherence to an alternative agriculture paradigm. *Rural Sociology* 60 (2): 297–309.

Allen, Patricia. 1999. Panelist: Alternatives to agribusiness? Exceptionalism revisited. Eleventh Annual Conference of the California Studies Association, at Clark Kerr Campus Conference Center, Berkeley, Calif.

Allen, Patricia, and Martin Kovach. 2000. The capitalist composition of organic: The potential of markets in fulfilling the promise of organic agriculture. *Agriculture and Human Values* 17 (3): 221–32.

Allen, Patricia, and Carolyn Sachs. 1993. Sustainable agriculture in the United States: Engagements, silences, and possibilities for transformation. In *Food for the future*, ed. P. Allen. New York: John Wiley and Sons.

Allen, Patricia, Debra Van Dusen, Jackelyn Lundy, and Stephen Gleissman. 1991. Integrating social, environmental, and economic issues in sustainable agriculture. *American Journal of Alternative Agriculture* 6 (1): 34–39.

Almaguer, Tomás. 1994. *Racial fault lines: The historical origins of white supremacy in California*. Berkeley: University of California Press.

Altieri, Miguel. 1995. *Agroecology: The science of sustainable agriculture*. Boulder: Westview Press.

Altieri, Miguel, J. Davis, and K. Burroughs. 1983. Some agroecological and socioeconomic features of organic farming in California. *Biological Agriculture and Horticulture* 1: 97–107.

American Vegetable Grower. 1996. Large farms getting larger. October, 10–11.

Arce, Alberto, and Terry Marsden. 1994. The social construction of international food: A new research agenda. *Economic Geography* 69 (3): 293–311.

Ball, Michael. 1980. On Marx's theory of agricultural rent—a reply to Ben Fine. *Economy and Society* 9 (3): 304–26.

Bardacke, Frank. 1999. Panelist: Alternatives to agribusiness? Exceptionalism revisited. Eleventh Annual Conference of the California Studies Association, at Berkeley, Calif.

Barham, Bradford, Stephen G. Bunker, and Denis O'Hearn. 1994. *States, firms and raw materials: The world economy and ecology of aluminum.* Madison: University of Wisconsin Press.

Barham, Elizabeth. 1997. Social movements for sustainable agriculture in France: A Polanyian perspective. *Society and Natural Resources* 10 (3): 239–49.

Barnett, Tracy L. 1996. Couple turns green into gold. *Santa Cruz Sentinel,* April 4.

Baur, John E. 1959. *The health seekers of southern California, 1870–1900.* San Marino, Calif.: Huntington Library.

Beardsworth, Alan, and Teresa Keil. 1997. *Sociology on the menu.* London: Routledge.

Beck, Ulrich. 1992. *Risk society: Towards a new modernity.* Translated by M. Ritter. Edited by M. Featherstone. Theory, Culture, and Society. Thousand Oaks, Calif.: Sage Publications.

Beeman, Randal S. 1995. "A green and permanent land": Agriculture in the age of ecology, 1935–1985. Ph.D. dissertation, History, Iowa State University, Ames.

Belasco, Warren J. 1989. *Appetite for change.* New York: Pantheon.

Bell, David, and Gill Valentine. 1997. *Consuming geographies: We are where we eat.* London: Routledge.

Benton, Ted. 1989. Marxism and natural limits: An ecological critique and reconstruction. *New Left Review* 178: 51–86.

Berry, Wendell. 1986. *The unsettling of America: Culture and agriculture.* 2d ed. San Francisco: Sierra Club Books.

Beus, Curtis E., and Riley E. Dunlap. 1990. Conventional versus alternative agriculture: The paradigmatic roots of the debate. *Rural Sociology* 55 (4): 590–616.

———. 1994. Agricultural paradigms and the practice of agriculture. *Rural Sociology* 59 (4): 620–35.

Blaikie, Piers. 1985. *The political economy of soil erosion in developing countries.* London: Longman Development Studies.

Blaikie, Piers, and Harold Brookfield. 1987. *Land degradation and society.* London: Methuen.

Blank, Steven C. 2000. Some facts about farmland values. *Agriculture and Resource Economics Update,* summer, 3–4.

Bonanno, Alessandro. 1987. *Small farms: Persistence with legitimation.* Boulder: Westview Press.

Boulton, Leyla. 1997. Accord on ozone depleting chemicals. *Financial Times,* September 19.

Bourdieu, Pierre. 1984. *Distinction: A social critique of the judgment of taste.* Translated by R. Nice. Cambridge, Mass.: Harvard University Press.

Boxall, Bettina. 1999. Vineyard neighbors see only wrath from grapes. *Los Angeles Times,* February 18.

Boyd, William, Scott Prudham, and Rachel Schurman. 2001. Industrial dynamics and the problem of nature. *Society and Natural Resources* 14 (7): 555–70.

Bramwell, Anna. 1989. *Ecology in the twentieth century: A history.* London: Yale University Press.

Brass, Tom. 1997. Popular culture, populist fiction(s): The agrarian utopiates of A. V. Chayanov, Ignatius Donnelly and Frank Capra. *Journal of Peasant Studies* 24 (3): 153–90.

Brussel, Juli. 2002. Collaborative marketing through MAICs: OFARM offers organic farmers collective bargaining power. *Organic Farming Research Foundation Information Bulletin,* fall, 1, 4–5.

Buck, Daniel, Christina Getz, and Julie Guthman. 1996. *Consolidating the commodity chain: Organic farming and agribusiness in northern California.* Oakland: Institute for Food and Development Policy.

———. 1997. From farm to table: The organic vegetable commodity chain of northern California. *Sociologia Ruralis* 37 (1): 3–20.

Burnham, T. J. 2000. Liquid assets. *California Farmer,* November.

Business Wire. 1999. North America's leading organic certifier projects continued robust growth in 1999. January 25.

Buttel, Frederick H. 1983. Farm structure and rural development. In *Farms in transition,* ed. D. E. Brewster, W. D. Rasmussen, and G. Youngberg. Ames: Iowa State University Press.

———. 1992. Environmentalization: Origins, processes, and implications for rural social change. *Rural Sociology* 57 (1): 1–27.

———. 1993. The production of agricultural sustainability: Observations from the sociology of science and technology. In *Food for the future,* ed. P. Allen. New York: John Wiley and Sons.

———. 1994. Agricultural change, rural society and the state in the late twentieth century. In *Agricultural restructuring and rural change in Europe,* ed. D. Symes and A. J. Jansen. Wageningen, The Netherlands: Wageningen University.

Buttel, Frederick H., and Pierre LaRamee. 1992. The "disappearing middle": A sociological perspective. In *Towards a new political economy of agriculture,* ed. W. H. Friedland, L. Busch, F. H. Buttel, and A. P. Rudy. Boulder: Westview Press.

Byrne, P. J., U. C. Toensmeyer, C. L. German, and H. R. Juller. 1991. Analysis of consumer attitudes toward organic produce and purchase likelihood. *Journal of Food Distribution Research* 22 (2): 49–62.

Cacek, Terry, and Linda L. Langner. 1986. The economic implications of organic farming. *American Journal of Alternative Agriculture* 1 (1): 25–29.

California Chapter of the American Society of Farm Managers and Rural Appraisers (Cal ASFMRA). 2000. Trends in agricultural land and lease values. www.calasfmra.com/landvalues/2000/index.html. Accessed January 2001.

California Department of Food and Agriculture. 1987. *California agriculture: Statistical review*. Sacramento: State of California.

―――. 2000. California agricultural statistics. Available from www.cdfa.ca .gov/statistics/california.html. Accessed February 2000.

California Service Agency. 1997. *California agricultural directory*. Sacramento: State of California.

Campbell, Hugh. 1996. *Recent developments in organic food production in New Zealand, Part 1: Organic food exporting in Canterbury*. Research Report #1. Dunedin, New Zealand: Department of Anthropology, University of Otago.

Campbell, Hugh R., and Brad L. Coombes. 1999. Green protectionism and organic food exporting from New Zealand: Crisis experiments in the breakdown of Fordist trade and agricultural policies. *Rural Sociology* 64 (2): 302–19.

Carnal, Jim. 1996. California's Cadiz Land Co. acquires Sun World International Inc. *Bakersfield Californian*, July 16.

CCOF. 1986. *Growers list*. Santa Cruz: California Certified Organic Farmers.

―――. 1987. *Growers list*. Santa Cruz: California Certified Organic Farmers.

―――. 1989. *Growers list and product index*. Santa Cruz: California Certified Organic Farmers.

―――. 1990. *Growers list and product index*. Santa Cruz: California Certified Organic Farmers.

―――. 1991. *Growers list and product index*. Santa Cruz: California Certified Organic Farmers.

―――. 1993. *Certified organic membership directory and product index*. Santa Cruz: California Certified Organic Farmers.

―――. 1994a. *Certification handbook*. Santa Cruz: California Certified Organic Farmers.

―――. 1994b. *Certified organic membership directory and product index*. Santa Cruz: California Certified Organic Farmers.

―――. 1995a. CCOF influences defeat of bill to ban hand weeding. *California Certified Organic Farmers Statewide Newsletter*, summer 1995, 9.

―――. 1995b. *Certified organic membership directory and product index*. Santa Cruz: California Certified Organic Farmers.

―――. 1997. Certified organic membership directory and product index. Santa Cruz: California Certified Organic Farmers.

―――. 1998a. 1998–99 membership directory. Santa Cruz: California Certified Organic Farmers.

―――. 1998b. Certification handbook. Santa Cruz: California Certified Organic Farmers.

Chayanov, A. [1924] 1986. *The theory of peasant economy*. Madison: University of Wisconsin Press.

Chiappe, Marta B., and Cornelia Butler Flora. 1998. Gendered elements of the alternative agriculture paradigm. *Rural Sociology* 63 (3): 372–93.

CIRS. 1999. Trends in California farmland use. *Rural California Report: Newsletter of the California Institute for Rural Studies*, spring, 1, 5.

Clunies-Ross, Tracey. 1990a. Agricultural change and the politics of organic farming. Ph.D. thesis, University of Bath, United Kingdom.

———. 1990b. Organic food: Swimming against the tide? In *Political, social and economic perspectives on the international food system*, ed. T. Marsden and J. Little. Aldershot, England: Avebury.

Clunies-Ross, Tracey, and Graham Cox. 1994. Challenging the productivist paradigm: Organic farming and the politics of agricultural change. In *Regulating agriculture*, ed. P. Lowe, T. Marsden, and S. Whatmore. London: David Fulton.

Cochrane, Willard W. 1993. *The development of American agriculture*. Minneapolis: University of Minnesota Press.

Conway, Gordon R., and Jules N. Pretty. 1991. *Unwelcome harvest: Agriculture and pollution*. London: Earthscan Publications.

Cook, Ian. 1994. New fruits and vanity: Symbolic production in the global food economy. In *From Columbus to ConAgra*, ed. A. Bonanno, L. Busch, W. Friedland, L. Gouveia, and E. Mingione. Kansas City: University Press of Kansas.

Cook, Ian, and Philip Crang. 1996. The world on a plate: Culinary culture, displacement and geographical knowledges. *Journal of Material Culture* 1 (2): 131–54.

Daniel, Cletus. 1981. *Bitter harvest: A history of California farm workers, 1870–1941*. Ithaca: Cornell University Press.

Daniels, Tom, and Deborah Bowers. 1997. *Holding our ground: Protecting America's farms and farmland*. Washington, D.C.: Island Press.

Davis, Mike. 1992. *City of quartz*. New York: Vintage Books.

DeLind, Laura B. 1993. Market niches, "cul de sacs," and social context: Alternative systems of food production. *Culture and Agriculture* 1993 (47): 7–12.

———. 1998. Presidential address: Close encounters with a CSA: The reflections of a bruised and somewhat wiser anthropologist. Paper read at Joint Meetings of the Agriculture, Food, and Human Values Society and the Association for the Study of Food and Society, San Francisco.

Department of Finance. 1997. *California statistical abstract*. Sacramento: State of California.

Douglas, Mary, and Baron Isherwood. 1996. *The world of goods: Towards an anthropology of consumption*. 2d ed. New York: Routledge. Original edition, New York: Basic Books, 1979.

Duncan, Colin A. M. 1996. *The centrality of agriculture: Between humankind and the rest of nature*. Montreal: McGill-Queen's University Press.

DuPuis, E. Melanie, and David Goodman. 2002. Knowing food and growing food: Beyond the production-consumption debate in the sociology of agriculture. *Sociologia Ruralis* 42 (1): 5–22.

Economic Development Agency. 1961. *California statistical abstract*. Sacramento: State of California.

———. 1971. *California statistical abstract*. Sacramento: State of California.

———. 1981. *California statistical abstract*. Sacramento: State of California.

———. 1991. *California statistical abstract*. Sacramento: State of California.

Economic Research Service. 1999. Genetically engineered crops for pest management. www.econ.ag.gov/whatsnew/issues/biotech. Accessed October 27, 1999.

———. 2000a. Contracting changes: How farms do business. *Rural Conditions and Trends* 10 (2). www.ers.usda.gov/Publications/rcat/rcat102.

———. 2000b. U.S. organic agriculture. www.ers.usda.gov/whatsnew/issues/ organic. Accessed November 21, 2000.

El Feki, Shereen. 2000. Growing pains: A survey of agriculture and technology. *Economist,* March 25–31, Supplement, 1–16.

Esbenshade, Jill. 2001. The social accountability contract: Private monitoring and labor relations in the global apparel industry. Ph.D. dissertation, Ethnic Studies, University of California, Berkeley.

Eysberg, Cees D. 1990. The California wine economy. Ph.D. dissertation, Geographical Sciences, University of Utrecht, Utrecht.

Farm Verified Organic. 1999. Organic certification standards. Farm Verified Organic, Inc., Southeast Medina, N.D.

Fetter, T. Robert. 1999. Economic impacts of alternative scenarios of organic products regulation. Senior thesis, Resource Economics, University of Massachusetts, Amherst.

Fine, Ben. 1979. On Marx's theory of agricultural rent. *Economy and Society* 8 (3): 241–78.

———. 1994. Towards a political economy of food. *Review of International Political Economy* 1 (3): 519–45.

Fine, Ben, Michael Heasman, and Judith Wright. 1996. *Consumption in the age of affluence: The world of food.* New York: Routledge.

Fisher, Lawrence M. 1991. Organic wines enter the mainstream. *New York Times,* November 19.

FitzSimmons, Margaret. 1986. The new industrial agriculture. *Economic Geography* 62 (4): 334–53.

Food Chemical News. 1998. California gourmet salad processor charged with food safety violation. January 19.

Fost, Dan. 1991. Organic food movement bearing fruit: Recent growth raises industry hopes that it may yet compete as agribusiness. *Washington Post,* October 13.

Fox, Nicols. 1997. *Spoiled: Why our food is making us sick and what we can do about it.* New York: Penguin.

Friedland, William H. 1984. Commodity systems analysis: An approach to the sociology of agriculture. In *Research in rural sociology and development,* ed. H. K. Schwarzweller. London: JAI Press.

———. 1994a. The global fresh fruit and vegetable system: An industrial organization analysis. In *The global restructuring of agro-food systems,* ed. P. McMichael. Ithaca: Cornell University Press.

———. 1994b. The new globalization: The case of fresh produce. In *From Columbus to ConAgra,* ed. A. Bonanno, L. Busch, W. Friedland, L. Gouveia, and E. Mingione. Kansas City: University Press of Kansas.

Friedland, William H., Amy E. Barton, and Robert J. Thomas. 1981. *Manufacturing green gold.* Cambridge: Cambridge University Press.

Friedmann, Harriet. 1978. World market, state, and family farm: Social bases of household production in the era of wage labor. *Comparative Studies in Society and History* 20 (4): 545–86.

———. 1980. Household production and the national economy. *Journal of Peasant Studies* 7 (2): 158–84.

———. 1992. Changes in the international division of labor: Agri-food complexes and export agriculture. In *Towards a new political economy of agriculture*, ed. W. H. Friedland, L. Busch, F. H. Buttel, and A. P. Rudy. Boulder: Westview Press.

———. 1993a. After Midas's feast: Alternative food regimes for the future. In *Food for the future*, ed. P. Allen. New York: John Wiley and Sons.

———. 1993b. The political economy of food. *New Left Review* 197: 29–57.

———. 1994. Distance and durability: Shaky foundations of the world food economy. In *The global restructuring of agro-food systems*, ed. P. McMichael. Ithaca: Cornell University Press.

Gates, Paul W. 1975. Public land disposal in California. *Agricultural History* 49:158–78.

Gaura, Maria Alicia. 1997. Birthplace of organics. *San Francisco Chronicle*, September 18, A15, A20.

Gereffi, Gary, and Miguel E. Korzeniewicz, eds. 1994. *Commodity chains and global capitalism*. London: Praeger.

Gilbert, Jess, and Raymond Akor. 1988. Increasing structural divergence in U.S. dairying: California and Wisconsin since 1950. *Rural Sociology* 53 (1): 56–72.

Gilbert, Jess, and Alice O'Connor. 1996. *Leaving the land behind: Struggles for land reform in U.S. federal policy, 1933–1965.* Madison: Land Tenure Center, University of Wisconsin.

Goldman, Barbara, and Katherine L. Clancy. 1991. A survey of organic produce purchases and related attitudes of food cooperative shoppers. *American Journal of Alternative Agriculture* 6 (2): 89–96.

Goldschmidt, Walter. 1947. *As you sow*. New York: Harcourt, Brace.

Goodman, David. 1999. Agro-food studies in the "age of ecology": Nature, corporeality, bio- politics. *Sociologia Ruralis* 39 (1): 17–38.

Goodman, David, and Michael Redclift. 1985. Capitalism, petty commodity production, and the farm enterprise. *Sociologia Ruralis* 15 (3/4): 231–47.

———. 1991. *Refashioning nature*. London: Routledge.

———. 1994. Constructing a political economy of food. *Review of International Political Economy* 1 (3): 547–52.

Goodman, David, and Michael Watts. 1994. Reconfiguring the rural or fording the divide. *Journal of Peasant Studies* 221 (1): 1–49.

———, eds. 1997. *Globalising food: Agrarian questions and global restructuring*. London: Routledge.

Goodman, David, Bernardo Sorj, and John Wilkinson. 1987. *From farming to biotechnology*. Oxford: Basil Blackwell.

Gottleib, Robert. 1993. *Forcing the spring*. Washington, D.C.: Island Press.

Groves, Martha. 1991. Brand 'em podnuh: Harris Ranch shifts to selling beef under its own label. *Los Angeles Times*, July 29.

Guither, Harold D. 1983. Citizen and consumer groups in policies affecting farm structure. In *Farms in transition,* ed. D. E. Brewster, W. D. Rasmussen, and G. Youngberg. Ames: Iowa State University Press.

Gunnison, Robert B. 1996. Wilson signs extension to methyl bromide use. *San Francisco Chronicle,* March 13.

Guthman, Julie. 2003. Fast food/organic food: Reflexive tastes and the making of "yuppie chow." *Journal of Social and Cultural Geography* 4 (1): 43–56.

Handel, Mary E. 1998. Conflicts arise on the urban fringe. *California Agriculture* 52 (3): 11–16.

Hanson, Victor Davis. 1996. *Field without dreams: Defending the agrarian ideal.* New York: Free Press.

Hartman Group. 1997. *The Hartman report: Food and the environment, a consumer's perspective.* Portland, Oreg.: Food Alliance.

Hartwick, Elaine. 2000. Towards a geographical politics of consumption. *Environment and Planning A* 32: 1177–1192.

Harvey, David. 1982. *Limits to capital.* Chicago: University of Chicago.

———. 2000. *Spaces of hope.* California Studies in Critical Human Geography. Berkeley: University of California Press.

Harwood, Richard A. 1990. A history of sustainable agriculture. In *Sustainable agricultural systems,* ed. C. Edwards. Ankeny, Iowa: Soil and Water Conservation Society.

Heffernan, William D., and Douglas H. Constance. 1994. Transnational corporations and the globalization of the food system. In *From Columbus to ConAgra,* ed. A. Bonanno, L. Busch, W. Friedland, L. Gouveia, and E. Mingione. Kansas City: University Press of Kansas.

Henderson, George L. 1999. *California and the fictions of capital.* New York: Oxford University Press.

Hill, S. B. 1985. Redesigning the food system for sustainability. *Alternatives* 12 (3/4): 32–36.

Hinrichs, Claire G. 2000. Embeddedness and local food systems: Notes on two types of direct agricultural market. *Journal of Rural Studies* 16 (3): 295–303.

Howard, Sir Albert. 1940. *An agricultural testament.* London: Oxford University Press.

Hundley, Norris. 1992. *The great thirst: Californians and water, 1770s–1990s.* Berkeley: University of California Press.

IFOAM. 1998. *Basic standards for organic production and processing.* Tholey-Theley, Germany: International Federation of Organic Agriculture Movements.

Ikerd, John E. 2001. Farming in the new century: Is organic farming sustainable? Paper read at 21st Annual Ecological Farming Conference, January 24–27, Asilomar, Calif.

Jackson, Wes. 1984. A search for the unifying concept for sustainable agriculture. In *Meeting the expectations of the land,* ed. W. Jackson, W. Berry, and B. Colman. San Francisco: North Point Press.

———. 1990. Agriculture with nature as analogy. In *Sustainable agriculture in temperate zones,* ed. C. A. Francis, C. B. Flora, and L. D. King. New York: John Wiley and Sons.

Jackson-Smith, Douglas, and Frederick H. Buttel. 1998. The conventional-alternative agriculture paradigm: A replication. Paper read at 61st Annual Meeting of the Rural Sociological Society, Portland, Oreg.

Jacob, Jeffrey. 1997. *New pioneers: The back-to-the-land movement and the search for a sustainable future.* University Park: Pennsylvania State University.

Jaffee, Steven. 1994. Exporting high-value commodities. Washington, D.C.: World Bank.

James, Allison. 1993. Eating green(s): Discourses of organic food. In *Environmentalism: The view from anthropology,* ed. K. Milton. London: Routledge.

Jelinek, Lawrence J. 1979. *Harvest empire: A history of California agriculture.* San Francisco: Boyd and Fraser.

Johnson, Nancy L., and Vernon W. Ruttan. 1994. Why are farms so small? *World Development* 22 (5): 691–706.

Jolly, Desmond A. 1991. Differences between buyers and nonbuyers of organic produce and willingness to pay organic price premiums. *Journal of Agribusiness* 9 (1): 97–111.

Jones, Keith. 2000. National organic update. Paper read at 20th Annual Ecological Farming Conference, Asilomar, Calif.

Katz, Cindi. 1998. Whose nature, whose culture? Private productions of space and the "preservation" of nature. In *Nature at the end of the millennium: Remaking reality and the end of the twentieth century,* ed. N. Castree and B. Willems-Braun. London: Routledge.

Kautsky, Karl. [1899] 1988. *The agrarian question.* London: Zwan Press.

Klonsky, Karen, and Laura Tourte. 1994. *State registration and organic certification: A guide for California growers.* Davis: University of California Cooperative Extension.

———. 1995. *Statistical review of California's organic agriculture 1992–1993.* Davis: University of California Cooperative Extension.

———. 1997. *Production practices and sample costs for organic raisin grape production: Southern San Joaquin Valley.* Davis: University of California Cooperative Extension.

———. 1998a. Organic agricultural production in the United States: Debates and directions. *American Journal of Agricultural Economics* 80 (5):1119–24.

———. 1998b. *Statistical review of California's organic agriculture 1992–1995.* Davis: University of California Agricultural Issues Center.

Klonsky, Karen, Laura Tourte, and Chuck Ingels. 1992. *Production practices and sample costs for organic wine grape production with an annually sown cover crop in the North Coast.* Davis: University of California Cooperative Extension.

Klonsky, Karen, Laura Tourte, Chuck Ingels, and Sean Swezey. 1994. *Production practices and sample costs for fresh market organic apples: Central Coast.* Davis: University of California Cooperative Extension.

Klonsky, Karen, Laura J. Tourte, Robin Kozloff, and Benjamin Shouse. 2001. *Statistical review of California's organic agriculture 1995–1998.* Davis: University of California, Agricultural Issues Center.

Kloppenberg, J., Jr., J. Henrickson, and G. W. Stevenson. 1996. Coming into the foodshed. *Agriculture and Human Values* 13 (3): 33–42.

Kloppenburg, Jack. 1988. *First the seed.* Cambridge: Cambridge University Press.

Kraus, Sibella. 1991. Working the land with a sense of community. *San Francisco Chronicle,* October 2.

Lampkin, Nicolas. 1990. *Organic farming.* Ipswich, England: Farming Press.

Lampkin, Nicolas, and S. Padel, eds. 1994. *The economics of organic farming.* Wallingford, England: CAB International.

Lappé, Francis Moore. 1971. *Diet for a small planet.* New York: Ballantine Books.

Lasley, Paul, Eric Hoiberg, and Gordon Bultena. 1993. Is sustainable agriculture an elixir for rural communities? *American Journal of Alternative Agriculture* 8 (3): 133–39.

Lee, Roger. 2000. Restructuring. In *Dictionary of human geography,* ed. R. J. Johnston, D. Gregory, G. Pratt, and M. Watts. London: Blackwell.

Le Heron, Richard. 1993. *Globalized agriculture: Political choice.* Oxford: Pergamon Press.

Leibman, Ellen. 1983. *California farmland: A history of large agricultural land holdings.* Totowa, N.J.: Rowman and Allanheld.

Lele, Sharachchandra M. 1991. Sustainable development: A critical review. *World Development* 19 (6): 607–21.

Levenstein, Harvey A. 1988. *Revolution at the table: The transformation of the American diet.* New York: Oxford University Press.

———. 1993. *Paradox of plenty: A social history of eating in modern America.* New York: Oxford University Press.

Liebman, James. 1997. *Rising toxic tide: Pesticide use in California 1991–1995.* San Francisco: Californians for Pesticide Reform.

———. 1998. Attacking pesticides and supporting small farmers. Paper read at 18th Annual Ecological Farming Conference, Asilomar, Calif.

Lighthall, David R., and Rebecca S. Roberts. 1995. Towards an alternative logic of technological change: Insights from cornbelt agriculture. *Journal of Rural Studies* 11 (3): 319–34.

Lipson, Mark. 1997. *Searching for the "O-word."* Santa Cruz: Organic Farming Research Foundation.

Lloyd, Erik. 1995. Boswell buy of Salyer reported. *Daily Sentinel,* February 2.

Lohr, Luanne. 2002. The Conservation Security Program: Leveling the playing field for organic farmers. *Organic Farming Research Foundation Information Bulletin,* fall, 1, 6–8.

Los Angeles Times. 1986. Briefly: Mobil said it will sell a farming subsidiary. April 1.

Lowe, Philip, Terry Marsden, and Sarah Whatmore. 1994. Changing regulatory orders: The analysis of the economic governance of agriculture. In *Regulating agriculture,* ed. P. Lowe, T. Marsden, and S. Whatmore. London: David Fulton.

McCarthy, James. 1999. The political and moral economy of wise use. Ph.D. dissertation, Department of Geography, University of California, Berkeley.

McMichael, Philip, ed. 1994. *The global restructuring of agro-food systems.* Ithaca: Cornell University Press.

McWilliams, Carey. 1949. *California: The great exception*. New York: Current Books.
———. [1935] 1971. *Factories in the field*. Santa Barbara: Peregrine Smith.
Mann, Susan A. 1989. *Agrarian capitalism in theory and practice*. Chapel Hill: University of North Carolina Press.
Markusen, Ann. 1985. *Profit cycles, oligopoly, and regional development*. Cambridge, Mass.: MIT Press.
Marsden, Terry. 1992. Exploring a rural sociology for the Fordist transition. *Sociologia Ruralis* 32 (2/3): 209–30.
Marsden, Terry, and Alberto Arce. 1995. Constructing quality: Emerging food networks in the rural transition. *Environment and Planning A* 27: 1261–79.
Marsden, Terry, Jonathan Murdoch, Philip Lowe, Richard Munton, and Andrew Flynn. 1993. *Constructing the countryside*. Boulder: Westview Press.
Martin, Philip. 1987. *California's farm labor market*. Davis: University of California, Agricultural Issues Center.
Massey, Doreen. 1984. *Spatial divisions of labor: Social structures and the geography of production*. London: Macmillan.
Medvitz, Albert G. 1998. Urban growth squeezes agriculture. *California Agriculture* 52 (3): 8–9.
———. 1999. Population growth and its impacts on agricultural land in California: 1850–1898. In *California farmland and urban pressures,* ed. A. G. Medvitz, A. D. Sokolow, and C. Lemp. Davis: Agricultural Issues Center, University of California.
Mergentime, Ken. 1994. History of organic. *Natural Food Merchandiser's Organic Times,* 62–66.
Mergentime, Ken, and Monica Emerich. 1995. Organic sales jump over $2 billion mark in 1994. *Natural Foods Merchandiser,* June 1995, 74–76.
Mitchell, Don. 1996. *The lie of the land: Migrant workers and the California landscape*. Minneapolis: University of Minnesota Press.
Moe, Michael T., and David M. Scharf. 1997. *Forever young*. San Francisco: Montgomery Securities.
Mooney, Patrick H. 1983. Toward a class analysis of midwestern agriculture. *Rural Sociology* 48 (4): 563–84.
Moore, Michael C. 1998. Permissive growth policies may encourage speculative investment in farmland. *California Agriculture* 52 (3): 23–27.
Morgan, Kevin, and Jonathan Murdoch. 2000. Organic vs. conventional agriculture: Knowledge, power and innovation in the food chain. *Geoforum* 31: 159–73.
Morris, Charles E. 1991. New tomato plant processes 90 tons per hour. *Food Engineering,* March/April.
Moses, H. Vincent. 1995. The orange grower is not a farmer. *California History* 74 (1).
National Agricultural Statistics Service. 2002. California's top twenty commodities. www.nass.gov/california. Accessed June 2002.
National Research Council. 1987. *Regulating pesticides in food: The Delaney paradox*. Washington, D.C.: National Academy Press.
Nation's Agriculture. 1971. "Crisis or challenge." 19 (July-August).

Nestle, Marion. 2002. *Food politics: How the food industry influences nutrition and health.* Berkeley: University of California Press.

Nowacek, David. 1997. The organic foods system from 1969–1996: A defense of associative order and democratic control over a market. M.A. thesis, Rural Sociology, University of Wisconsin–Madison.

O'Connor, James. 1989. Capitalism, nature, socialism: A theoretical introduction. *Capitalism, Nature, Socialism* 1: 11–38.

OFRF. 1998. *National organic certifiers directory.* Santa Cruz: Organic Farming Research Foundation.

———. 1999. Third biennial National Organic Farmers' Survey. Santa Cruz: Organic Farming Research Foundation.

OMRI. 1998. Preliminary overview of the USDA/NOP proposed rule as it applies to materials. Eugene, Oreg.: Organic Materials Review Institute.

O'Neill, Molly. 1995. Organic industry faces an ethics question. *New York Times,* May 17.

Orden, David, Robert Paarlberg, and Terry Roe. 1999. *Policy reform in American agriculture.* Chicago: University of Chicago Press.

The Packer. 1996. Consumption influences. *Fresh Trends 1996,* 60.

Parr, J. F., R. I. Papendick, and I. G. Youngberg. 1983. Organic farming in the United States: Principles and perspectives. *Agro-Ecosystems* 8: 183–201.

Pease, W. S., R. A. Morello-Frosch, D. S. Albright, A. D. Kyle, and J. C. Robinson. 1993. Preventing pesticide-related illnesses in California agriculture: Strategies and priorities. Berkeley: California Policy Seminar.

Peters, Suzanne. 1979. The land in trust: A social history of the organic farming movement. Ph.D. dissertation, Sociology, McGill University, Montreal.

Pfeffer, Max J. 1983. Social origins of three systems of farm production in the United States. *Rural Sociology* 48 (4): 540–62.

Pincetl, Stephanie S. 1999. *Transforming California: A political history of land use and development.* Baltimore: Johns Hopkins University Press.

Pisani, Donald J. 1984. *From the family farm to agribusiness: The irrigation crusade in California and the West 1850–1931.* Berkeley: University of California Press.

Podger, Pamela P. 1999. A growing controversy; fear in Sonoma County over bigger wine industry. *San Francisco Chronicle,* October 7, A1, A14.

Polanyi, Karl. 1944. *The great transformation.* Boston: Beacon Press.

Pollan, Michael. 2001a. *The botany of desire.* New York: Random House.

———. 2001b. The organic-industrial complex. *New York Times Magazine,* May 13.

———. 2002. Power steer. *New York Times Magazine,* March 31.

Pressly, Thomas J., and William H. Scofield, eds. 1965. *Farm real estate values in the United States by counties, 1850–1959.* Seattle: University of Washington Press.

PR Newswire. 1987. Texaco completes sale of its California agribusiness operations. February 2.

Proctor, Robert N. 1995. *Cancer wars: How politics shapes what we know and don't know about cancer.* New York: Basic Books.

Public Law 101–624. 136th Cong., 2d sess., 28 November 1990. *Food, Agriculture, Conservation, and Trade Act of 1990.*

Pulido, Laura. 1996. *Environmentalism and economic justice: Two Chicano struggles in the Southwest.* Tucson: University of Arizona.

Quarles, William. 1995. What does organic mean? *IPM Practitioner* 17 (10): 9–13.

Reed, Matthew. 2001. Fight the future: How the contemporary campaigns of the UK organic movement have arisen from their composting of the past. *Sociologia Ruralis* 41 (1): 131–45, 161.

Reisner, Marc. 1993. *Cadillac desert.* 2d ed. New York: Penguin.

Rhode, Paul W. 1995. Learning, capital accumulation, and the transformation of California agriculture. *Journal of Economic History* 55 (4): 773–99.

Rodman, Paul. 1988. *The Far West and the Great Plains in transition, 1859–1900.* New York: Harper and Row.

Romm, Jeff. 2001. The coincidental order of environmental injustice. In *Justice and natural resources: Concepts, strategies, and applications,* ed. K. M. Mutz, G. C. Bryner, and D. S. Kennedy. Covelo, Calif.: Island Press.

Rosset, Peter M., and Miguel Altieri. 1997. Agroecology versus input substitution: A fundamental contradiction of sustainable agriculture. *Society and Natural Resources* 10 (3): 283–95.

Sachs, Carolyn E. 1996. *Gendered fields: Rural women, agriculture, and the environment.* Boulder: Westview Press.

Sachs, Wolfgang. 1992. *Development dictionary.* London: Zed Press.

Sale, Kirkpatrick. 1985. *Dwellers in the land: The bioregional vision.* San Francisco: Sierra Club Books.

Sanders, Steve. 1998. Statewide farmland protection is fragmented, limited. *California Agriculture* 52 (3): 5–11.

Sawyer, Richard C. 1996. *To make a spotless orange.* Edited by R. D. Hurt. Henry A. Wallace Series on Agricultural History and Rural Life. Ames: Iowa State University Press.

Scheuring, Ann Foley, ed. 1983. *A guidebook to California agriculture.* Berkeley: University of California Press.

Schilling, Elizabeth. 1995. Organic agriculture grows up. *California Journal,* May 1995, 21–25.

Schlosser, Eric. 2001. *Fast food nation: The dark side of the American meal.* Boston: Houghton Mifflin Company.

Schumpeter, Joseph. 1939. *Business cycles.* New York: McGraw-Hill.

Scott, James C. 1998. *Seeing like a state.* New Haven: Yale University Press.

Severson, Kim. 2002. Agribusiness goes organic: New law and growing appetite for wholesome foods bring mega-growers to the table. *San Francisco Chronicle,* October 13, A1, A18.

Shennan, Carol, L. E. Drinkwater, A. H. C. van Bruggen, D. K. Letourneau, and F. Workneh. 1991. Comparative study of organic and conventional tomato production systems: An approach to on-farm systems studies in sustainable agriculture research and education in the field. Washington, D.C.: National Academy Press.

Shoemaker, Robbin. 1989. *Long run determinants of land values.* Washington, D.C.: Economics Research Service, USDA.

Smith, Jerd. 1998. Going natural: Green revolution takes root in the grocery business. *Denver Rocky Mountain News,* August 16.

Smith, Ralph E. 1946. Protecting plants from their enemies. In *California agriculture,* ed. C. B. Hutchinson. Berkeley: University of California Press.

Sokolow, Alvin D. 1998. North bay leads Central Valley in protecting farmland. *California Agriculture* 52 (3): 17–22.

Soule, J. D., and J. K. Piper. 1992. *Farming in nature's image.* Washington, D.C.: Island Press.

Steffen, Robert, Floyd Allen, and James Foote, eds. 1972. *Organic farming: Methods and markets.* Emmaus, Pa.: Rodale Press.

Stegner, Wallace. 1953. *Beyond the hundredth meridian.* New York: Penguin.

Steingraber, Sandra. 1997. *Living downstream: An ecologist looks at cancer and the environment.* New York: Addison-Wesley.

Stevenson, Richard W. 1987. Farming in a corporate age. *New York Times,* September 11.

Stoll, Steven. 1995. Insects and institutions: University science and the fruit business in California. *Agricultural History* 69 (2): 216–40.

————. 1998. *The fruits of natural advantage: Making the industrial countryside in California.* Berkeley: University of California.

Storper, Michael. 1997. *The regional world: Territorial development in a global economy.* Edited by M. S. Gertler and P. Dicken. Perspectives on Economic Change. New York: Guilford Press.

Storper, Michael, and Richard Walker. 1989. *The capitalist imperative: Territory, technology and industrial growth.* Oxford: Basil Blackwell.

Strange, Marty. 1984. The economic structure of a sustainable agriculture. In *Meeting the expectations of the land,* ed. W. Jackson, W. Berry, and B. Colman. San Francisco: North Point Press.

————. 1988. *Family farming: A new economic vision.* Lincoln: University of Nebraska Press/Institute for Food and Development Policy.

Thevenot, Laurent. 1998. Innovating in "qualified" markets: Quality, norms, and conventions. Paper read at Workshop on Systems and Trajectories of Agricultural Innovation, April 23–25, Institute of International Studies, University of California Berkeley.

Thirsk, Joan. 1997. *Alternative agriculture: A history.* New York: Oxford University Press.

Thomas, Robert J. 1985. *Citizenship, gender, and work.* Berkeley: University of California Press.

Thompson, Kevin. 1998. Solid state. *California Farmer,* April.

Turner, R. Kerry, David Pearce, and Ian Bateman. 1993. *Environmental economics.* 1st ed. Baltimore: Johns Hopkins University Press.

U.S. Bureau of the Census. 1910. *Thirteenth census of the United States, 1910: Agriculture.* Washington, D.C.: GPO.

————. 1950. *Seventeenth census of the United States, 1950: Agriculture.* Washington, D.C.: GPO.

————. 1999. *Statistical abstracts of the United States.* Washington, D.C.: GPO.

USDA. 1980. *Report and recommendations on organic farming.* Washington, D.C.: United States Department of Agriculture.

———. 1999. Census of agriculture. Vol. 1, part 5, chapter 1: California state level data. www.noss.usda.gov/census/census97/volume1/ca-5/toc97.htm. Accessed August 2003.

———. 2001. National Organic Program. Web page. www.usda.ams.gov/nop. Accessed August 2002.

———. N.d. Farm real estate values (86010). http://usda.monnlib.cornell.edu/usea/usda.html. Accessed January 2001.

Vaught, David. 1999. *Cultivating California: Growers, specialty crops, and labor, 1875–1920.* Baltimore: Johns Hopkins University Press.

Villarejo, Don. 1989. *Farm restructuring and employment in California agriculture.* Davis: California Institute for Rural Studies.

Villarejo, Don, and Charles V. Moore. 1998. *How effective are voluntary agricultural pesticide use programs? A study of pesticide use in California almond and walnut production.* Davis: California Institute for Rural Studies.

Vink, Erik. 1998. Land trusts conserve California farmland. *California Agriculture* 52 (3): 27–31.

Vos, Tim. 2000. Visions of the middle landscape: Organic farming and the politics of nature. *Agriculture and Human Values* 17 (3): 245–56.

Walker, Richard. 1974. Urban ground rent: Building a new conceptual framework. *Antipode* 6 (1): 51–59.

———. 2001. California's debt to nature: Natural resources and regional capitalism, 1848–1940. *Annals of the Association of American Geographers* 91 (1): 167–99.

Warde, Alan. 1997. *Consumption, food and taste.* London: Sage.

Wargo, John. 1998. *Our children's toxic legacy.* 2d ed. New Haven: Yale University Press.

Watts, Michael. 1983. *Silent violence: Food, famine and peasantry in northern Nigeria.* Berkeley: University of California Press.

———. 1987. Drought, environment and food security. In *Drought and hunger in Africa,* ed. M. Glantz. Cambridge: Cambridge University Press.

———. 1993. Life under contract. In *Living under contract: Contract farming, agrarian restructuring, and flexible accumulation,* ed. M. J. Watts and P. Little. Madison: University of Wisconsin Press.

Wells, Miriam. 1984. The resurgence of sharecropping. *American Journal of Sociology* 90: 1–29.

———. 1996. *Strawberry fields: Politics, class, and work in California agriculture.* Ithaca: Cornell University Press.

Welsh, Rick. 1998. The importance of ownership arrangements in U.S. agriculture. *Rural Sociology* 63 (2): 199–213.

Whatmore, Sarah. 1995. From farming to agro-business. In *Geographies of global change: Remapping the world in the late twentieth century,* ed. R. J. Johnston, Peter J. Taylor, and Michael Watts. London: Blackwell.

White, Richard. 1991. *"It's your misfortune and none of my own": A new history of the American West.* Norman: University of Oklahoma Press.

Whorton, James. 1974. *Before "Silent Spring": Pesticides and public health in pre-DDT America.* Princeton: Princeton University Press.

Wolf, Steven, B. Hueth, and E. Lison. 2001. Policy mechanisms in agricultural contracts. *Rural Sociology* 66 (3): 359–81.

Worster, Donald. 1979. *Dust bowl: The southern Plains in the 1930s.* New York: Oxford University Press.

———. 1985. *Rivers of empire.* Oxford: Oxford University Press.

———. 1992. *Under western skies: Nature and history in the American West.* New York: Oxford University Press.

———. 1994. *Nature's economy: A history of ecological ideas.* New York: Cambridge University Press.

Youngberg, Garth, Neill Schaller, and Kathleen Merrigan. 1993. The sustainable agriculture policy agenda in the United States: Politics and prospects. In *Food for the future,* ed. P. Allen. New York: John Wiley and Sons.

Zwerdling, Daniel. 1993. California's vineyards discovering organic farming. National Public Radio, November 1.

Index

absolute rents, 209n6

Adamchak, Raoul, 17

agrarian capitalism, 20–21, 111

agrarian populism, 10–12, 176–78, 184; in California, 174–75, 217–18n4; family-owned farm role, 14, 174–76, 201n15; organic movement role, 17–18, 43, 117, 120

The Agrarian Question (K. Kautsky), 61

agribusiness. *See* conventional agriculture

agricultural economics, 4, 165, 202–3n2; 1980s farm crisis, 33, 36, 79, 85, 110, 114, 203n3; land use restructuring, 89–90; post-productivist period, 23–24, 203n4. *See also* land values; price premium for organic crops; taxation of agricultural land

agricultural exceptionalism, 63–65

agricultural innovation, 66–67, 77, 78–79, 83, 209nn4,6; appropriation role, 65–66, 68–69; land values and, 61, 65, 67–68, 169, 178; year-round production, 80, 84, 103. *See also* intensification

agricultural zoning, 86–87, 212n25

agrochemical industry, 181

agroecological principles, 46–47, 71, 117, 175, 207n11, 219; adoption by growers, 47–51, 87–88, 92, 147–52, 170; grower assessment tables, 48, 149; marketing perspectives, 53–54, 56; in study regions, 102, 105, 106–7;

subscription farm practices, 59–60, 184–85

agroforestry, 47

Alar and Aldicarb food scares, 20, 25, 27, 36, 113, 115, 202n21

Alien Land Laws, 210n10

alternative agriculture, 6–7, 24, 178–79, 202n1, 208n19, 219; history, 4, 16–18; pest control strategies, 36, 38

Altieri, Miguel, 46

apples, 57, 105, 216n2; high-value varieties, 33, 81; organic, 30, 31, 106, 166, 205n14

appropriate technology movement, 8

appropriation, as aspect of innovation, 65–66, 68–69, 79, 209n4

arsenical compounds, 76, 210n13

artichokes, 151, 166

avocados, 31–32, 57, 73, 101–2, 151, 166

azinphos methyl, 38

Bacillus thuringiensis (bt), 201n18, 215n9

Balfour, Lady Eve, 4, 120

beef. *See* livestock production

Berkeley, California, 27

Berry, Wendell, 9–11, 201n14

beyond organic, 166, 169–71, 173

BIFS (Biologically Integrated Farming Systems), 107

biodynamic agriculture, 120, 148, 170, 219

237

Text:	10/13 Sabon
Display:	Sabon
Compositor:	Binghamton Valley Composition, LLC
Printer and Binder:	Maple-Vail Manufacturing Group
Indexer:	Ellen Davenport
Cartographer:	Bill Nelson